CONTEST FOR A CAPITAL

About the author —

T.L. Loftin during 20 years of work in the National Geographic Society's Special Publications Division in Washington, D.C., did research for numerous books, wrote chapters for books, and authored the book *America's Beginnings: The Wild Shores.* Before joining the National Geographic staff, and while she was bringing up two children, she wrote for radio, TV, and, as Washington correspondent and columnist, for her hometown daily, *The Kinston, N.C. Free Press.* In 1980, she produced in her spare time an adventure book *Staying Alive in Alaska's Wild* for trapper Andy Nault, published it, and sold twenty thousand copies. Ms. Loftin has a Bachelor of Journalism from the University of Missouri, and an M.A. in Journalism from American University, Washington, D.C.

About the illustrator—

Sofia Zarambouka during the past 17 years has written and illustrated 40 books for children. Among them are Aristophanes' plays *Irene, Lysistrata, The Birds, Plutus* and *The Frogs*; a 10-book *Mythology* series, and *Odyssey.* She is widely known as an artist-writer for children in Greece, where she lives and works. About 500,000 copies of her books have been published in 10 countries.

About the portrait artists—

Betty Wells of Virginia Beach, Virginia, does rapid-sketching of people and scenes, particularly courtroom scenes, for news programs on NBC television. Her Supreme Court drawings have been exhibited as a one-man show. Her most recent sketches were daily scenes at the Oliver North trial in Washington, D.C.

Tita Mendoza reports and broadcasts news and features on Mexico City television. An accomplished artist, she has exhibited numerous times in Mexico City, various states in Mexico, and in France. She recently returned from a year-long journey in a small sailboat with two companions. An earlier adventure was as TV war correspondent in Iran during the American hostages crisis.

CONTEST FOR A CAPITAL

George Washington, Robert Morris, and Congress, 1783-1791 Contenders

Dramatized Events of America's
Founding Years

BY

T.L. Loftin

Line drawings by **Sofia Zarambouka**

Individual portraits by
Sofia Zarambouka
Betty Wells
Tita Mendoza

"History come to life!"

Tee Loftin Publishers, Inc.
3100 R Street, N.W.
Washington, D.C. 20007

CONTEST FOR A CAPITAL

George Washington, Robert Morris, and Congress, 1783-1791 Contenders

by **T.L. Loftin**

Line drawings by Sofia Zarambouka

Small portraits by
Sofia Zarambouka
Betty Wells
Tita Mendoza

Basic book design
Sofia Zarambouka

Issue Editor
Suzanne Snell Tesh

Technical assistance
Bradley Tesh, computer
Suzanne Snell Tesh, photostats

Printing consultant
Willard Brown

Printed by Kirby Lithographers
Arlington, Virginia

Tee Loftin Publishers, Inc.
3100 R Street N.W.
Washington, D.C. 20007

202-338-6049

Library of Congress Cataloging-in-Publication Data
Loftin, T.L.
Contest for a capital : George Washington, Robert Morris, and Congress, 1783-1791 contenders : dramatized events of America's founding years / by T.L. Loftin; line drawings by Sofia Zarambouka; individual portraits by Sofia Zarambouka, Betty Wells, Tita Mendoza.
        p.   cm.
   "History come to life!"
   Bibliography: p.
   Includes index.
   ISBN 0-934812-04-7 : $19.95
1. United States--Capital and capitol--History--18th century.
2. United States--Politics and government--1783-1789.
3. United States--Politics and Government--1789-1797
4. Washington, George, 1732-1799. 5. Morris, Robert, 1734-1806. 6. Washington (D.C.)--Politics and government--To 1878. I. Title.
F195.L84 1989   973.4--dc20   89-12842 CIP

COVER
Georgetown, Maryland (lower right corner) at the head of navigation on the Potomac River, won the national capital at the end of an eight-year contest that was often raucous, sometimes bitter. The public stage was sessions of Congress, both Continental and First Federal, with the players its members. But the two principal forces at work were George Washington and Robert Morris, essentially South pulling against North.
The bird's-eye view of Georgetown and the adjacent Georgetown Flats is a small section of a poster, "City of Washington - 1800" by T.L. Loftin, author of *Contest For a Capital*. The 25 by 31-inch poster shows the wilderness capital on the first day that Congress convened there. Shoreline and street pattern were traced from a 1796 map. Buildings are primarily those listed in an 1802 inventory made for President Jefferson. Poster is available from the publisher, address at left. Mailed rolled, with descriptive booklet, $10 postpaid.

A WORD TO THE READER—

Your first question when you begin reading this book may be, "Is this fiction or facts?" My answer is, "Facts—but personalized, dramatized as reconstructed events you are witnessing, enhanced by conversation and a context of place, time, and circumstances." I would add that most of the events are from written records. A few others are more likely to have happened than not—linkages that, though not recorded, can be discerned as inevitable.

A prime example is the final scene in this book. I have not seen a written word to confirm that Pierre L'Enfant and Thomas Jefferson had a conversation with Washington when L'Enfant passed through Philadelphia on his way from New York to Georgetown, Maryland.

Yet, the surrounding facts shape an event: the stagecoach schedule keeping L'Enfant overnight in Philadelphia, the short walk, four blocks, between the depot and the President's house, Jefferson's designation as the contact man between the President and L'Enfant, Washington's intense interest in the creation of the new city.

Your next question may be, "What about the conversation, the words your historical personages are saying in your book? Did they say those exact words?" My answer is that wherever any written record exists—diary, journal, letter, account book, official record, unofficial record, newspaper or magazine article—I have used their words, even though the occasion at which they are spoken in this book may have occurred before or after the recorded words.

Other words have been derived from historians' studies of the characters in the story, studies describing everything from physical appearance, home, and horses, to the people they liked or respected immensely, those they hated passionately, and their opinions about the issues of the day.

Since far more was said than was ever recorded 200 years ago, I have reconstructed some conversations as logical expansions of the fragments, the clues, left to us. "Interpreting! Guessing!" you may say. All historians, even those whose studies read like legal briefs, must, when they confront a gap in a story, guess at what they think is the closest probability to truth.

I liken this reconstruction to drawing the shape of a missing piece of a jigsaw puzzle by tracing along the edges of the pieces surrounding the hole. To fit well, the created piece must not only have the right shape, it must also have the right style, tone, character, and point of view.

This applies to both conversations and scenes. The sequence of events before and after the gap, the known character and behavior of the persons involved, practical details like geography of the place, weather, health, stage coach schedules, can point clearly to an "inevitable happening" that nobody recorded.

Some call this enhancement and reconstruction "fleshing out the bones of known facts." It can also be compared to an amplifier that takes a tiny radio signal from faraway and enlarges it to a size we can hear and see—or to the paleontologist who finds one tooth and can quite accurately reconstruct a whole animal long extinct. I have not had to start with so little and do so much. With the quantity of solid evidence left us by our founding fathers, I have only created missing teeth.

To remind you all along the way through these 65 scenes that you are not reading fiction, I have placed alongside in the margins the source of the facts or direct quotes in the text column. These citations will also serve as informal bibliography for anyone who wishes to consult the source for more detail, or confirmation.

In addition, to further assure that the facts I present are accurate, I have submitted to scholars and to local history groups those sections of the book that concern people or events they have studied. The names of these reviewers are listed at the end of the book. Many improvements and new information came from them, making the stories much stronger, more dramatic, human, and accurate.

It is my hope that you can hear and see our founders of 200 years ago talking, wrangling, competing, showing anger, tears, joy; talking, talking, walking about in streets and buildings familiar to them, participating in dramatic episodes that produced the foundations for our sturdy republic. If I should ever hear that many of you have made remarks similar to my son's after he read several chapters—"These are fascinating stories! If I had been taught history this way in school, I would have loved it instead of hating it!"—I shall feel amply rewarded.

Perchance you will, for it is said around the world that all people love a story—and what is hi-story but the high art of story telling?

T.L. Loftin

"Your 'creative non-fiction' is a fascinating idea. A wonderful job of research—I am in awe of the detail you have in your command."
Kathryn S. Smith, President, The Historical Society of Washington, D.C., and Editor, *Washington History*.

"Fascinating fun to read! My admiration grows hourly. The research is awe-inspiring. I can't praise your work highly enough."
Judith Frank, Editor for the Junior League's *History of Washington, Illustrated*; local history columnist *Washington Times*.

"Engrossing storytelling. The First Congress, First Session chapters I read are quite accurate."
Dr. Kenneth Bowling, First Federal Congress Project; author of many articles and a forthcoming book about locating the capital.

"I carefully read the chapters you sent me. They seem fine to me."
Dr. Eugene R. Sheridan, Associate Editor, The Papers of Thomas Jefferson, Princeton University.

"Enjoyed what you wrote and the style it's written in. I think you have a winner."
Jay S. Moler, U.S. Park Service, Harper's Ferry, W. Va.

"All in all, a good feel for Washington puttering around the river. The drawings are fresh and alive."
Dick L. Stanton, Superintendent, C and O Canal National Historical Park, Sharpsburg, Md.

"I enjoyed the lively, evocative style, and particularly the speeches of Patrick Henry and Lafayette."
Minor Weisiger, Archives, Virginia State Library, Richmond, Va.

"It's very, very good. The characters are clearly and sharply drawn, the dialogue has the proper tone, and the story moves along quickly. This is the way history should be written—as dramatic, human stories."
Marion Boyars, Publisher-Editor, London & New York

"A tour de force—fascinating, painstakingly researched, history come to life..."
Jean van der Tak, Editor, Population Reference Bureau, Washington, D.C.

"On-the-scene, authentic background, real characters, interpretation based on current historical scholarship—entertaining too."
Dr. E. James Ferguson, author of *Power of the Purse*.

"This book will raise the historical IQ of a couple of generations by a quantum jump."
Merrill Windsor, Editor, *Arizona Highways Magazine*; formerly Editor in Special Publications, National Geographic Society.

"It's a winner! I read four chapters at one sitting. Didn't have time to, but couldn't put it down."
Janice Windsor, Family Counselor, Phoenix, Ariz.

"Many formerly disconnected threads concerning efforts and purpose are picked up and woven into an orderly pattern in your Allegheny chapter."
Betty Harr Koontz, Marion County Historical Society Museum, Fairmont, W.Va.

"It's a captivating story. I hope it's a best seller."
David Dutcher, Historian, Independence National Historical Park, Philadelphia, Pa.

"Quickly I was swept along by interest in what was happening, the reality of the events, and the strengths of the characters."
Peg Morrison, Administrator, Woman's Clinic, Wichita, Kansas

"I enjoyed the two chapters you gave me—wonderful appetizers. I know this book will be a triumph."
Bart McDowell, Senior Editor and Writer, *National Geographic Magazine*

"What a marvelous job of spinning a tale and bringing in the facts."
Clem Gardiner, President, Catoctin Furnace Historical Society, Thurmont, Md.

TABLE OF CONTENTS

Part One
District of Congress:
From Idea to Law of the Land
1783-1789

Mutinous soldiers, brandishing muskets with fixed bayonets, demand overdue pay as they surround Congress and state officials meeting in the State House, Philadelphia, on June 20, 1783. When the Pennsylvania Council refused to call militia to control the threatening soldiers, angry and fearful Congress delegates resolved that Congress would have a capital territory under its control, independent of any state.

2

CHAPTER 1

Continental Congress Under Siege

SCENE: First floor room, to the left of Chestnut Street entrance, the State House, Philadelphia, Pennsylvania.
TIME: Saturday, June 21, 1783, from about 12:45 to 3:15 p.m.

In the room where rebellious colonists seven years before had signed the Declaration of Independence, 14 Congressmen of the victorious United States listened intently as President Elias Boudinot, plump, 50, wigged in curls, and Alexander Hamilton, small, trim, 26, handsome and handsomely attired, had spoken in high excitement, the words of one at times mixing with those of the other.

"I tell you, Gentlemen," declared Hamilton, wagging his forefinger, "the mutineer soldiers have taken possession of the Powder House and several public arsenals with some field pieces from the public yard of Philadelphia! Two officers—one Captain Carbery and a Lieutenant Sullivan—have devised a plan of the most diabolical nature against not only the Congress and the Council of Pennsylvania, but also against the Bank of North America, and the city of Philadelphia!"

"When they begin marching," Boudinot was saying, "they'll be in the hundreds—not just the 80 who came yesterday from camp in Lancaster!"

Hamilton hurried on with his story. "They—these officers—have the men and the guns of the Continental Army, and are inciting violence to obtain money! After executing their horrid purposes, they expect to go off with their plunder to the Indies!" Exclamations of incredulity and dismay arose from the circle of men. "However unsensible this may

appear," Boudinot's voice proclaimed, "such action and violence appeal to soldiers who have been doing nothing for months, and who are led into thinking that the Congress and the State Council are going to cheat them of several months' pay, as well as bounties and free land in the West! An army that refuses to lay down its arms until its demands are satisfied could ruin America."

"Yes—I learned last night that soldiers in Philadelphia's barracks, including South Carolinians on their way home, have joined them!" Hamilton added. "Carbery and Sullivan were at work here last week—recall the insolent and threatening message that came to Congress from the barracks a few days ago. 'We refuse to go home on furlough without first being paid!' it said—"

"—a mutinous remonstrance!" cried James Madison of Virginia.

"'Give a satisfactory answer or we take our own measures to settle accounts!' they said," Hamilton went on. "This morning, rumors were running through the barracks that hundreds of soldiers will attack the Bank tonight! God knows what will happen if they find Congress has no money!"

"But the State Council—President Dickinson—do they still resist calling the militia to deal with this situation?!" exclaimed Madison.

Hamilton quickly replied, "So far, they refuse. At

Journals of the Continental Congress June 19, 20, 21, 1783 (Vol. 24) p410-421, p971-974

Elias Boudinot (G.A.Boyd) p125

Elias Boudinot Report to Congress, July 15, 1783

Jour. Cont. Cong. (E.C.Burnett) p573

E. Boudinot (G.A.Boyd) p125

Jour. Cont. Cong. July 1, 1783, p414

"New Light on Philadelphia's Mutiny of 1783" (K.Bowling) Penn.Mag.Hist. Oct. 1977

Cont. Cong. (Burnett) p575

Elias Boudinot

E. Boudinot
(G.A. Boyd) p124-126

Boudinot Report,
July 15

this special meeting of Congress, we hoped to persuade the Council to protect itself, and Congress, against armed force. So far, we have NOT been able to convince the State Council to do ANYTHING to halt the threatened violence!"

Ralph Izard of South Carolina drawled grimly, "These Pennsylvanians will do nothing. If you, Richard Peters, and you, Oliver Ellsworth, couldn't get a Council member to go yesterday with our Assistant Secretary of War to TALK the Lancaster men out of coming into this city, surely no measures will be taken today to CONTROL them. So, our lives hang by a state-held thread! By God—"(he hissed in his breath)—"if this City and State will not support Congress, it is high time Congress removes to some other place!"

"Listen! Fifes and drums!"

"Sounds like a regiment marching!"

The 16 Congressmen, faces drawn, eyes wide, nervously hurried to windows on each side of the room. "Oh Lord!" cried Peters of Pennsylvania, looking out on Chestnut Street. "Instead of going to the Bank, they're coming here!"

Suddenly, the door to the lobby swung open and James Wilson of Pennsylvania, panting audibly, quickly entered, hurriedly slammed the door, and turned the key to lock it. When he looked up, his eyes, magnified by thick lenses in his spectacles, seemed to bulge with fear. "I was only a block ahead of them," he gasped. "There are about 25 of them, all with muskets, bayonets fixed!"

"There they are!" called Hamilton from a window. Several men scurried to his side to look. "Halt!" they heard clearly. "About face!" In narrow, gravel-covered Chestnut Street, two short lines of soldiers, muskets shouldered, faced the great doors of the building. Fifes shrilled and drums rumbled.

Suddenly, the sound of those doors snapping open and crashing shut, then heavy, quick footsteps thumping in the lobby just outside the door of the

Congressmen's chamber. In a few seconds, at the far end of the lobby where long, curving marble staircases embraced the entrance from the garden, two loud voices debated which steps to take. Footsteps then clacked up those on the right.

"They've gone upstairs where the State Council is meeting," remarked Hamilton. "They probably don't know Congress is here since we don't usually meet on Saturday."

"This seems a good moment for us to depart," declared Izard.

"Dangerous! Much too dangerous!" cried Wilson and Maryland's Daniel Carroll at the same moment. Carroll added, "They likely have guards at the outer door controlling who goes in—or out. Worse, the rest of the mutineering hundreds are probably marching this way."

Bird-like Elbridge Gerry of Massachusetts dropped nervously in his chair, his bony face grim. "We should never have mm-met this morning!" he declared. "We're short a quorum, so we cannot take any action. We're c-caught in a dangerous corner. As soon as these mutineers learn they have both Congress and Council to frighten, there is no telling what they will demand—or do. Robert Morris did the wisest thing—he l-locked up the bank and went to visit a friend."

Robert Morris Official
Journal. June 21, 1783

President Boudinot, back in his chair, replied that he had called them to come immediately after he learned at noon that several hundred armed soldiers planned to attack the bank. "With the Council already in session upstairs in this building, I expected to hear that militia—which the state has, but Congress does not—was on its way to protect the bank. No such assurance came.

"No one expected the mutineers to come here— and the mutineers, not expecting to catch Congress as well as the Council, will rejoice to find us both. We have heard two soldiers mount the stairs. I suggest we invite no insults by intruding on their meeting. Instead, we could select a committee to confer with the Council after we hear those soldiers leaving the building."

They had just chosen Hamilton, Theodorick Bland of Virginia, and Boudinot when they heard the clatter of boots descending the stairs and the lowered voices of two men. Only seconds after they left the building, the Congressmen heard pounding on their door, and the voice of John Dickinson, President of Pennsylvania's Council. When the lock was turned, he entered breathing hard. His voice squeaky-tight with anxiety, he told the Congress his visitors were Sergeant Nagle, commander of the mutineers, and Sergeant Morrison. "They presented us with an ultimatum!" exclaimed Dickinson, and held up a piece of paper.

"They demand the right to send their choice of officers to confer with us and 'procure justice' for the revolting soldiers. They give us 20 minutes to write out such an agreement. If we don't (Dickinson read from the paper) 'we shall instantly let in those injured soldiers upon you and abide by the consequences!'"

"AND upon Congress, since everyone in this building will be under attack!" Hamilton declared.

"That is true," Dickinson acknowledged, "and Congress's debts to the army are as well-known to them as the debts of Pennsylvania."

Hamilton, arms crossed, expression stern, declared, "We asked you yesterday to call upon your militia to suppress this mutiny, and you refused. What say you now?" he demanded.

Dickinson, a Quaker known for his work for peace with England while vigorously but non-violently opposing King George, shook his head. "I must repeat, Colonel Hamilton, what I told you yesterday. It is the opinion of the Council that our militiamen cannot be relied upon to take arms against soldiers whose grievances they feel much sympathy for—unless those soldiers commit some

actual outrage—"

"Such as breaking into the State House—this room—and firing their muskets at us, or thrusting a bayonet into yourself?" demanded Hamilton, his eyes flashing indignation.

Dickinson shook his head impatiently. "I cannot believe any such thing will happen. By the time the sergeants return with their chosen officers—who, we think will turn out to be the instigators of this business—General St. Clair will have written the agreement they have demanded. The sergeants are surely only puppets. The Council will confer with those officers, explain that Morris has sent money to Lancaster camp. They will accept that, I believe, and send the soldiers back to their barracks, peacefully."

"Did the sergeants know that we—the Congress—are in the building?" asked Wilson.

"We did not ask them, nor did they mention it," Dickinson replied.

"Listen! More fifes and drums! The rest of the mutineers are coming!" called Ben Hawkins of North Carolina. The Congressmen rushed to the windows. Shortly, they saw an orderly, double line of uniformed soldiers ("We've had more uniforms to hand out since Yorktown than we ever had before," grumbled Hamilton) entering the State House expanse of gardens through openings between the building and adjoining sheds. Each man shouldered a gun, its bayonet flashing in the sun.

"They're surrounding us!" cried Hamilton.

Congressman Ellsworth of Connecticut suddenly flinched, cried out, and jumped away from a window. He had seen a bearded, wild-eyed soldier swing out of line, run toward the building, and point his gun at the window where Ellsworth was standing. As the Congressman drew back, the soldier jabbed the air with his bayonet, and ran back to the line.

"Cover the windows!" Ellsworth shouted, and

Alexander Hamilton

Jour. Cont. Cong.
1783. Vol. 24 p973-4

E.Boudinot (G.Boyd)
p124

Cont. Cong. (Burnett,)
p577

Signers of the
Constitution
(R.Ferris/J.Charlton)
p158

grabbed at the cords of the venetian blinds.

As if in answer, the soldiers, now standing in a loose line and looking at the first floor windows, began to shout, aware that the meeting room of Congress was occupied.

"GIT US OUR PAY!!"

"SIX MONTHS—NO PAY!"

"TWO YEARS—NO PAY!"

"NO FURLOUGHS WITHOUT PAY!"

"SETTLE UP—OR WE STORM THE BANK!"

"CONGRESS LIED! COUNCIL LIED!"

"WHERE'S OUR 6.66 A MONTH?!"

"WHERE'S OUR BONUS?!"

"DAMN WAR'S OVER! WE WANT OUR DUE!"

"WE GOT THE GUNS TO TAKE IT!"

"WHERE'S DICKINSON?!"

"IN THERE—SCARED!" (Laughter)

"PARLEY! PARLEY! PARLEY!"

Odd Destiny (M.Hecht)

R.Morris (Oberholtzer)

Inside, Hamilton, peering through a crack between slats of the blinds, exploded, "Assassins!"

James Madison, standing beside him, murmured, "How much do they imagine Congress has in the bank? Millions of dollars? Morris told you yesterday our bank shares total less than $54,000—all committed to feed the army—"

"—while Robert Morris every day signs Morris money to PAY the army," Hamilton broke in, "backing it with his own silver. These Lancaster soldiers became ugly yesterday when we told them we had sent their money to Lancaster, and they must return there if they wanted to be paid."

Robert Morris
(F.Wagner) p102-3

Hamilton lifted the blind slat for another squint at the scene outside. Some soldiers still were yelling,"Pay!Pay!" and a few burst out with insults and threats from time to time. "Damn politicians!" "Lying bastards!" "Rich aristy-crats!" "We'll hold you prisoner until we're paid!"

Hamilton suddenly jumped back from the window. "That man—he must have seen me—he ran up to the wall just below the window and jabbed his bayonet into the brick! His face—I saw faces like his—all hate and fury—among a rioting mob during the Revolution!"

"Gentlemen! Take your seats!" called out President Boudinot. "Remind them, Mr.Wilson, of the Philadelphia mob that attacked your house during the war, shot dead an officer standing in front of a window, then set your house on fire! We must avoid anything that invites violence or mischief! Gentlemen! Move away from the windows! Please sit down! Let us think what to do in this situation! Mr. Gerry, sir! Mr. Williamson! Gentlemen, please!"

Ellsworth had not been able to tear himself away from the crack at the side of a blind. "Shocking! Shocking!" he said over and over. "There are so many of them! Three, four—no, FIVE hundred. They keep yelling, shouting. I've heard obscenities. Listen! That fellow just ran up close to the building to holler 'We've brought ropes and lashes!'"

"Surely he said 'ladders', Mr. Ellsworth," said Nathaniel Gorham of Massachusetts.

"Is the Revolution to be subverted by the swords of a victorious but mutinous army?" bemoaned Hugh Williamson of North Carolina.

Col. Hamilton, still standing, banged his fist on a desktop. "Mobs and riots! Guns and insults! What a fine way to start a nation's history! Mutinous soldiers surround, overrun, KILL the delegates attending the Continental Congress! Murder in the room where the Declaration of Independence and Articles of Confederation were signed!"

"I can't believe they have in mind to go that far," ventured George Read of Delaware.

"To predict what a mob will do is folly! Many a riot has started off as a quiet gathering," Hamilton answered hotly. "But if a mouthy leader fires tempers, in a flash, disaster strikes!"

"So we merely sit here," Izard spoke up irritably, "listening to the insults and threats of this armed mob, waiting to hear the doors crashing open—?"

6

BAM! The striking of a rifle butt against the chamber's great door resounded through the building. Loud voices shouted in the lobby. Stern voices gave orders. Footsteps of departing soldiers faded and the outer door banged shut. The Congressmen and Pennsylvania's Executive had stood rigidly attentive in those few minutes. Mr. Mercer broke the silence. "We must find a way out of this trap—or we may be living our last hour!"

"I move that we adjourn!" Izard's voice boomed. "Into the embrace of the soldiers?" Madison's small,clear voice inquired.

"President Boudinot, I have a motion," said the tremulous voice of Mercer. "I move that we get down on our knees, pray, and think of eternity, for it seems certain we will all be there within the next few hours."

Hamilton's impatient voice stormed out, "A motion to direct the Congress President to send a message at once to General Washington requesting his best troops for our defense, immediately!" The vote was unanimous.

"Mr. President, I move that we send a spokesman to confer with the soldiers outside, persuade them to disband peacefully by assuring them of the disposition of Congress to do them justice," Read declared.

"Do I have a volunteer?"

"No, no—that is f-foolish," Gerry of Massachusetts stammered, "and would look as if we were bowing to them from fear. Besides, I do not see anyone acting like a leader with these soldiers."

"But if we wrote a statement they could pass around—saying that Congress can be trusted not to fail to settle their accounts, and settle them fairly, but need time—"suggested Bland of Virginia.

"That would not work!" Hamilton said, shaking his head vigorously. "Words on paper will merely anger men who haven't been paid for months. They want silver coin—not paper promises—NOW,this

very hour! For God's sake don't anyone walk out there to SAY words or hand out paper—you only expose yourself to humiliation at best. At worst, you could become a hostage, or the cause of a musket's discharge, exciting a riot!

"Remember what General Washington told us months ago, when his own camp officers almost mutinied. He said, 'Congress must pay the soldiers or expect commotion that could end in bloodshed!' Well, my friends, the commotion is here. Let us pray this is not the first day of such bloodshed."

"Congress HAS been doing something about paying the soldiers," spoke up James Wilson. "Our Superintendent of Finance has been signing his Morris notes to pay them."

"I doubt he can write fast enough to defuse this situation," answered Hamilton. "And to do any good, the soldiers must believe that his pieces of paper are as good as silver. What a rock-bottom position when men have more faith in one merchant than in the United States government!"

Boudinot shook hands with Dickinson, who was leaving, and mounted the two steps to his seat on the platform."Gentlemen,the soldiers have quieted this quarter-hour. I trust we can all agree we, too, had best watch and wait, do nothing about the soldiers or their demands—I doubt the guilty officers will return with the sergeants to press demands.

"If in spite of our restraint, however, they should become violent, begin to destroy property and threaten our lives, surely the Pennsylvania Council will then order its local militia to action—to save the Council as well as the Congress. Are we agreed on this course, Gentlemen?"

"YEA."

"Now, I beg you once more to resist looking through the blinds. Some foolish soldier might shoot at the movement—making you an accidental target," Boudinot warned the men by the windows.

"We should have accepted last month's offer of

Old Philadelphia
(H.Eberlain) p85-87

Jour. Cont. Cong.
(Burnett)p578

Jour. Cont. Cong.
June 21,1783 p973

Odd Destiny:
A.Hamilton
(M.Hecht) p85-7

GW Writings Vol.26,
p285, 296, 342

Robert Morris
(F.Wagner)p102

John Dickinson

In the room where Congress in 1776 declared America's independence from England, nervous delegates of the 1783 Congress peer through window blinds at perhaps 500 soldiers threatening violence. Two hours or so later, noting the lounging mutineers, the beseiged delegates risked leaving, and walked through the crowd unharmed. Rumors of violence persisting, Congress fled to Princeton, New Jersey.

a square of land at Kingston, New York," New Yorker Hamilton began.

"Or Williamsburg!" threw in Bland of Virginia.

"—and moved our sessions from this hostile city of Philadelphia," Hamilton added.

Madison's thin but intense voice took up the subject. "Would either of those villages have come forth with any more protection than the great city of Philadelphia? Would New York or Virginia have ordered militia to stand between us and armed mutineers? Brother might be asked to shoot brother. We can see from our present situation that this peripatetic Congress MUST attend to the matter of a PERMANENT residence—"

"—AND," Hamilton broke in, "itself govern that seat of government, DETACHED FROM ANY STATE! In such an independent district, Congress would command the militia. Then, should Congress ever call for help, help WOULD COME!

"As it has developed," he rushed on, "we used Philadelphia as our capital during the war, but ran hither and yon when threatened by the British. Always, we must rely on state generosity for a room to meet in. States decide to protect us—or not. State officials now have no respect for us. They call us 'the little Congress,' and laugh. They think Congress so little, they ignore its calls—be it for money to pay the army, or militia to deal with violence."

"Hear, hear!" agreed the delegates. President Boudinot had left his platform during these remarks, and joined the men standing on the floor. He raised his hand and voice for attention. "Gentlemen," he called, "assuming that by some means we escape harm this day, I suggest New Jersey could provide a safe home for Congress. Princeton has suitable space in Nassau Hall, home of New Jersey College for which I am a trustee. Several mansions, my sister's home 'Morven' among them, offer worthy accommodations for the officers of Congress. Many smaller houses and taverns have comfortable quar-

Old Philadelphia.
(*H.Eberlain*) p85-87

E. Boudinot
(*G.A.Boyd*) p126

ters for all of you."

"I quite agree," Gerry said, "that New Jersey would offer us safety. But I have heard both North and South delegates speak of Trenton at the Falls of the Delaware as a location half-way geographically, thus acceptable to both. Trenton, too, has great houses, and several hostelries since the stage between Philadelphia and New York stops there for the night, and since it is one of the towns where the state Assembly meets."

"Well, yes," said Boudinot. "Both New Jersey towns, furthermore, have the wide Delaware River as a barrier against mutinous soldiers."

"Listen! The mob is cheering! What's going on?!" Ellsworth exclaimed, and made a crack at the edge of the blind to look out.

"Come! Come! Look—the men are moving away from the building! They're cheering for barmen bringing them drinks! It seems the hot sun has worked for us! Thirsty soldiers forget rioting when drink appears!"

"Tipsy soldiers, however, are murderous," said Madison, looking out a peekcrack of his own.

"It must be only ale or beer they're getting. It looks to be free—it would have to be since the soldiers have no money," deduced Daniel Carroll. "I doubt the workmen who have gathered to watch the show would pay for spirits for 500 soldiers."

"I think the taverns across the street and nearby have moved to douse the fires of riot," ventured Hugh Williamson of North Carolina. "It's expected that soldiers on a spree of violence will attack taverns to seize the drinkables thereof. Usually they meet resistance, and end up wrecking the premises. Our noble tavern keepers are saving themselves—and us—with a barrel of beer!"

Wilson guessed that more than one barrel would be drunk. "Lucky tavern keepers to have two breweries within a block."

With murmurs of gratitude to tavernkeepers and

Ency.Brit. 11th ed.
Trenton, N.J. entry

Jour. Cont. Cong. June
21,1783, p973

James Madison

praise to God, the Congressmen crowded around the windows and peered for an hour at the scene in the open garden area outside one end of the room and at Chestnut Street on the other. The more nervous predicted trouble from the soldiers' tippling. The more experienced felt certain that soldiery daring would be blurred rather than enhanced by a half-pint of ale.

"That's about the most each one will get, I'd estimate," remarked Carroll. "And it will take much time for the little band of barmen to bring and pour even a half-pint 500 times."

About 2:30 o'clock, when the Congressmen observed that most of the soldiers had sought the shade of the trees, stacked their muskets, and sat—even lain—down, the Congressmen concluded that the soldiers still waited for leaders to appear and tell them what to do.

Boudinot opened the question of how the Congressmen could extricate themselves.

Picture map of Philadelphia (Bob Terrio) Friends of Ind.Natl.Hist. Park

Shortly, they agreed to follow his suggestions, Hamilton's dire predictions notwithstanding. "I propose," Boudinot said, "that we wait quietly until three o'clock, our usual adjournment time—then march out in a body. By then, if the tippling is only ale, the soldiers should be reduced to general mellowness, or better still, corporal sleepiness."

When the clock in the tower of the building sounded three o'clock, BONGNGNG-BONGNGNG-BONGNGNG! all was quiet. Most of the soldiers had retreated from the sun into the shade of trees in the garden, or the shadow of its high, encircling brick wall. Ever-changing clusters of a dozen or so men hung about a few barmen with pitchers and much passed-around mugs.

Inside the Hall, the Congressmen gathered by the door that opened to the lobby, its outside doors, the gravel sidewalk, and Chestnut Street.

Penn.Mag.Hist. (K.Bowling) Oct. 1977, p.433

At that moment, Pennsylvania's Council President, John Dickinson, was heard calling and pounding on the other side of the door. The door unlocked, he pressed a paper into Boudinot's hand. "It's General St. Clair's written agreement that we will meet with the Sergeants' chosen officers," Dickinson quickly declared. "Since Congress is involved, the Council would like its approval of this paper. Could you act on this, even without a quorum, informally—whatever—so we can have the signature of the Congress President?"

Jour. Cont. Cong. July 1, 1783

Boudinot quickly read aloud the short document, looked around at the faces of the delegates, saw only nods, and said, "I will sign it. The Council will remain in session to meet with the mutiny leaders?" Dickinson nodded.

Jour. Cont. Cong. July 1, 1783, Report p.417

Glaring at him, Hamilton exclaimed, "This menacing situation is the greatest of insults to the United States government, and it is a certainty that when the disturbance has been quelled, Congress will insist on courts martial for the guilty!"

Dickinson replied that the Council regretted the insult to Congress, and was sensible of having a principal share in its occurrence. "I see that you are adjourning. God grant that the soldiers have no inclination for violence against any of us. I believe they have none. God be with you." With a bow, he departed.

"Let us now leave with ceremony and calm dignity, Gentlemen," Mr. Boudinot said. "Arrange yourselves side by side in threes and form a column. Myself and the Secretary of Congress, Charles Thomson, and a volunteer—thank you, Mr. Hamilton—will head the procession. We will walk briskly, with firm step. The column of threes will follow close behind.

"Keep your rows and the column steady and in step. SAY NOTHING. Let no one taunt you into emitting a single word. Walk boldly, without any suggestion of fear—or haughtiness. Press on steadily, politely, strongly—let all insults pass. This is no time to risk argument or attempt reason.

"Have faith that no outrage will attend the adjournment of a session of the United States Congress. We shall cross Chestnut Street and turn right. Each of us will leave the column as he reaches his turn for home. I bid you to meet with me at six o'clock in this Hall, unless notified (he paused) that it is not feasible. Now, if we are all ready, I will start." They murmured, "Ready."

Immediately, the President of Congress, Hamilton, and Thomson marched briskly into the lobby, opened and proceeded out the great doors, walked unhesitatingly down the few steps, and crossed the street. They turned right on the sidewalk. Behind them marched five sets of three Congressmen.

"They're coming out!" someone shouted. The Congressmen then heard a babble of exclamations, rustles of movement, running feet, whackings of wood on wood as muskets were snatched from their stackings. Soldiers ran to the street.

Suddenly, a burly, bearded soldier was half-blocking the sidewalk where the Congress was proceeding. "Yaa—Congress bigwigs! Did YOU ever wait for y' $6 a DAY whilst y'family starved at home?!"

Silently, eyes straight ahead, steps never faltering, the column marched on. Velvet coats and lace wristlets brushed the soldier as they passed. He stood still, staring. His expression seemed one of fascination, gazing at these officers of the Revolutionary Army, signers of the Declaration of Independence, governors of states, judges, lawmakers, attorneys, owners of great plantations. He stared at them long after he could hear the rhythmic sound of the column's marching feet.

Others shouted to the soldiers running from the grounds behind the Hall into Chestnut Street, "Form a cordon! Block their way!" A few rushed into the street waving their muskets, but stopped short of the sidewalk, gazing at the elegantly dressed men whose names, if not their faces, had become known to all during eight years of war.

Details implied in <u>*Jour. Cont. Congress,*</u> *Madison, Boudinot accounts.*

Suddenly, a shout: "Cowards you are! What did we come here for? Arrest the rascals!" A soldier broke into a tipsy run toward the Congressmen. A rumble of disapproval accompanying a surge of the crowd of soldiers and townsmen stopped him.

The column of Congressmen marched on. A block farther, at Fourth Street, four soldiers on the corner had a close look at the parade of famous men, the government of the United States. One soldier raised his ale mug in salute. Two glowered; one spat on the ground.

President Boudinot, leaving the column to go to the Indian Queen a block away, passed between the soldiers. Three of them followed him.

He had walked past several houses when a man in a second-floor window called out, "That is the President of Congress! Why do you let him go?!"

"Stop! Come back here! You're under arrest!" the soldiers yelled, rushing towards the President.

"Stop yourselves, Privates!" called the soldier who had saluted with his ale mug, and who had been watching from the corner. The three Privates turned to face him. "I am Sergeant Townsend, Your Excellency," he said as he ran up, "and we have no orders from anybody to arrest, molest, or insult the Gentlemen of the government—or any Gentlemen whatsoever. My apologies, Your Excellency. Privates! Return to your barracks!"

President Boudinot, concealing his agitation and thinking of the hostile citizen who had shouted from the high window, strode rapidly the half-block to the entrance of the tavern. Inside, he was climbing the stairs to his room when he met his Boston friend, Josiah Bailey, merchant, coming down.

"Your Excellency! What is wrong?!! Your face tells me something terrible must have just happened!"

"ALMOST happened!" Boudinot replied "Close enough that I shall insist Congress leave this dreadful city forthwith, go to Princeton, Trenton, anywhere, and never, never return to Philadelphia!"

E. Boudinot (G.A.Boyd) p125 (letter to Washington, Sergeant's deposition)

E.Boudinot (G.A.Boyd) p126

Congress with only $53,000 in the bank, millions in debt, and no credit, borrowed Robert Morris's money and credit to pay disgruntled soldiers. He signed at least $500,000 of "Morris notes", guaranteeing he would redeem them in silver if the government did not. Mary (Molly) Morris, mother of seven, sister of a bishop, dressed in high fashion as befitted the wife of America's richest merchant, famous as "the financier of the Revolution."

CHAPTER 2

Robert Morris's Delaware River

SCENE: Office of the United States Superintendent of Finance, Robert Morris, merchant, in Philadelphia.
TIME: July 4, 1783, about 3:30 p.m.

Major source: The Papers of Robert Morris Vols. 7 & 8

In the heat of afternoon on the seventh anniversary of the Declaration of Independence, Robert Morris sat at a large table in his office writing his name again and again. Along one wall of the room, wooden boxes filled with thousands of specially printed pieces of paper lay in a row.

The only sound was that of Morris's quill pen scratching on one of the rectangles of printed forms. Scritch, scrritch, scritchy-scritch-scritch. "Rob-ert Mm-orr-is, the seven hundred and ninth time today." A deep sigh. A noisy yawn trailed off into a moan, "My God, it's hot!" Small sounds of movement as Robert Morris, 49-year-old finance officer for the Continental Congress mopped his large round face, double chin, and the folds of his short, plump neck.

The richest merchant in America, famous all over the country as the financier of the Revolution, had started hours earlier writing his name. He had worn out a handful of quills scratching "Robert Morris" on the three-by-six-inch pieces of paper, instantly changing them into money, more accurately called "Paper Anticipation" of hard coin. Tomorrow was delivery day for another $100,000 in "Morris notes" to the army paymaster, and a few hundred blanks remained to be signed. After that, only $90,000 more to reach the total of half a million dollars that Morris was guaranteeing the government—or himself—

Robert Morris Report to Boudinot, July 18, 1783 (Papers of RM, Vol.8)

would redeem in silver six months hence.

"Thousands of signatures in June from the sixth on—except for the week I spent with Congress in Princeton, discomforted, out of place. But how else can I keep an idle army from starting a war of its own against Congress and me?" Morris mumbled to himself.

"The army must be sent home before it eats all our resources—and Congress agree with General Washington that the men must depart with three months' pay in their pockets. In camp, they're disgruntled and dangerous, as we saw two weeks ago. Money! The states send none and the bankers of Europe probably will loan none, but I shall keep asking them. The Paper Anticipations of Congress being scorned by the soldiers, Congress must resort to paper not scorned—mine."

Another sigh. Dully he read, "Office of Finance. Six months after the date, pay, on account of the United States, fifteen dollars.." Scritch, scritchy, scritchy. "Rob-t Morrissss...and so it goes for 5s, 10s, 15s, 20s, 50s, and 100s.

"Well, it's an interesting if uneasy sensation to be in a position where my credit is better than the credit of the government of a nation. But then my credit would be as bad as the Congress's if I had to depend on stingy, petty, unreliable state governors for an income."

He heard noises in the hall—a heavy footstep, then a thump. He turned toward the door with a smile. A sudden rap, and the door swung open. "Gouv-ner!" Morris exclaimed. "Come in, come in! You're back from congressing in Jersey!" As Gouverneur Morris—no kin to Robert Morris except in mind and spirit—opened the door wide, returned the greeting and stepped aside, tall, lavishly dressed, smiling Mrs. Robert Morris walked in. "Molly!" exclaimed her husband, rising from his chair. "My dear, you look splendid in your new silk gown and satin turban! What magnificent plumes!"

Mrs. Morris beamed and tossed her head gingerly. "I'm about to depart for the country to see that all preparations for today's party move forward. You, however, MUST have some replenishment if you insist on working all afternoon. Samuel!" she said to a middle-aged black man following her with silver dishes on a silver tray. "We've brought some specialties from the cook. Place the tray exactly in front of Mr. Morris, Samuel—yes, there, never mind the little stacks of paper. That's fine. You may return to the house now. Gouv! Don't give my dear husband any news of Congress until he eats everything on the tray! Gouv raced his horse from Princeton in less than seven hours! arriving as I was entering the coach. I must hurry along—much to do when 40 men and their wives are coming to a party. We'll use up half the store of ice on such a hot night!"

She departed in a flurry of goodbyes, affectionate embraces, and wisps of French perfume. Her husband returned to his chair saying, "My wife is such a wizard at organizing, making decisions, and getting things done efficiently, we should press Congress to hire her to run their meetings!

"Ah me—Congress. What have they been doing since I left at the beginning of the week?"

Gouverneur Morris, assistant to the Superintendent, laughed and shook his head. "Oh, there is a

RM office in 1783 was in the store of Jacob Barge, corner of Market and 5th. Home on Front Street below Dock St.

bit of news, but I promised your wife I would not give it to you until you have eaten this food." The tall young man in brown silk knee breeches and brocade coat stepped with peg leg and one shiny leather shoe, silver-buckled, toward a chair. Braced by his walking stick, he let himself down into the seat and extended a slender wooden post attached at mid-calf.

He had been without his own flesh and bone for more than two years—ever since two run-away horses crashed his phaeton into a tree. His foot and ankle were so splintered, the doctors had amputated them. The wooden substitute had not stopped him from riding a horse better than many men, nor adding to his reputation as a successful gallant, nor serving Robert Morris as the perfect assistant.

"Your wife says you will kill yourself manufacturing money for Congress, Mr. Superintendent," Gouverneur said.

"There's no 'Mr. Superintendent' working here today, my friend. Just Bob Morris, merchant. All this—" he waved at the boxes by the wall—"will be leaning on my financial shoulders for the next few months. Well, I'm glad to rest my fingers," he said, lifting silver lids from the dishes, and beginning to eat as he talked.

"It's the glorious Fourth, Gouv, and everybody should be celebrating our new independence, but nobody in Philadelphia seems to have the spirit. Maybe the mutineers took it back to Lancaster with them. When I arrived two days ago from Trenton where I had retreated from Princeton's meager fare, I found that not a soul in Philadelphia had planned any kind of celebration for this great day!

"Right away I invited a company of 40 Gentlemen—foreigners, military and civil officers, and citizens—to come at seven o'clock this evening to 'The Hills' for food, festivity, and fireworks. Come along, Gouv! You need reminding—like the rest of

Robert Morris (E.P.Oberholtzer) p77

G.Morris (J.Sparks)

Robert Morris Office Journal June 30/July 4, 1783

Gouverneur Morris

*RM letter to Boudinot,
July 18, 1783*

*Journ. of Cont.
Congress, July 1, 1783*

us—of the great days in our history! You can ride with me. I will leave from home at six o'clock sharp—I enjoy my 'Hills' house and its view of the Schuylkill so much, I will even stop making paper money to go there!"

Gouverneur watched Morris eating and talking, and wondered how this broad-faced, broad-bodied, balding man could be so amusing, so ebullient, so jolly despite the worries that pressed from all sides. Here was a man who two weeks ago thought his life was in danger from armed, mutinous soldiers roaming the streets. Just days ago, he had sweated in Princeton, New Jersey's, Nassau Hall where Boudinot had led the Congress. Now he sat making jokes while perhaps digging his financial grave with his pen, promising to pay out a half-million dollars in silver coin by New Year's Day, 1784, if the government could not.

"The crisis with the soldiers might not have happened," Morris said between bites, "if I had written my name twice as fast during June. I signed only two-thirds of the notes needed, just enough to quiet Washington's rebellious men in the Newburgh camp, thereby discontenting the unpaid elsewhere. My best record was—oh, it must have been 10,000 notes in six days. Had I learned in school how to write my name with my left hand at the same time I wrote it with my right, the Lancaster sergeants might have been pacified in camp, Congress would be at peace in Philadelphia, and fireworks for the public would light our sky tonight!"

Morris had raised his cider mug to the sky and drained it while Gouverneur had a good laugh. Smacking his lips, Morris asked, "What happened in Princeton after Congress freed me to come home and create money?"

"Oh, there are still too few Congressmen to make a quorum and hold a proper session. But the committee of Hamilton, Ellsworth, and Peters has not only done a lot of talking, dissecting the mu-tiny and the Pennsylvania Council, it has also written it all down for the record. But you have heard about that, and so have I, ad tedium.

"This morning, before I hurried away to recuperate during the next four days from Princeton's dirty taverns and disgusting cooking, the Congressmen still on hand met very early and briefly to hear your five-minute report of June 22 read. They then accepted your resolution formally authorizing you and the paymaster to settle accounts with the army for rations, clothing, and pay."

Robert Morris jabbed the air with his quill. "Thank you, Congress! Thank you!"

Smiling, Gouv added, "The gentlemen also acknowledged another welcoming paragraph from Princeton people, followed by another invitation from Trenton, 10 miles away, to move over there. Ah, yes—Secretary Charles Thomson told me he put into the post, as instructed, letters to all the state governors telling them about New Jersey's recent offer for the seat of government—30,000 pounds for constructing a capitol, and total jurisdiction over a federal district.

"So the bidding begins for the seat," concluded Gouv, "a wide-open auction!" Gouv gave a short, unmirthful laugh.

"Everybody wants the $100,000-a-year flow of money that follows Congress to a place," he added. Robert Morris observed that every Congressman wanted to live close by the seat of government so as to travel little on abominable roads, and every squire and merchant wanted Congress next door so as to hear valuable news the day it happened, not weeks later. "I regret that Congress has moved from Philadelphia, a great inconvenience for me. Is there any talk in Congress of moving back? Some of them—Gerry, Lee, Izard—appear glad of an excuse to leave my town. They see me as the devil incarnate. My money stabilizing the country is BAD, they tell each other." The Superintendent of Finance

*Journal Cont. Cong.,
July 4*

*Congress at Princeton:
Thomson's Letters to his
Wife
(E. Sheridan/J. Murrin)*

*Journ. Cont Cong.,
June 23*

*"Whither Potomac?"
(L.Cress) Wm&Mary
Quarterly, Oct.1975*

screwed up his face in anger and disgust.

"Well, yesterday," Gouverneur informed him, "Hamilton and a Virginian, John Francis Mercer, did make a move for Congress to adjourn to Philadelphia when it was safe, and when soldiers sent by Washington had arrived in the city. But South Carolina's Izard, one of the cowpasture-for-capital delegates, jumped up with a motion to postpone, and a resolve that it's not safe or honorable to return any time soon. That group, Sir, on that day, had the strength to win. They're dead set on locating the seat of government in a country town far away from the bad influences of big city wickedness, politics, money—"

Jour. Cont. Cong.,
July 2

"—and Robert Morris!" exclaimed Robert Morris.

"They say, 'strong personalities and commercial interests,'" said his friend. "They say, 'an innocent town where no powerful, selfish, money-making influences pollute the virtuous business of law-making.' You should hear Elbridge Gerry's lecture on this theme.'Y-yes, the seat should lie mid-way between North and South, and should have no commerce, no rich financiers, no fashionable society or court-like manners, and no threatening m-mobs.'

"The Southerners say the same, but their geography shows Virginia as mid-way, while the virtuous New England and New York men say midway is Trenton, 200 miles north! They say 'Falls of the Delaware' generally, and name Lamberton, adjacent to Trenton, specifically. They see the obvious—that giving Congress total control of a town used as a state capital is politically impractical."

The Superintendent, digging into a sizeable trifle topped by thick, whipped cream, glanced at Gouv. "They're serious about their total control over everything in a federal district and no state capital?"

Gouv nodded solemnly.

"Then Philadelphia is out of the running," Robert Morris said, "except as a place where Congress can argue about where to locate its permanent seat,

and wait while it's built. But the virtuous-village advocates have the votes, you think, to keep Congress in Princeton, and name 'Falls of the Delaware' for permanent?"

Gouv threw up his hands, laughing. "Congress may never have a quorum, and so may never vote anything! But if ever enough delegates arrive to make a quorum in Princeton, they won't find a bed there without another man or two already renting space in it! The only delegate who is comfortable is Boudinot who lives in his sister's mansion and even he says Princeton is unsuitable for Congress."

James Madison
(R.Ketcham)

The Superintendent moved his dinner tray aside and wiped his hands on a napkin before picking up a quill. "Trenton," he said slowly. "Lamberton. Falls of the Delaware." He wrote his name.

Congress at Princeton
(E. Sheridan/J. Murrin)

"Gouv, Pennsylvania has a small village at the Falls of the Delaware—Colvin's Ferry. If Congress refuses to return to Philadelphia, and Philadelphia as state capital cannot be a candidate for permanent seat of the national government, we must promote another Pennsylvania candidate. Virtuous delegates now smile at New Jersey villages by Delaware Falls. They could easily—virtuously—stretch their smile across the river to Pennsylvania's village."

He looked up and winked a sparkling, uncommonly blue eye at his young friend.

Gouv flexed his knees and drew up his peg leg into a new position. Who owns the land at Colvin's Ferry? he wondered, and wasn't there some kind of manufacturing operation, Delaware Works, on a large island by the ferry?

His plump face beaming, Robert Morris suggested that Gouv look into those matters, and to include Lamberton on the Jersey side.

"The falls—our side preferably—would provide a perfect, moral setting for Congress," he went on, "being half-way between the evils of Philadelphia and New York. Colvin's Ferry, Pennsylvania, has a fine view of the river, its mile of hardly visible rapids, and of Trenton upon the bluff opposite. I've admired Colvin's site many times on my way to and from New York. To build a house there—and stables, especially stables—ah! that would afford me much convenience. My horses and I would stop there overnight at the end of the 30-mile, day's ride from Philadelphia. I'd happily miss barely tolerable dinners and beds in Trenton's taverns, especially when they're filled with assembly delegates."

Gouv settled back in his chair, smiling. His witty, talkative friend's ideas were sparking hot and fast, exciting, entertaining.

"Pennsylvania's side of the Falls has a fine advantage—the rock-strewn river separates it from Trenton and state politicians! Also, I know that Delaware Works on the island is turning out goods well suited to Congress delegates. A snuff mill would keep them in sneezes! A hat manufactory could produce fine felts, lending style to delegate dignity! A quarry and a plaster grindery would provide cheap building materials for a capitol! Grist mills, a malthouse, and shad fishery would furnish plentious food and drink!"

Then with a whoop of laughter, Morris's eyes almost closed as his face puckered from a mirthful thought. "Politicians—"he said, waving his quill in the air, "would know from long practice on each other how to make good use of the island's SLITTING mill, WIREPULLING mill, ROLLING mill, HOOP-IRON mill and TRIPHAMMER! Haw-haw-haw!!"

When both Morrises had wiped their eyes, the Superintendent with a big sigh declared, "Gouv, I've got to get on with this note-signing or the army paymaster will have too little for the soldiers tomorrow. Ah me—if you will kindly take this stack of signed notes to the nearest box under the window, I'll start on another pile.

"Do you realize, Gouv, that I have so far spent about 30 workdays of my life doing nothing but sign my name to paper money? Remember last year's money crisis when I wrote my name on many more than 10,000 'Morris notes'—'long Bobs' and 'short Bobs' according to the time of maturity. I was very proud that I had given the country a currency that, for the first time in years, all Americans would accept in trade, and which had the same value in every state. But this time, I may be called upon to sign twice as many to pay thousands of soldiers to go home and keep the peace. Those army privates will never know how unremittingly I scribbled and worried to create their $6.66-a-month pay. I tell you, I am propping up the country with three numb fingers."

Scritch, scritchy, scritchy. Gouverneur took his seat and watched the Superintendent quietly sign a set of blank notes. As Morris turned to the next set, he exclaimed, "Five hundred thousand dollars! Probably more later! Six months, and merchants who accepted them from ex-soldiers will be presenting them to Congress, expecting redemption in silver.

"For Congress to pay off my notes, I must begin now to beg states for coin, and beg our foreign banker friends for loans to Congress. I put a letter on a ship yesterday to Netherlands. I must write France—and our 13 governors,pressing them once more to pay Congress millions of dollars they owe. No one knows better than I what a hard tree that is to shake. I have waged continual warfare for years with the state governors, and have few dollars and much ill will to show for it."

Suddenly he pulled a page from the book of blanks he was signing, and handed it to Gouv. "Hold it up to the light," he said. "Do you see 'United States National Debt' written in WATER? That's my guarantee—besides a lot of talk—that Congress will get the money and pay off the notes in time. If they don't—paying is my responsibility. It's a chance

Place Names in Bucks County (G.MacReynolds) p264-5

Bucks Co.Hist. Soc. Papers, Vol. III, 1909

History of Bucks County (W.Davis) Vol.II, p164

RM (Oberholtzer) p155, 156, 296

RM, (F.Wagner) p102

RM (Oberholtzer) p103-4-5

RM letter to Congress (p128, Oberholtzer)

Trenton, New Jersey (above) at the Falls of the Delaware, received Congress's votes between 1783 and 1787 as the place for a permanent United States Capital. Surveys always included land on the opposite bank in Pennsylvania. A village developing there centered around Colvin's Ferry on the Philadelphia-Trenton-New York road, and on neighboring Delaware Works, a group of small industries. Robert Morris bought land on both sides of the river, but Congress, lacking money, built nothing.

18

I'm taking for this country in a desperate moment—letting Congress borrow my personal credit temporarily because it has none of its own. You know how devastating time lags can be, Gouv, either when you owe or are owed.

RM(Oberholtzer) p202

"Damnation! Another blot!" Morris sprinkled sand on paper. Grimly, he muttered, "TONS of coin! More silver than the French coin hauled by ox and cart in '81 from the ship in Boston harbor to our treasury in Philadelphia. God help me, I will be ruined if Congress fails to redeem, and silver must flow from my pockets! I am willing to risk as much for this country as any man in America. But is it expected of me that I put myself in so desperate a situation as absolute ruin?"

RM(Wagner) p207

Gouv tapped the tip of his peg leg on the floor nervously. "People believe that Robert Morris has many more millions of dollars, and that the notes are proof of it."

"Let them think that—it builds confidence, and confidence is the source of credit," Morris rejoined.

RM (Oberholtzer) p207

Gouv's peg tip drew agitated lines on the floor. "Yes sir, but perhaps you'd best be careful in the coming days—until all the soldiers in the area have been paid. The talk is that you have agents to purchase your notes as soon as they fall in value—which everybody expects. When Congress redeems them in silver, you'll reap a big profit, they say, on those you bought at discount."

Robert Morris suddenly and forcefully flung his right arm in the air and sent his quill flying out the open window. "Oh, this cursed job of drudgery and vexation! How can any soul continue to work for people who reward him only with calumny, jealousy, and hate!" he cried out. "If only I had stuck to my resignation and freed myself last month! To be liberated from this painful office!

RM (Oberholtzer) p200, 202

"But I gave in, desiring to free General Washington from HIS embarrassments by procuring some relief for his wretched, idle army. I tell you, my

RM to GW May 29, 1783

good friend, I will continue only as much longer as is required to send these soldiers home. When—WHEN?—will the peace treaty ever be done and over with!"

Gouv leaned to pick up a quill from the desk, and offered it to the Superintendent. "Sir, many do appreciate you. I heard James Madison decry the malice with which your character and services are murdered. Alexander Hamilton has told me he believes no man in this country but Robert Morris could have kept the money machine a-going for Congress for so many years. General Washington says openly that if any one man had to be singled out, Robert Morris is the one most responsible for our success in the Revolution."

RM (Wagner) p101

"God bless the man," said Morris, his voice quiet and tense with feeling. "If this country ever amounts to anything, it will be because George Washington has held us together and will hold us together. He understands business and money—that nobody can do business without money in hand. So give me that quill and let me create more money to keep the money machine a-going a little longer."

Scritch, scrrrritch, scritchyyy...

"My dear fellow," Morris said without looking up or stopping his quill, "thank you for your astute account of the events and talk in Princeton—especially about locating the seat of government. Once more I can say you are indispensable to me—and America. Nobody knows better than I how many times your ability and industry have made the impossible happen. Just being able to talk French to Rochambeau saved us at Yorktown."

"Sir, I thank you. I am your greatest admirer. You never will have a more sincere friend than Gouverneur Morris."

"I was about to say the same to you, young man." Robert Morris looked up. "You'd best go rest from your day of riding, and let me scribble faster. We have a Fourth of July party to attend shortly."

Life of Gouverneur Morris (Sparks)

As Gouv pulled himself up to stand, and made his final plans for accompanying the Superintendent to the country, he suddenly thought of an important piece of news. "Sir, nothing has happened yet, but in the taverns the delegates had much to say about asking General Washington to move his headquarters close to Princeton. The Southern gentlemen thought his presence would be particularly beneficial."

Morris stared at Gouv thoughtfully for a few seconds, then began scritch, scritch on another page of blank notes. "Ummm. They're thinking of the Potomac, of bringing the seat of government to Virginia or Georgetown, Maryland.

"Well, General Washington has been planning big things for his river Potomac, beginning before the Revolution. If he tells Congress about his preference, it will have a powerful influence.

"But, I have power too, and I intend to treat my honored friend to a lively contest."

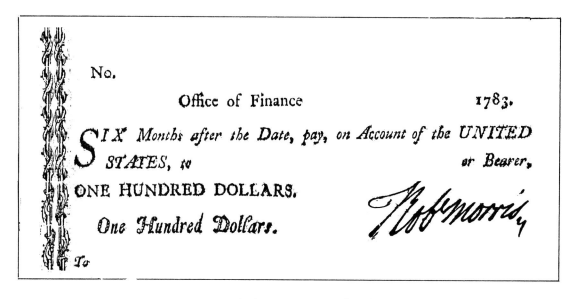

Blank "Morris Note" of 1783

At his country place on the Schuylkill less than three miles from his downtown Philadelphia office, Robert Morris could rest from business and politics, and enjoy exotic fruits and vegetables from his hothouse (right). Washington's main rival in the contest to locate the national capital, energetic, acquisitive Morris fought vigorously to draw the seat of government to his land at the Falls of the Delaware.

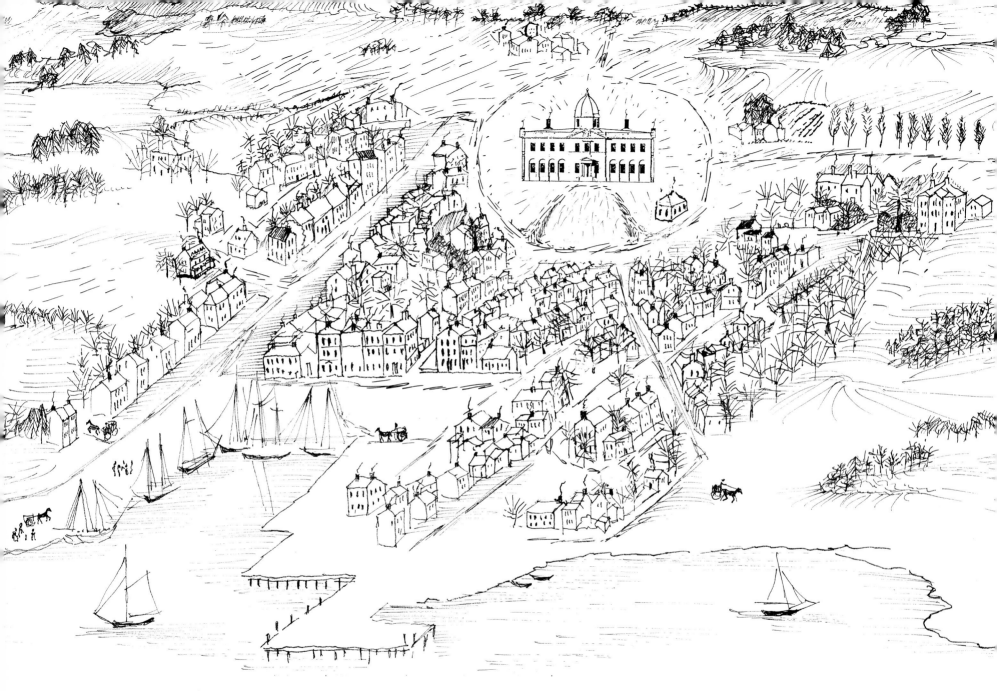

In a few hours in snow-covered Annapolis, General Washington and Continental Congress members will ride from Mann's Tavern (left center with porch and dormers) to Maryland's Capitol (circle). There on December 23, 1783, Washington will return the power Congress gave him eight years before. The event takes place in Congress's Southern temporary capital, alternate to Trenton, New Jersey, in the North. Alternate permanant capitals had also been voted—Trenton, and in the South, Georgetown, Maryland.

CHAPTER 3

Congress at Annapolis

SCENE: Mann's Tavern, corner of Main (Church) and Conduit Streets, Annapolis, capital of Maryland, on Chesapeake Bay.
TIME: December 22, 1783, eve of the ceremony when General George Washington returns the military power Congress gave him eight years ago.

Mann's Tavern,
Annapolis

Out of the Past
(R.L. Van Horn) citing
details from local
newspapers of
Dec.1783, and other
local sources

In the walnut-paneled foyer of Mann's Tavern, the escort group of 20 Congressmen awaited General George Washington's descent from his room. As soon as he, Governor William Paca, and Congress President Thomas Mifflin joined the Congressmen, the group would board coaches-and-four waiting outside the door in the frosty night. Uphill they would ride a few blocks to the second mammoth celebration of the day, a grand ball attended by planters and their wives whose carriages had been arriving all day from as far as 40 miles away.

The Congressmen in the tavern foyer were noisily talking about the afternoon's banquet, a feasting that had gone on some four hours.

"AAAhhh! It will take me another w-week to recover from today's eating!" groaned Elbridge Gerry, probably the skinniest man there. "Oh, it was the most EXTRAORDINARY banquet I ever attended—outlandish in its extravagance! Mr. Mann left out nothing from his pro-ff-fuse repertoire! Chesapeake oysters on the half-shell, in the sauce, in the stuffings, with the crabmeat! Then Maryland hens, roosters, and biddies glazed, dumplinged, gravied, barbequed! Followed by Maryland turkeys, partridges, d-ducks, and pheasants! And then! At least 40 Maryland recipes of puddings, casseroles, breads, pastries, cakes, pies, candies—and let us not count the free-flowing beverages or we shall

become tipsy from the memory!" Mr. Gerry ended his comments with one of his nervous tics—contracting and expanding the muscles around his eyes and eyebrows.

"But did you observe, Mr. Gerry, that not a single man among the 200 drank himself staggeringly drunk!" commented George Partridge of Massachusetts. "Most unusual! But then the exalted company was so intensely interesting—"

"Indeed, we were all too occupied with watching the General—no time to drink a lot!" observed David Howell of Rhode Island. "How much was he drinking? What dishes did he chose? How many helpings? We are no different from the citizens in the streets who stop and gaze at him, the man to whom we owe our present security, and future liberty, and peace."

"He's put on weight since I saw him a year ago," Cadwalader Morris of Pennsylvania said with several nods of his head to confirm his observation.

In the group behind him, Daniel Carroll of Maryland, his voice rising above all in the area, declared, "The noisiest banquet I ever attended! The only time those 200 voices went silent, the only moments the clattering of dishes, forks, knives, and spoons stopped, were the few seconds for each of the 13 toasts and accompanying cannon boom."

His voice lower and more intense, Carroll added,

Elbridge Gerry
(G.A.Billias) all details
about Gerry

"But a profound silence fell over the hall when the General stood to answer the toast to his happiness and health. 'Competent Powers to Congress for General Purposes, ' he said. I hope he's prophetic."

"I wish he would tell us HOW to put competent power in the hands of Congress," said Hugh Williamson of North Carolina. "Under the Articles, we can't make anybody—legislator or governor, or even ourselves—do anything. We have no money, no power to tax, thus no power. So we spend time instead. We can make motions and resolves, dissolve resolves, re-arrange motions, or lose track of motions entirely. We are best at backing and forthing. For example, in Princeton we spent most of our—uh—debates deciding what towns we would go to for our meetings."

His fellow delegate from North Carolina, young Richard Spaight, patted him on the back and said, "As a new member, I thank you for moving from Princeton to Annapolis instead of north to your alternate, Trenton, especially in winter and at Christmas. Besides being much closer to Carolina, this is a very pretty seaport, a neat, elegant place. Not a lot of buildings, but three-fourths of the houses are fine mansions!"

"And such beautiful women!" chimed a heavy-set man in velvet, lace, and tricorn hat who was just then squeezing past.

"Who is that?" mumbled Jacob Read of South Carolina. "Edward Lloyd of Annapolis," whispered James McHenry of Baltimore, and continued, saying that Lloyd's sister-in-law employed a French hairdresser at 1,000 pounds a year—"more than we pay the secretary of Congress. It follows," he whispered, that she's called the most beautiful woman in America and her husband is Mr. Jealousy."

"I have observed during the week I have been here," Gerry said over his shoulder to George Partridge, "that a surprising number of Annapolis gentlemen enjoy a princely style of living, and look upon themselves as aristocrats in the society. Excessive materialism and luxury! They undermine the virtue of the people and bring corrrr-uption of every kind!

"I hear many of the planters and ship owners have annual incomes of many thousands of pounds—Charles Carroll of Carrollton, a Declaration 'Signer', is one of them. He's said to be the richest man in America. His fortune is made from that vile weed, tobacco.

"What high style and frippery they live in! I hear that the French army officers, themselves addicted to the luxury that breeds corruption, went home from here last year after weeks of constant partying. They—General Rochambeau, General Armand, and a troop of young noblemen—declared Annapolis society more 'stylish' than Philadelphia's!"

"Why, Mr. Gerry, you'll have us thinking you've switched your permanent-capital vote from the Potomac—or is it today the Delaware?—to Chesapeake with your recitation of the delights of Annapolis!" teased elderly William Ellery, wit and humorist of Rhode Island.

The others laughed at the joke, but the skinny, birdlike Gerry deepened his usual squint, drew himself up, and, head tilted, glared. At 39, he was well-to-do but frugal, disciplined, and serious, a merchant of Marblehead, Massachusetts. Wagging a stern forefinger to emphasize each word of his reply , he said, "I have not sh-sh-shifted my ground, Gentlemen! I have only t-tried to be FAIR to every place outside of uncomfortable, unsuitable Princeton! Three months—July, August, and September—Congress slept poorly, worked uncomfortably, and ate badly, except when we rode an hour to Rocky Point to dine at General Washington's table. Some proposed to return to Philadelphia—but were defeated by those of us abhoring the corruptive influences of our large cities.

"In October when, as scheduled before we left

Elbridge Gerry

*Story of Dec.
Independence*
(D.Malone) p124

*Journals of Cont.
Congress July-Nov.
1783*

24

Philadelphia, it was the time to decide WHERE to build the permanent home Congress needs, and WHERE to meet more comfortably until that home was habitable, I offered every state a chance for the prize. The states refuse to give Congress money, but half of them beg for our company! AND the $100,000 a year in trade we bring! Annapolis wants us! Kingston, New York, wants us! Williamsburg and Georgetown and Wilmington and a dozen others smile and beckon. All of you know my mo-oh-oh-tion (Mr. Gerry's hesitation stammer almost stopped him) left out no place! Every state was voted upon. BUT— NO state won!"

Some delegates who had attended in Princeton began to laugh. Gerry drew himself up and rebutted. "Bu-Bu-Bu-BUT, it was FAIR!" The men around him laughed again. A voice in the little crowd called, "Just an idle chance for North to vote North and South to vote South, and each state for itself!"

Laughter, Gerry, and the subject had drawn all the Congressmen, including Virginia's three, to the circle.

Feisty Gerry continued undaunted, his brows drawn together, his head tilted to one side. "I then offered the PRINCIPLE that Falls of the Delaware OR Potomac—rural places where the purity of republican principles and manners could be preserved—was a principle acceptable to all!"

"Sir, did you expect anybody to say 'yea' to Delaware AND Potomac in the same breath?" said Delaware surgeon James Tilton."Even your Massachusetts colleagues couldn't. They kicked out Potomac—and 16 of us north of Maryland agreed—everybody except YOU, Mr. Gerry! You threw your vote away to the losing South!"

Gerry frowned mightily, shaking his head, then stretched his eyes open wide ."You missed the point of my motion—for delegates North and South to AFFIRM that the American capital should sit on EITHER of those quiet riverbanks, away from the

evil influences of a large, dominating, commercial city!"

"Really, Mr. Gerry?" growled Arthur Lee of Virginia. "Have you forgotten, Mr. Gerry? The very next day, you turned your back on us when your motion was reconsidered."

Nathaniel Gorham, a Boston-area merchant, could hardly wait to throw the next barb. "And have you forgotten, Mr. Gerry, how only one WEEK later, you leaped South again with your motion to build a federal seat on Potomac IN ADDITION to a seat on the Delaware?!"

A slightly falsetto voice from the edge of the group remarked, "Oh, Mr. Gerry! Could it be that no idea is a good idea unless it's YOUR idea?"

"Who s-s-said that!?" demanded Mr. Gerry. David Howell of Rhode Island, who was standing at Gerry's elbow, quickly and loudly said, "And Mr. Gerry! You scare-talked us New England delegates into voting for two capitals. The Southerners, you said, would kill any money bill for a Delaware capital—unless Potomac was included! TWO permanent capitals! Georgetown and Trenton! TWO temporary capitals—Trenton and Annapolis—while we waited for buildings to go up! Back and forth, forth and back, we'd be traveling through mud, dust, and river fords year-round! No sir! We'll not let that vote last through this session, I warn you!"

Gerry stretched his eyes wide and rose on tiptoes. "TWO capitals will be the only way to have ANY capital, for North and South will never agree on one! Besides, the committee to survey the two sites has already done half the job—with our geographer, Thomas Hutchins, we stopped two days at Delaware Falls on our way home after Congress adjourned! He surveyed a site at Lamberton by Trenton, and a second one at Colvin's Ferry across the river in Pennsylvania. As for Georgetown, we engaged Charles Beatty to go there and survey—"

Abel Foster of New Hampshire, red-faced from

"Whither Columbia? " (L.D.Cress) *Wm&Mary Qrtly.,* Oct.1975

"Neither in a Wigwam nor the Wilderness" (K. Bowling) *Prologue Mag.* Fall 1988

Jour. Cont. Congress Oct.7 , 1783

Oct.8

Oct. 20, 21

Oct. 7

Oct.17, 20, 21

Journ. Cont. Cong. Committee Report, Dec. 27

"A Place to Which Tribute is Brought" (K.Bowling) *Prologue,* Fall 1976

holding down his temper, burst out, "Aside from the extra 200 or so miles we in New England would have to travel to Potomac, we should consider how the Europeans will react when they learn they must build or rent TWO houses, with diplomats constantly bumping along our wretched roads between them!"

Still stretching on tiptoes to spot the delegate guilty of taunting him, Gerry spluttered, "The salutary effects—" but Ellery of Rhode Island brusquely interrupted—"are figments of your imagination, Sir! We will have convoluted confusion with regional capitals! Soon we will have a third capital at Fort Pitt, and another on the Mississippi—if we should ever expand so far! Multiple capitals! Ridiculous! You've led us astray, sir!"

"Gentlemen!" called McHenry of Maryland. "Not so noisy! General Washington is due here any minute! What will he think if he walks in and finds us going at each other tooth and nail?"

"He will know it is Congress who awaits him, and it is not cured of disputation!" rose Thomas Jefferson's slow, musical voice.

Laughter and the babble of voices broke off as Mr. Mann, the portly tavern keeper, stepped briskly into the room. "Gentlemen of Congress! We have the honor of welcoming General George Washington! with President Thomas Mifflin! And Governor William Paca!"

The familiar, towering figure in his heavy black cloak and three-cornered hat strode into the foyer.

"Gentlemen!" The General's voice ended the word on an upbeat. He bowed as he lifted his hat, uncovering his powder-white hair with long queue enclosed in black silk.

The delegates returned the bow and uncovered their heads briefly, responding, "Your Excellency!" "General!"

At one side stood the Governor in red velvet and gold lace, and at the other side, the President of Congress, handsome, stocky Mifflin in stylish grey-blue velvet and ruffled lace cravat. "We are ready to proceed to the State House and the Grand Ball, Gentlemen," announced the strong baritone of Governor Paca. Mifflin flashed a smile at the delegates and said, "The Congressional escort is ready, I trust? Then let us board the coaches. Mr. Jefferson, Mr. Hardy, Mr. Monroe, Mr. Lee—General Washington has requested that you, the Virginia delegation, join him, Governor Paca, and myself in the coach of state. I see that Mr. Mann, whose catering today has excited our greatest admiration, has opened the door to the dark, frozen world. Let us make haste to the coaches!"

Servants appeared and draped cloaks about the Congressmen. Virginians quickly followed Washington, Paca, and Mifflin, facing a chill wind. An icy coverlet of snow now three days old lighted the scene, outlining roofs, blanketing the tavern's wide yard all the way to Main Street.

Shivering black attendants in red coats and gold knee pants swung open the doors of the four coaches. Horses snorted and tossed their heads, while the men hurried to sit down in seats warmed by charcoal burners beneath them.

In a matter of minutes, the heavy wheels of the line of coaches were grinding into the half-frozen ruts of the drive. Flickering whale-oil lanterns on the outsides of the vehicles played their light on the snowy ground and the faces of the distinguished men.

In the last coach, the delegates from New Hampshire, Massachusetts, and Rhode Island began immediately to discuss General Washington. "He looks very plump in the face," said Gerry. "I hear he's 30 pounds heavier than his usual weight."

"Sitting around two years waiting for the peace treaty plays more hell with a general's flesh than a hot battle or two every season," observed Ellery.

"Still, he hasn't put it on as thick as General Lin-

George Washington

GW (D.Freeman)

coln," said Partridge. "Have you seen him? He's up to 224, I'm told. General Knox is worse. He's at 280 pounds, a bison of a man, breathing heavy and walking slow."

"General Gates is here, and St. Clair, and Small-wood, and they're ALL fat," said Ellery.

RM(Oberholtzer) p176

"Perhaps these Generals are fat in direct p-pro-portion to the leanness of their finances," said Gerry. "When I stopped in Philadelphia on my way here, I heard that General St. Clair's plight melted Robert Morris's famous resistance to pitiful stories, and he gave the General $300 from his own pocket."

"I heard something even more interesting," said Sam Osgood, 35-year-old Massachusetts merchant. "General Washington's war-time expense account—how much it totaled. Oh—by the way, I passed through New York on November 25th when the last of the British army boarded ships and departed, and when Washington and the troops came march-ing in. Great crowds of people yelling, shouting, crying! I did, too. I think all 20,000 inhabitants turned out to see him. I went on to Philadelphia, and a week later when he arrived there, I witnessed the same crowd scene.

"What I heard about his expense account came in a roundabout way from Robert Morris's office," Osgood said. His five companions leaned to hear him better. "The General brought his records show-ing year by year how much money Congress sent him, and what it was spent for."

"How much did it total?" several voices asked simultaneously.

Accounts, GW with U.S. June 1775/ June 1783 Recapitulation

Triumph of Freedom (J.C.Miller) p661

"Something over 16,000 pounds spread over eight years. That covered his headquarters, travel, secret intelligence, but not food and drink from the com-missary. Nothing for salary. It works out to 2,000 pounds a year—six a day.It's meaningless to figure silver pounds into paper dollars now worth noth-ing or less."

"Six pounds a day!" exclaimed Abel Foster of New Hampshire. "Not much more than it costs to pay my board and room in this town. Annapolis has many attractions, but it's the most expensive place I ever stayed—much more than Philadelphia!"

Md.State House exhibit

Amid murmurs of agreement, Gerry declared the General's 2,000 pounds a year for his military fam-ily, travel, and spies was not much more than the Gerry family spent in a year.

"Well, he HAS asked to be repaid now for the cost of Mrs. Washington's travel back and forth from Mount Vernon to army camp every year —a matter of 2,000 pounds," added Osgood.

"I hope Morris pays him in coin, not in Conti-nental paper," said Gerry. The sounds of unani-mous approval moved Osgood to tell how Morris had boxes of silver loaded at night into the Gen-eral's baggage coach.

"By the way," Osgood said, "The General stayed with the Morrises. They're the closest of friends."

"I wonder," remarked Partridge of Massachusetts, "what they said to each other about TWO capi-tals—one on Washington's Potomac, the other on Morris's Delaware—especially since Morris and his merchant friends are also trying to lure Congress from New York to Philadelphia while the perman-ant seats are built."

Ellery snapped, "Since Congress may remain pen-niless, a temporary seat lasting forever will be the winner over any permanant seat needing money to materialize."

In the next to the last coach, the North and South Carolina delegates spent half the drive to the State House comparing the miseries of their journeys on 300 to 600 miles of bad roads or rough seas. "Only to arrive and join a handful of Congressmen—in-cluding Mr. McComb here, down from Delaware—who have sat here for weeks unable, for lack of a quorum, to start the session!" complained Benjamin

Continental Congress (E.C.Burnett) p592

Hawkins of North Carolina. "We have the peace treaty in hand—and New York, New Jersey, Connecticut, and Georgia have no delegate here! Mr. Read, if your other South Carolinian would get well, ride down from Philadelphia—"

"Mr. Beresford has fever—he's really quite ill," Jacob Read injected.

"—if you, Mr. McComb, will cancel your urgent trip back to Delaware, and if New Jersey will quickly send two men, we would have nine states and could get to work!"

Eleazer McComb shook his head. "I am as concerned as anybody about dealing with the treaty to meet the English deadline. But I predict that I will have time to go home and return before a quorum assembles. It's Christmas and bad weather time—expect no one until the January thaw."

Hugh Williamson did not laugh with the others. Solemnly he observed, "Every session, it takes longer for Congress to get to work, and the work accomplished amounts to less and less."

Thomas Mifflin

Five of Maryland's delegates, and one each from Pennsylvania and Rhode Island, had squeezed into the facing seats of the coach behind the State coach. The door had barely closed when Cadwalader Morris of Philadelphia leaned toward McHenry of Maryland and remarked tartly, "Did you notice General Mifflin waiting by the coach and bowing and bowing—and Washington smiling and bowing to Mifflin?"

McHenry nodded. "Yes—but I also noticed that General Gates, here for the occasion, was NOT invited to join Mifflin in escorting Washington."

Edward Lloyd of Annapolis cleared his throat elaborately, and said, "Gentlemen, perhaps you are unaware that General Gates is an old friend of my family—he is, in fact, a guest in the Lloyd family mansion. His Excellency, General Washington, has courteously sent two of his aides to escort General Gates, who is not part of the Congress as President Mifflin is, to the ball in the Capitol."

After a few seconds of silence, McHenry said, "Nevertheless, Mr. Lloyd, you as well as everyone else must be aware of the curiously ironical scene we will witness tomorrow. At noon, victorious Washington, with Gates on hand to watch, will present to Congress President Mifflin the army commission—and power—that Gates, Mifflin, and Conway tried so hard to take from him during the winter of Valley Forge. They argued that Washington was losing battles that Gates could win. Congress did not listen, thank God."

Three other Marylanders—Carroll, Stone, and Annapolis Mayor Jeremiah Chase—with Howell of Rhode Island and Cadwalader Morris of Pennsylvania chorused, "Thank God!" Lloyd murmured, "It was all Conway's doing."

"The odd thing to me," said Cadwalader Morris, "is that Washington seems to have accepted Mifflin's story that he was only an innocent bystander. But I was at Valley Forge that winter—Philadelphia Light Horse—and know how much the army suffered from Mifflin's poor job as Army Quartermaster. Later we heard he had been too busy conspiring against Washington to round up and deliver food and clothing to the soldiers."

Mayor Chase shifted his large frame and growled that his kinsman, Sam Chase, a member of Congress that year, helped approve the advisory to Washington that he should investigate Mifflin's quartermaster accounts.

"Did he?" inquired Daniel Carroll.

"No. I can't imagine why not—except that Mifflin had been one of his aides a year or so before, and he thought he was too good a man to ruin."

"How VERY interesting," responded Morris, "for I heard Mifflin say recently that General Washington was THE best friend he ever had. Now I know

GW (Freeman)

GW (D.Freeman)

Dict.Am.Rev. (Boatner)

how true that is!"

McHenry gave a short laugh. "Well, no matter what he's thinking or feeling tomorrow, the General will be Grace itself when he gives his speech, and hands to Mifflin his army commission."

Thomas Jefferson

In the crowded Coach of State, Thomas Jefferson's calm, expressive voice kept the talk moving. "What a pleasure to learn that the new duties assigned me by the Virginia Legislature will confront me in my neighbor state, in comfortable, beautiful Annapolis—not Trenton, a VERY cold place." The coach began making the turn into Main Street, horses straining to pull the great coach onto the long incline to the Capitol circle.

"I confess I was dismayed in October," Jefferson continued, "when a letter from Mr. Madison informed me that Congress had voted to locate the seat of government at the Falls of the Delaware— Trenton forever! A month later—Trenton part-time, Georgetown on the Potomac equal-time! Annapolis and Trenton—split-time as temporaries, which might be forever also."

"Whither Columbia"
(Cress) Wm&Mary
Qrtly Oct.1975

All the men laughed, even Washington. "Well, we had to work on Mr. Gerry of Massachusetts to resuscitate Potomac," said Arthur Lee. "He then worked on the New England men. In spite of his odd stammer and facial distortions, he obviously is persuasive. They voted with us. Perhaps they were impressed with news he brought them that we would not support funding for Trenton buildings. Or perhaps it was the news that we would join those who wanted to go back to Philadelphia, no matter the high drama that drove us away."

The chortles of the Southerners ceased as Washington began to speak.

"The judges in the courts martial rated the story exceedingly high drama," General Washington answered. "They sentenced two sergeant leaders

Journ. Cont. Congress
Sept.14, 1783

to hang, and four other men to suffer whippings. Congress, as you know, chose to pardon them all and send them home. The two officers who stirred up the business probably would not have fared so well had they been captured before fleeing to Europe.

"The soldiers they led into revolting were soldiers of a day," he continued. "They had borne none of the heat and burden of the war —unlike the 1500 (almost my entire force) at Newburgh which I sent to quell, if need be, the disgraceful behavior of the troops in Philadelphia. By then, of course, the Lancaster troublemakers had gone back to camp, and Congress had moved to Princeton. I cannot sufficiently express my surprise and indignation at the arrogance, the folly, and the wickedness of the mutineers."

GW letter July 1783

Governor Paca responded, "A shocking affair, and Congress must never be faced with such again! I have pointed out to our legislators that Congress has included in its seat of government bills its requirement of total jurisdiction over the capital district. I believe they will add it to our offer of 300 acres with the statehouse, governor's mansion, public circle, and 13 buildings for the delegates."

Jour. Cont. Cong.
Oct7-21, 1783

Washington spoke quickly to say, "I heartily concur with Congress's move to make the seat of a national government entirely independent of any state."

"Whither Columbia?"
(Cress) Wm&Mary
Qrtly Oct.1975

The other six men waited expectantly. Would he mention his attitude toward having two capitals? For a moment, no one, including the General, spoke.

Then, with a little cough, Washington addressed Mifflin. "I am overjoyed, President Mifflin—"(he stopped and cleared his throat) that the final peace treaty, revised by the British to take care of most of our objections, is now in the hands of Congress. Mr. Jefferson, I understand you have the task of shepherding the treaty through. It is, therefore, in

Map of Annapolis

Maryland Gazette, Dec. '83. Out of the Past (R.L.Van Horn)

The State House at Annapolis (M. Radoff)

the best of hands."

Jefferson was saying his thanks when the coach reached the top of the hill and turned to the right. A long block away, the State House illuminated with a thousand candles in windows from the top of its dome and tiny cupola to the ground, flashed into sight.

All the men in the caravan of coaches suddenly stopped thinking of politics, exclaimed with pleasure at the thrilling sight, leaned and twisted for a better view. Another right turn, and within minutes they had traveled the circular drive downhill far enough around to see the Capitol floating high like a dream palace of lights against the black sky. On the streets leading to the circle, they saw the flickering lamps of a hundred coaches moving slowly toward the great event of the season—or perhaps the decade.

"Gentlemen," laughed Governor Paca, "you see why it is so necessary to have these grand and glorious social occasions: For a few seconds, they shut off the flow of political talk!"

"Time's up!" drawled Jefferson. "General, did you have time to look at the order of business drawn up for tomorrow's ceremony in the Senate chamber of this Capitol?"

"Yes. It is a good procedure."

Journ. Cont. Congress 1783, p820 Committee Report

"You approve then. Mr. Monroe, Mr. Gerry, Mr. McHenry, and I were appointed a committee to draw it up. Of course, we had plenty of advice. May I call to your attention that the President and members of Congress will be sitting when you arrive, and will remain seated while you speak. They will also remain covered."

Washington nodded and said, "It goes without saying that I would wear no hat out of respect to Congress. I would bow before I make my address, and also as I retire, even if it were not written into your instructions."

"Your Excellency," said Mr. Mifflin, heard for the first time on this ride, "as President of this session of Congress, I assure you that our respect for you is so great, we will have difficulty remaining seated and with our hats on during this ceremony tomorrow. Only with great effort will we be able to limit ourselves to uncovering but not bowing in response to your bows to us. You have served Congress long, faithfully, and triumphantly, and you have our full affection!"

Washington responded without hesitation. "President Mifflin, if my conduct through the war has merited your confidence, and that of the Congress I have long served, I owe my actions to that Supreme Being who guides the hearts of all, and who has bestowed on me the greatest of earthly rewards—the approbation and affections of a free people in this now independent nation." *GW resignation speech Dec. 23, 1783*

Governor Paca said jauntily, "General, the outpouring of approbation and affection from many thousands during the past few weeks has been truly phenomenal! Indeed, Your Excellency, it was soul-shaking in Baltimore when you attended the mammoth banquet and ball—" *GW (Flexner)*

"I heard that you danced all night, General," Jefferson interrupted.

"—and I have heard descriptions of the adoring crowds in New York, Trenton, Philadelphia, and Wilmington," continued Paca. "Your popularity is so great, General, you have only to ask for any position, any particular thing, and the people will give it, nay, THRUST it into your hands. 'Our King' some call you."

"Gentlemen," answered Washington, "my greatest desire is to go home in time for Christmas dinner with my family. I hope to spend the rest of my days under my own vine and figtree at Mount Vernon, which I have but once visited, and that briefly, in eight years of war. I shall be content to farm my acres as a private citizen there on the banks of the Potomac." *Writings of GW Vol.27*

The coach had rounded the State House drive and stopped at the brightly lit portico. Footmen jumped down from the coaches to open the doors, pull down the steps, and bow and smile as the gentlemen climbed out.

Washington was rising from his seat when Jefferson suddenly inquired whether he needed to leave the ball early to prepare his speech.

"It's here in my pocket," answered Washington, putting his hand on his breast. "I have been ready for weeks. Tonight I will remain as long as it takes to dance with each and every lady, starting with the beautiful Mrs. Mackubin, as ordered by the ball committee."

"Sixty belles are attending, General," laughed Governor Paca, "all of them eager to get their hands on you!"

Maryland Gazette Dec. 1783. Out of the Past (Van Horn)

CHAPTER 4

George Washington's Potomac River

SCENE: Southwestern corner of Pennsylvania, and adjacent western Virginia, in the Allegheny mountain area of the Monongahela and Cheat rivers, and headwaters of the Youghiogheny near Potomac's source.
TIME: From Thursday afternoon, September 23, to Saturday night, September 25, 1784.

Persons, places, routes, events from GW Diary, Sept. 1784

GW Diary, Vol.2, p301

Now Uniontown, Pennsylvania

Left: Searching out waterways in the Allegheny Mountains of western Pennsylvania and Virginia, George Washington slept in cabins of frontiersmen along the trail. He questioned all about streams in the area that could possibly connect the western end of the Potomac to the Ohio and Mississippi rivers. As an east-west waterway, the Potomac could offer the best capital site for an expanding nation.

Bushrod Washington's horse jerked its head and snorted. The young man released tension on the reins to let the animal crop the grass close to the ground. Near Bushrod and his two companions, tall golden-brown grass rippled in a late September breeze that chilled this high, open meadow and the lightly rolling woodlands bordering it in the distance. On the southeast, the land rose in a series of hills to the foot of long and rugged Chestnut Ridge. Ahead, on the west, two ridges marked the banks of the Monongahela River.

"Tolerably level land here, Colonel, compared to the hills in our past hour from Beason Town," remarked Bushrod's tall, gray-haired Uncle George. He stood head and shoulders above the stocky frontiersman striding beside him, returning to their horses from a walk.

"Tolerably level, General, and only tolerably good for growing anything. Not as rich as I'd like, this Allegheny country. I may move on west one of these years."

The two men stirruped and swung themselves up into their saddles.

"We're only about 10 miles from my house," Colonel Phillips said, clucking his horse into starting. "It's on the far edge of this flattish area, so we'll git there in a coupla hours, a good spell before dark. My farm and cabin, as I said, are just two

miles short of where the Cheat comes into the Monongahela."

The three horses moved along smartly toward the sun hanging over the western ridges. "The Cheat is a fair-size river coming out of the Blue Ridge mountains in Virginia," said Washington. "I've heard from some that, though rough with rapids, it will accommodate at least rafts and boats the 25 miles from Dunker's Bottom to its junction with Monongahela. Some say not. I am looking for local men who have traveled the Cheat, and have accurate information. On the way here from Virginia, I traveled on the east side of Chestnut Ridge. Several times I met parties taking ginseng roots to Philadelphia, and heard from some that the Cheat is mostly impassable, being blocked with boulders.

"What is the truth about this river? Have you gone up the Cheat yourself, Colonel? Have you ever traversed the land between the upper end of the Cheat and the upper end of the North Branch of the Potomac—30 miles or so one man told me. Is there a good way? Or is it rough and a good way not to be found, for I've heard both." The Colonel shook his head. "Never went up the Cheat nor tramped the mountains to the east of it. But I know a man near its forking with the Monogahela who knows hunters that go up the Cheat and prowl the nearby wilderness."

GW Diary, Vol. 2, p290

p300

"I'd like to talk to those men. Who is your neighbor, Colonel?"

GW Diary, Vol.2, p302

"Captain Samuel Hanway, and he's the surveyor of Monongahela County. He's mostly in Morgan Town on the river, but tomorrow he'll be in his office in John Pierpont's cabin up on the ridge that crosses the triangle of land where the rivers fork. We'll have to climb to the top and ride eight miles east along the crest. But once we're at the cabin, it's only two miles more, downhill mostly, to the mid-section of the Cheat."

"Then I must go there tomorrow to obtain further information on the feasibility of connecting the Cheat with the Potomac," said Washington. "Would you be agreeable to accompany me, or provide me a guide?"

"I m'self will be proud to escort you, General," replied Phillips.

"I'm much obliged to you, Colonel. My trip to the Allegheny country was mostly to look after my lands close to Fort Pitt—which now has 20 log houses inhabited by traders and Indians. I dealt with my incompetent manager and tried reasoning with squatters—to no avail. I am forced to sue. A second reason for my trip was to search out waterways that could best link the Potomac River to the Ohio and thereby to the Mississippi.

GW Diary, Vol.2, p299

"I had intended to go down the Ohio from Fort Pitt," Washington explained, "as I did in 1770. At that time, I went to stake claims to the lands the Crown gave Virginia militia who fought in the French and Indian War. We walked and canoed for days through rich and beautiful river country, which abounded in deer and buffalo herds, bears, and wildfowl. But this week I was advised not to go. The Indians are generally in arms, attacking some of our settlements. I therefore resolved to return home through the Cheat area to learn whether, as some informants have told me, that river, or the 'Yawky-gany' can link the Potomac to

the Monongahela, which joins the Ohio at Fort Pitt.

"There is a matter, which (tho' it has not come before Congress), in my opinion, is of great political importance and ought to be attended to in time. It is to prevent the trade—grain, furs, peltry—of the Western territory from settling in the hands either of the Spanish at New Orleans or British at Montreal. If either of these happens, there is a line of separation at once drawn between the Eastern and the Western Country, the consequences of which may be fatal to our expansion.

GW Writings, Nov.3 letter

"I hear," he added, "that settlers in the far western lands of North Carolina have organized and are talking of applying to the Spanish for confederacy and trade. Last January, Mr. Madison brought me news that the Spanish at New Orleans were offering money and land to settlers between the mountains and the Mississippi to become Spanish subjects—or not be able to sell tobacco in New Orleans."

Washington as a Business Man (H.L. Ritter)p156

GW Diary, Jan.25, 1784

Bushrod, seeing that his uncle had warmed stronger and stronger to his subject, moved closer for better hearing. Colonel Phillips, already beside the General, was gazing intently at the calm, peaceful man he last saw as the stern commander at Yorktown lighting the powder fuse of the first cannon to bombard the enemy.

The General looked straight ahead as the horses walked steadily on. His gaze focused on the higher ridges beyond the river, and on a distant time. His voice strong, his words came in a steady flow.

GW Writings, p489

"We must extend the inland navigation of the Eastern rivers, communicate them as near as possible—by excellent roads—with those which run to the westward, open these to the Ohio, and even others extending from the Ohio towards Lake Erie. Then we shall not only draw the produce of the western settlers, but the fur and peltry trade of the lakes also, to our eastern ports. We will see how astonishingly our exports will be increased, while

GW Diary Vol.2, p327

GW letter to Lafayette
(*Col. Hist. Soc. Records*
Vol.12) p157

we bind those people to us by a chain of interest and habit which can never be broken.

"I wish to see," he said, "the sons and daughters of the world in peace and busily employed in the more agreeable amusement of fulfilling the first and great commandment, 'Increase and multiply.' And as an encouragement, we shall open the fertile plains of the Ohio to the poor, the needy, and the oppressed of the Earth. Anyone who is heavy laden, or who wants land to cultivate, may repair thither, and abound as in the Land of Promise with milk and honey. But the way must be prepared and the roads made easy."

Washington, sitting erect in his saddle, gestured toward the sun. "Already beyond the mountains, settlers number at least 100,000 souls. They are groaning under the inconveniences of a long land transport across the mountains, over bad roads, or mere trails, to eastern markets. They are wishing for the extension of inland navigation. None is so convenient as that which offers itself through the 'Yawky-gany' or Cheat connected to the Potomac, the Monongahela, and Ohio.

GW Diary Vol. 2, p328

p327

"We must open a wide door, and make a smooth way for the produce of that country to pass to our markets—Georgetown, Alexandria, and perhaps at the seat of government, should Congress choose to locate it on the Potomac."

Bushrod leaned forward with a question on the tip of his tongue, but the calm, deep tones of his uncle's voice did not stop.

p318

"The more, then, the navigation of Potomack is investigated and duly considered—which I have been doing since before the Revolution—the greater the advantages arising from it appear. The expense, comparatively speaking, deserves not a thought, so great would be the prize. The Western inhabitants would, I am persuaded, do their part towards accomplishing the creation of an inland waterway. They would meet us half way rather than be

p327

p326-7

DRIVEN into the arms of foreigners on the flanks and rear of the United States. The consequences of an alliance or dependency on Spain or Britain would be separation from us, or a war.

"This continent stretches another 500 miles or so from here to the Mississippi. Far beyond that river rise towering mountains I'm told. I would like to see them some day. God preserve the United States to expand and gain it all. Not to do so would be the greatest folly."

Bushrod's eyes and mind as well as those of the Colonel were concentrated upon the man between them, his head tilted slightly upward, eyes half-closed, caught up in a dream of the future.

"He is the handsomest, grandest man I ever saw," thought Bushrod.

"Now that was some eloquent talking," thought the Colonel. "I always heard he didn't talk much, but he sure has loosened up today." Aloud he responded gravely to Washington's message, "Yes sir, that is powerful thinking, General. People out here would like nothing better than easy, cheap transport to market. It's hard now, it's hard—worse most of the time than fending off Indians."

During a silence of some minutes while they passed through a woodland's heavy shade, the Colonel thought, "I'd like to hear him talk some more. Do I dare ask him a question?"

The bright sun in the clearing encouraged him. In a sudden rush of words, he remarked, "General, Your Excellency, sir, you've traveled in these parts before, and had many adventures that I've heard much talk about. In Great Meadows just on the other side of Chestnut Ridge back there, you fought the French at Fort Necessity. I'd dearly love to hear you tell about that, if it's your pleasure, Your Excellency."

Washington looked around at Phillips, smiled faintly, and answered, "As it happens, I spent time in Great Meadows only two weeks ago, and recalled most vividly the events that occurred there 30 years ago. I own part of the land now. The road across it is the same trail Braddock's army marched on its way through the wilderness to the fort the French had just built. It was at the junction of the Monongahela, Ohio, and Allegheny Rivers—now Fort Pitt.

"I fought my first skirmish on the north tip of Great Meadows when I was barely 21, not quite as old as you are, Bushrod. I was leading a surprise attack at daybreak against a party of French. A month later I fought my second battle, this time defending a small fort we had built—Fort Necessity, we called it—at the south end of Great Meadow. French and Indians numbered about 1500 against our 300 or so Virginians. We lost our fort, but I bargained for the men and we marched out with the honors of war. That was July 3, 1754.

"Those battles were the start of seven years of fighting in these mountains before the French left the Great Lakes, the Ohio Valley, and all of Canada to the British.

"For us, the big battle of that war took place the year after the Fort Necessity affair. I came back to Great Meadows with General Braddock and about 1200 British troops neatly uniformed in red coats and white trousers, and about the same number of Virginia, Maryland, and North Carolina militia.

"The trail we used to get there from Winchester in western Virginia to the southwestern corner of Pennsylvania, some 150 miles, had been cut through the wilderness by my Virginia militia the year before. North of Great Meadows, the British ever so slowly cleared a new wagon trail and built dozens of bridges for the wagons and artillery to cross 40 miles—almost to the French fort on the Ohio.

"However, I took no part in this, for by the time I reached Great Meadows, I had been lying in my wagon for some days with severe fever and delirium. Not until I took Dr. James's Powder, a most

Adapted from Writings of GW, Vol.29, p46-50 (biographical statement GW wrote in 1793)

Hist.of Cumberland, Md.(W.Lowdermilk)

GW Writings, Vol.29 (autobiog.)

French and Indians ambush Braddock and Washington's army, July 1755.

excellent medicine that General Braddock sent to me, was I recovered enough to ride and catch up with the half of the army Braddock was leading. It was then approaching the French fort. The other half of the army, his reserves, stayed encamped above Great Meadows.

"The next morning after arriving in Braddock's camp, I took up my duties as one of General Braddock's aides. Very weak, I mounted my horse, though obliged to sit on cushions. In the next hour, I began a day (he paused, his face grim) the memories of which still haunt me. It was July 9, 1755. It became known to us who were there as The Bloody Day.

"French soldiers and hundreds of Indians hidden in the woods all of a sudden began whooping, hallooing, and firing their muskets. Our troops seeing no enemy, but seeing themselves falling every moment from the fire, fled in general confusion.

"No exertions of the officers could recover them. Many attempts to dislodge the enemy from an eminence proved ineffectual, and fatal to the officers. Three horses were killed or wounded from under me. A ball passed through my hat, and three made holes in my clothes. I escaped unhurt.

"The General was not so lucky. After 12 hours of slaughter, the General, who was badly wounded, ordered me about midnight to ride back 40 miles to the encampment above Great Meadows, order provisions sent to his men, and start arrangements for the retreat.

"The journey took up the whole night and part of the next morning. The shocking scenes my two guides and I experienced in those hours many of them in darkness so impervious the guides had to grope on the ground with their hands to know when we were in, or out of the track, remain painful memories. The groans, lamentations, and cries of the wounded for help would have pierced a heart

of adamant stone. Lying dead or crawling in agony through those miles of dark woods were more than 800 men. The next afternoon, General Braddock, arriving at the Great Meadows encampment, breathed his last."

Bushrod saw his gray-haired uncle look away, sigh deeply, and bow his head.

Abruptly, the General clucked to his horse and trotted ahead on the trail. When they came out of a thicket to a path alongside open fields of corn rows dotted with shocks of dried stalks, the General was waiting for them, and ready to pick up his story.

"But my very first trip to Great Meadows had taken place two years previous, before any battles with the French.

"I was a newly appointed major in His Majesty's Virginia militia, eager for duty, and volunteered to carry a message from Governor Dinwiddie to the French in a camp close to Lake Erie. I rode alone finding my way through 200 miles of uninhabited wilderness between Williamsburg and Great Meadows. There I was to find the noted scout and woodsman, Christopher Gist. At that time, Gist was one of the best-known men in Virginia, which, as you know, extended until last year all the way to the Great Lakes.

"I would hire Gist to guide me through the mountains on more than 100 miles of trails to the French camp at Presque Isle. To its commander I would deliver Governor Dinwiddie's message, which was that they were trespassing on Virginia land, and were ordered to depart. Their answer I would bring back to Williamsburg as quickly as possible.

"It was late October of a very cold winter. Guided mostly by compass, I rode the first 200 miles at a steady five miles an hour the better part of a week along muddy roads, rocky roads, steep paths, animal trails, tangled woods with no trail, up and down ridges, through dozens of streams.

Based on GW's account written in 1753, published by Gov. Dinwiddie's order, and sent to King George III.

Major George Washington

GW Vol.6. (Freeman)
p17

"I found Gist living in a log house at the foot of a ridge overlooking a grassy plateau he called Great Meadows. We saw the house, Bushrod, when we stopped for a meal at Gist's brother, Thomas, the other day.

"Gist and I did the assignment during a most eventful six weeks. I delivered the Governor's message, heard the French commander's laugh and his refusal. By now it was Christmas and intensely cold with snow falling. Gist and I and our Indian company started on the return journey. I was anxious to get back to Williamsburg with the news that the French were claiming the area and would proceed to build a fort on the Ohio.

"Just north of the three-river junction, site of the proposed French fort, our progress was so slow that Gist agreed we should leave our worn-out horses with our Indian escorts and walk 30 miles to a settler's cabin to hire fresh mounts.

"We counted on walking across the frozen Allegheny River. However, the Allegheny was still running, though crowded with blocks of ice. With one poor hatchet, we cut saplings and lashed together a small raft. Just before dark we cast off.

GW Diary, Oct-Dec.
1753

"A fierce current caught us, and great chunks of ice attacked us. In an effort to hold back the raft and save us from going downstream, I jabbed my pole into the river bottom. The raft, pushed forward by the rushing current, struck the pole. All at once I was levered from the raft and tossed into the icy water. I grabbed at the raft. By the will of Providence, I caught hold. Straining and hauling, I pulled myself aboard, the water stiffening as it froze, and crackling in my clothes.

"Providence was still with me, for within minutes, the current ran the raft close enough to a small island that we could wade and tramp over ice to shore. Gist's fingers were frost-bitten, but with his knowledge of surviving in the most desperate of wilderness circumstances, and with our luck in

saving our backpacks, we survived the bitter night.

"At daybreak, we saw the river had frozen across and we walked to shore. It took us several days to ride the borrowed horses through snow storms and drifts to Gist's cabin at the northern tip of Great Meadows."

Bushrod leaned forward to inquire, "Uncle, sir—"

"There's my house, General!" interrupted the Colonel. "And there's my nearest neighbor coming to meet us. Somehow, word raced ahead of us that Your Excellency was coming this way. We are greatly honored to have this visit from you, sir. I am sure a venison dinner awaits us on the table."

In near-dawn's gray light, General Washington and Bushrod, guided by the Colonel, rode west over very hilly ground to reach the ferry on the north bank of the Cheat River, in sight of its junction with the Monongahela. The General paid the fares, a shilling for each horse with rider.

GW Diary Vol.2, p302

Bushrod heard the ferryman describe how the brown Cheat waters and the clear Monongahela waters have a repugnancy to mix. Bushrod could see a visible line of division between the two for some distance. As the ferryboat docked, Washington asked, "Colonel, are we now in Pennsylvania or Virginia? I hope I was misinformed by travelers who told me the mouth of the Cheat is now in Pennsylvania."

"Well, they were right, General," replied the Colonel. "It is actually a fact that Virginia lies two miles farther south, beyond the river fork. The state line surveyed last year runs along the top of that first ridge—the very ridge we're heading for to find Surveyor Hanway."

Washington's lips tightened, and he frowned fleetingly. "With the junction of the two rivers in Pennsylvania, Colonel, that state, not Virginia, controls traffic on both rivers. We in Virginia—and

GW Diary Vol.2,
p308, 320

During the last week in September 1784, Washington rode horseback exploring the practicality of joining the Potomac by 30 miles of road and canal to the Cheat River (above), and thereby to the Monongahela and Ohio. He heard conflicting reports about the Cheat from local hunters, trappers, farmers, ginseng gatherers, and other mountain men. Finally he rode off to look with his own eyes.

Maryland—expect hinderance, not help, from Pennsylvania, in connecting the Potomac to the Ohio. Such a connecting would be the means of withdrawing from Philadelphia the trade of Pennsylvania's western territory."

The General's talkative mood vanished. Across a wide river flat, the horsemen rode in silence to the foot of the first ridge running across the point of land separating the Cheat and Monongahela. A steep trail through thick woods that screened out all but glimpses of the Monongahela brought them to the ridge crest. "Here's the Virginia line, General. The trail turns east, stays on the crest, and will bring us in six miles to John Pierpont's house where Captain Hanway is."

"Below the ridge on the Virginia side, how is the terrain? Could a wagon road be had to connect the two rivers there?" Washington inquired. The Colonel was sure it could be, for already a path crossing six miles was in use. Washington's face lit up. "Then," he said, "if Pennsylvania blocks us out of the lower Monongahela, traffic from Potomac and the Cheat can portage to the upper Monongahela, be poled UP river to a road—or canal—joining the Kanawha flowing into the Ohio. I explored and staked a claim around the mouth of the Kanawha in 1770.

"In addition to land on the Kanawha, I was offered and accepted 2500 acres on the Little Kanawha. I have wondered what happened to them— I received no further word. If Captain Hanway could bring the area land books, I'll spend some time on a title search," Washington said.

When they reached the Pierpont cabin about nine o'clock, they saw tied to the rail fence around the clearing the horses of two other visitors. As Washington walked in the door, both the visitors, as well as Pierpont and Hanway sprang to their feet, startled, staring.

"Is it possible?! General Washington?!" cried Hanway.

Colonel Phillips made the introductions, and Washington immediately stated his questions concerning the Cheat. None of the men had sure and first-hand information. "General," said Hanway, "you need to talk to Colonel Zack Morgan of Morgan Town. He will know, or he will know who knows. I propose that you plan to stay here all night, which will give John here time to go for Colonel Zack, time for them to get back here, and to return home by dark."

"Do you have the land records for the area around the Little Kanawha's mouth?" Washington inquired, glancing at the same time at the cabin's sparse accommodations.

"Right here, General," said Hanway.

"And," added John Pierpont, "you will have the bed to yourself, Sir."

Washington smiled and nodded, John hurried to his horse, and Hanway laid the land book on the pine board table.

By two o'clock when Pierpont arrived with Morgan and a troop of men in 'possum hats, coon hats, leather jackets over homespun shirts and deerskin trousers, Washington had recovered from his disappointment and flush of temper at finding his land registered in the name of another. He had dined on cornbread, roasted squirrel and 'possum Hanway cooked on fireplace spits, and was sipping fiery Pierpont whiskey.

Introductions over, Morgan and his men crowded around the table to drink toasts that dissolved their awe of the General, and rowdied their voices.

"Here's to liquified corn crops, General! It's light on our wagon wheels and heavy in our purse!"

"Here's to General Washington who led us to victory! Here's to John Barleycorn who is leading us to solvency!"

Washington stood and raised his glass. In the hush, he toasted, "Easy transport eastward by the waters of Monongahela, Cheat, and Potomac!" The men responded "Yay! Yay!" noisily and drained their mugs.

Remaining standing, Washington pursued his purpose. "Gentlemen, do I understand that you agree a good wagon road can be made on the Virginia side of this ridge from the Cheat to the Monongahela?"

"Yes," they chorused. "It's only a few miles, General. We can widen what's there!"

"From the end of that road, how many miles up the Monongahela can a canoe easily go?" Washington asked.

"About 70, General," replied Morgan.

"From there, how many miles to portage to the Kanawha?"

"Oh, 'tain't more 'n nine and a half miles, a good road, with only one hill in the way, and that not bad!" called out a trapper. "Down the Kanawha to the Ohio is 50 miles, easy water," declared several voices.

"Excellent!" said the General. "Now, for the connecting river with the Potomac—the Cheat."

The news, extracted from the rambles and layers of talk of a dozen men, was not encouraging. The rumored boulders were real. Rapidly descending water dashed against and between those giant rocks; a canoe could hardly squeeze through without wrecking. Was there room beside the river for a canal? Probably not, but no one could say for sure.

Once past five or six miles of rapids (though no one in the crowd had ever accomplished that) the going was said to be good for five miles to Dunker's Bottom, the point closest to the Potomac.

"But, General! You shouldn't go the path from Dunker's to the Potomac! Overgrown for miles with briers! That path is blind!! Everybody tells us that! Yes sir, there is another route—"

"How many miles?"

"Oh, 35 or 40, we hear."

Hanway brought paper, an inkpot, and quill for Washington to write down the figures and begin a calculation. A loud, young, impatient voice, heavily accented, announced, "I have the totals—143 miles of river, Potomac to Ohio, and at least 65 miles of roads or canals!"

Bushrod glanced at his uncle just in time to see him turn a brief but withering stare upon the speaker, a 20-year-old introduced earlier as Albert Gallatin. Bushrod winced at the sudden, silent tension in the cabin. The General proceeded to finish his calculation, while Gallatin's glance was making a rapid survey of the disapproving faces around the table. Minutes later, Washington laid his pen down, turned his stern gaze on Gallatin and said flatly, "You are right, sir."

No one laughed. Bushrod shivered, thinking, "That character will never forget the look my uncle gave him."

"You say there is another, a better route from the Cheat to the Potomac?" Washington said, turning the sheet of paper over and drawing lines for the Cheat and the North Branch of the Potomac. Patiently, he marked the sketch with the plentiful details his advisers offered.

Two hours before dark, Morgan and his men left—except for Albert Gallatin, whom Washington was questioning as to his origins (Switzerland) and his business in the Alleghenies (bringing settlers to land he held, and selling them supplies). He, too, had been exploring possibilities for linking the Potomac to the Ohio. The conversation lasted so long, it was too near dark for the young Swiss to start for Morgan Town. He stretched out on the floor between Bushrod and Colonel Phillips for the night.

At dawn, having slept fitfully on a narrow wooden cot's cornshuck mattress, Washington arose, impatient to depart. He waited only long enough for Pierpont and Hanway, who had slept like guards on the floor by the door, to brew coffee and cook

GW (Freeman) Vol.6, p204

A.Gallatin,
Jeffersonian Financier
and Diplomat
(R.Walters)

Gallatin became
Jefferson's Secretary of
the Treasury.

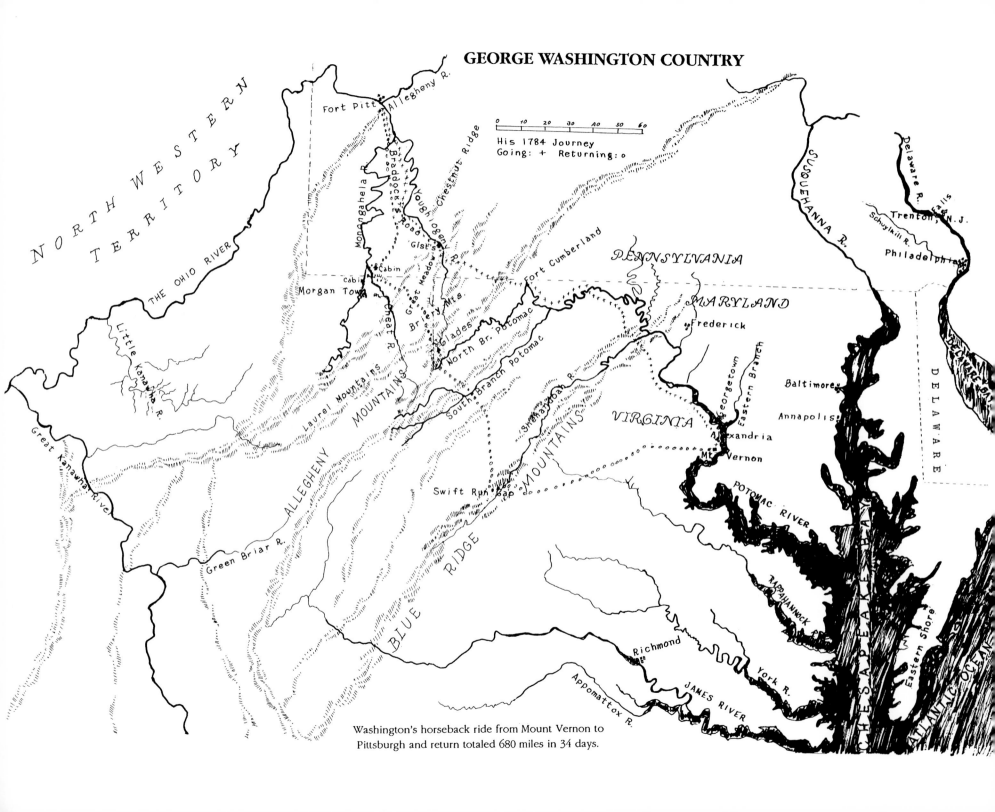

GEORGE WASHINGTON COUNTRY

His 1784 Journey
Going: + Returning: o

NORTH WESTERN TERRITORY

THE OHIO RIVER

Little Kanawha R.

Great Kanawha River

Green Briar R.

ALLEGHENY MOUNTAINS

Laurel Mountains

Cheat R.

Morgan Town

Cabin

Cabin

Monongahela R.

Braddock's Road

Fort Pitt

Allegheny R.

Youghiogeny R.

Chestnut Ridge

Gist's

Great Meadows

Briery Mts.

Glades

North Br. Potomac

Fort Cumberland

South Branch Potomac

Shenandoah R.

BLUE RIDGE MOUNTAINS

Swift Run Gap

PENNSYLVANIA

MARYLAND

Frederick

VIRGINIA

Georgetown

Eastern Branch

Baltimore

Annapolis

Alexandria

Mt. Vernon

POTOMAC RIVER

SUSQUEHANNA R.

Delaware R.

Falls

Trenton, N.J.

Schuylkill R.

Philadelphia

DELAWARE

CHESAPEAKE BAY

Eastern Shore

ATLANTIC OCEAN

Richmond

Rappahannock R.

York R.

JAMES RIVER

Appomattox R.

Washington's horseback ride from Mount Vernon to
Pittsburgh and return totaled 680 miles in 34 days.

cornmeal hoecakes on a griddle.

Colonel Phillips led them through light fog along the ridge top, and down its rough, steep side into the sunshine. At the edge of the Cheat, Adam Ice and his ferry were on the job, ready for customers.

GW Diary Vol. 2, p304-5

"No, Morgan's men are wrong," said Adam Ice to Washington as the raft was poled and paddled across. "I have myself just run the Cheat in that very canoe you must have saw on the bank by the ferry. I went, and I come, Dunkers Bottom to here, and though meandering through the large rocks choking the river does render steerage dangerous by the sudden turnings, I have done it many a time, and could do it very easy were some of the rocks removed. Oh, there's room, there's room I believe, on one side or the other at each of the rapids, for a canal."

He deposited a smiling General on the east bank of the Cheat.

"I have no doubt now of the practicality of opening an easy passage," Washington told Bushrod as they followed an easy road south along the southwestern edge of Great Meadows. "Or of cutting canals to bypass the rapids."

Ascending Laurel Hill by a good road of gentle slope, and descending with less conveniences, Washington described to his nephew how canals, only recently built in England, channel river water around rapids, and how canal locks lift boats from sea level through hills and mountain ranges.

Some miles on, they forded Sandy Creek, water up to their stirrups. "Here we cross McCulloch's Path. He was probably the first man to go from Virginia to Ohio country, and from here west. He followed buffalo trails, very crooked," Washington informed Bushrod.

They pressed on another two hours on a not bad path to the first cabin. There, a Mr. Lemon fed them and the horses, then insisted on guiding them through the next intolerable country, as he called it. Bushrod trailed Mr. Lemon and Uncle George, struggling his horse through deep, rich soil, over treacherous rock and up steep slopes, then across the Briery Mountains.

"Intolerable now," Washington observed, "but these tracks can be eased if a little pains are taken to slant them."

The sun was going down when they entered Youghiogheny ("Yawky-gany") Glades, 33 miles from Ice's ferry. Heavy clouds were gathering. Lemon led them to a massive oak tree, whose thick and well-leafed arms would canopy them for the night. "From here," he told the General, "it's not mor'n eight miles to Dunker's Bottom on the Cheat." Bushrod mumbled that meant their day's long journey was a buffalo trail of their own making.

Mr. Lemon, glancing anxiously at the darkening sky, went off with Bushrod to cut armsful of tall grass and ferns for bedding. "Watch out for water courses hiding under the grass and ferns," he warned. "The Yawky-gany gets its start out of this high, water-cut meadow. It don't look like a regular meadow, what with being rolling and having so many high spots thicketed with oaks and alder—AND it ain't. These low, grassy stretches are crisscrossed with little streams."

Under the great oak, Washington gathered dry grass and twigs, struck sparks from a flint and started a campfire. By the time his companions returned with bedding, he had stacked enough sticks and dead branches to feed the fire through the chill night. Horses turned loose to find their supper stayed close, keeping in sight of the light.

Heavy storm clouds deepened the darkness as the men ate bread, venison strips, and apples by firelight. "Gentlemen," Washington said, looking out over the glades, "this ground would admit an exceedingly good wagon road with a little causeying—raising up the roadway—in some parts of the Glades—"

He stopped in mid-sentence at the sound of heavy rain striking the tree leaves above and the grasses of the glades beyond.

"It's essential to keep as dry as we can, Gentlemen," the General said, and advised them to draw their wraps about them and lie beneath their beds of grass and reeds.

In the wet night some time later, Bushrod, rousing when Mr. Lemon put wood on the fire, saw by the flickering light that his uncle was raising himself on one elbow. His mellow, calm voice blended with the sound of heavy rain without, and the light shower dripping through the umbrella of leafy tree branches above.

"Mr. Lemon," he said, "the more I investigate the western streams that could, joined to each other, extend the Potomac waterway to the Ohio, the more advantages I see resulting from it, and the more determined I become to press for an early start. The present epoch is favorable above all others. Not only have canals with locks been perfected to lift boats upstream, but there is also Mr. Rumsey's self-propelled boat. I saw him demonstrate a model of his invention at his tavern in Bath when we began this trip. This mechanism, which will move boats upstream without men working oars or poles could revolutionize transport as much as canals. With such a discovery perfected, to move a boat against the current will cease to be difficult."

Present Berkeley Springs, West Virginia

"It's all coming together, and in our time! As soon as I arrive at Mount Vernon, I shall draw up a bill for a Potomac development company, and present it to the Virginia Assembly. Potomac River extends deeper into the west than any other eastern river. It is fated to become the roadway from the west, bearing trade and giving western settlers easy access to their government!" Mr. Lemon murmured agreement to the General and began to snore lightly. The General, his tricorn still firmly on his head, settled under his grass blanket, stared at the camp-

fire, and listened to the sizzle of raindrops that fell into it. Half-whispering, he said, "With all that is at stake, we must view rocks, rapids, mountains, and marshes as trifling difficulties, Gentlemen, only trifling difficulties."

After crossing rough, rocky terrain, steep inclines, briery paths, and cold streams, all in intolerable country, Washington, his nephew Bushrod, and his local guide spend the night sleeping under a great oak tree. Growing on a hummock or high spot in watery glades of a high plateau, the tree shelters them from a shower. Despite the hardships, Washington's conviction has deepened that a road can be built across the area to join the Potomac to the Cheat and create a waterway to the West.

Arriving by coach at the 1784 Virginia capitol (above), Washington and Governor Benjamin Harrison—whose son and grandson would later lead the nation—would have entered a tobacco warehouse renovated for the Assembly. The elegant Capitol at Williamsburg was abandoned in 1779 when Governor Thomas Jefferson led the delegates to Richmond village 60 miles up the James River in the mistaken belief that the British army would not raid so far west.

CHAPTER 5

Washington's Potomac Company

SCENE: Richmond village, Virginia's capital, 60 miles upriver at the Falls of the James.
TIME: November 18, 1784, a rainy, windy day.

"Almost time to go down to The Warehouse," Governor Benjamin Harrison said to his guest as they rose from the dining table in "The Palace." Ordinary but spacious, the two-story wooden executive mansion sat on top of Shockoe Hill overlooking Richmond village lying a half-mile down a steep slope. In a little cluster of wooden buildings there, the Capitol, formerly a tobacco warehouse owned by a British exporter, stood out, being the biggest. The Assembly met in it, and the Senate met in a small adjacent house. The several state bureaus occupied other nearby small houses.

Towering six-feet-four, and broad with fat, Governor Harrison outsized his old friend and comrade-in-arms, George Washington, in town these past few days on Potomac business.

"I am ready," replied Washington.

While the Governor went off to complete his arrangements for riding down to the Capitol and a meeting of the Assembly, Washington viewed the scene out the parlor window. Beneath dark skies and beating rain, the muddy little road bringing traffic from the east and north was empty. The coach he had looked for during each of the past three days might not come today either.

"Where is 'The Boy'?" Washington wondered with a pang of anxiety. The visiting Marquis de la Fayette, his "adopted" son, after a two-week stay at

Mount Vernon had gone on a nostalgic tour of the northeast while Washington was exploring in the Allegheny Mountains. They had agreed to meet in Richmond in mid-November. Washington, at home again, spent two weeks thinking out and writing down his Potomac-to-Ohio plan, then rode south 90 miles to present it to the Assembly in Richmond—and to meet LaFayette. Richmond's 1,200 people, half of them slaves, had also watched eagerly for the coach of the popular young aristocrat from France. They knew him well from his almost yearlong stay there in 1781 when he commanded troops sent to harass British General Cornwallis.

Rain beat down on the village, blurring Washington's view of the James River, of the road that was also Main Street—nobody called it "D" Street, though using alphabet names for other streets. Thomas Jefferson, governor at the time the capital was moved to Richmond from Williamsburg, had devised the name plan.

Washington saw little movement of people around the 300 or so mean, wooden houses, except for umbrella'd figures scurrying from The Warehouse to, or from, three taverns nearby. In these "ordinaries", legislators roomed, ate, drank wine and whiskey, gambled, socialized, and played billiards or cards. A creek with a small wooden bridge separated the state government side from the town government—the Courthouse, the jail, the open-air punishment cage. Near them on a knoll stood Henrico Parish Church, St. John's, where Patrick Henry not 10 years before had hurled "Give me liberty or give me death!" like a flaming torch across America.

By the river and creek mouth sat a cluster of warehouses for the sale and storage of tobacco, main money crop, and even the main money of the area. Paper money of the Continental Congress became equal in value with oak leaves as long ago as the Yorktown victory in autumn 1781.

Washington once more scanned the road, but saw only a few pigs rooting in the mud.

The Governor's coach, however, had pulled up in front of the door, and Governor Harrison's strong bass voice was calling, "We must go, General! The Assembly waits for us!"

Down the hill to the Capitol, the two old friends reviewed the chances for quick action by the Assembly on the urgent business that Washington would present—a bill to set up a public Potomac River development company, and to grant money for a survey of western Virginia rivers to link the Potomac to the Ohio. "Well, General, judging from the reception you have had during the past three days, I predict that if you gave them only 24 hours to approve everything, they'd break their necks to do it," the jovial Governor said. "As soon as they heard you were here, they boomed the cannon, illuminated this pitiful town with candles, and threw a speech-making party.

"Since then, General, you have told us about the Potomac plan, and we all agree it is grand— Governor-elect Henry, our great scholar Madison, our brilliant if slovenly young John Marshall, Attorney General-Secretary of State Edmund Randolph, and the rest of the State Council—and we want it.

"We esteem you, General! Besides saving our country for us, you play cards for pennies with us

at the tavern, praise our rockfish, brave clouds of loathsome tobacco smoke, and show interest in gossip from and about old friends and army comrades. It all counts! It all counts! Everybody here longs to give you more than you ask for—all of Richmond, IF you would have it!"

"Benjamin, you could make a horse laugh!" Washington declared.

In the warehouse-capitol, the voices of more than a hundred Assemblymen—delegates and Senators, in a joint session—had risen to the rumble of a great waterfall. The babble of talk concerned horses, horseraces, runaway slaves, cockfights, yesterday's card games, politics, buying goods and selling crops, weather, and General Washington.

From time to time, the burly doorkeeper in the wide vestibule shouted a name. "Mr. Richard Bland Lee!" "Mr. Alexander White!" "Mr. James Madison!" "Mr. Ebenezer Zane!" The delegate answering would find at the door a man with a problem or request, or a friend who talked him into a quick drink at Formicola Tavern almost next door.

Hardly audible, the Speaker called the Assembly to order. The clerk began to read. No one paid attention. Dressed in boots and trousers, or in Indian leggings, or hunting clothes, work clothes, great coats, ordinary coats, short jackets, gentlemen's velvet and ruffles—each to his own notion and comfort—the delegates and senators moved from one knot of talkers and backslappers to another. Some left the room or building, some entered, all causing a constant motion about the door. At each opening, cold, wet air flew inside, so that, despite two roaring fireplaces, removing coats or cloaks was soon regretted.

Suddenly, the doorkeeper's voice sounded in bugle volume on a great draft of cold air. "THEIR EXCELLENCIES GENERAL WASHINGTON AND GOVERNOR HARRISON!!"

The cold, the glimpse of the state coach and

Travels in the Confederation, 1783-84 (J.D.Schoepf/ Morrison, translator)

Richmond newspaper: GW arrived Nov.14, Marquis Nov.18

GW (D.Freeman)

Travels in Virginia in Rev.Times (A.J. Morrison) p54-55

handsome horses, the two big men dressed elegantly in fine suits, flowing cloaks, satin cravats, and three-cornered hats, froze the Assemblymen's tongues. A hesitant scattering of applause, then hurrahs, and a grand clapping of hands. The crowd of men parted for the distinguished visitors to make their way to the low platform of the Speaker.

Voices rose in excited conversation while official greetings and handshakes took place. "I heard that one of the Governor's servants got up at four this morning to go to the necessary, and ran into the General shaving, getting ready for the day!"

"How does he do it—sleep so little, work so hard and long? He stayed at the dance the other night until past midnight—"

"I wish I had his energy! But maybe he slept better in four hours than we did at the ordinary piled up 20 snorers to a room!"

BANG!BANG!BANG! the gavel called for order. Only half the roar died down. "I heard the Marquis should've shown up here by now. Where's he coming from?" "Just about every town north of us and maybe Williamsburg, down east, too." "But with the weather so bad—"

"Gentlemen! GENTLEMEN!" shouted Governor Harrison. "QUIET! QUIET! General Washington is waiting for silence so he can speak to you on important business for Virginia's future! The next man I see opening his mouth, I'm coming down there, pick him up, and carry him outside!"

GW's Expense Account
(Kitman) p238

The Governor's huge frame, his known inclination to ignore and disturb decorum, his fame as the man who, on the floor of the 1775 Congress exuberantly swept little John Hancock off his feet and deposited him in the President's chair to which he had just been elected, brought total silence.

With a satisfied smile, the Governor said, "The most effective governor is the man who has the loudest voice and can outwrestle any Assemblyman! Now, General Washington, the floor is yours!"

Washington stood to applause, his speech in hand, a broad smile for Harrison, who never failed to amuse him. For almost an hour, he gave the Virginians an account of his exploring trip among the streams to the west, weighing the information he gathered, pondering which streams, canals, and roads would best connect the Potomac to the Ohio. He spoke warmly, vividly, of a westward-expanding United States, of tens of thousands of people coming from many countries to the Ohio Valley and the urgency of drawing their goods and trade eastward by easy waterways.

He ended by reading the bill now drafted to set up a Potomac Company for raising money from stockholders to construct canals and portage roads. To start the project quickly, he asked for a grant of $3,000 for a survey of the rivers to find the best routes to connect the Potomac to the Ohio.

Enthusiastic applause and a noisy wave of comment broke out simultaneously.

"GENTLEMEN! I renew my threat!" boomed the Governor's voice. "If you must talk, speak one at a time and address the Speaker. I recognize—but Mr. Speaker, this is your job! Please take over."

"The Chair recognizes Senator Henry Lee."

"Your Excellency, you know that last June, this Assembly adopted a resolution calling for a conference with Maryland delegates. Our neighbor owns ALL the Potomac, and at the conference, scheduled for next spring, we were going to ask to share ownership and navigation. Now, we don't know what the Marylanders will agree to—so how can we proceed with your bill to develop the Potomac when no part belongs to us?"

Washington had his answer ready. "What I hear from Thomas Johnson, former governor of Maryland, leads me to expect that Maryland will come forth with an agreeable arrangement for the Potomac. As for this bill, if the Assembly desires, I will go immediately to Annapolis to consult with

GW (D.Freeman)

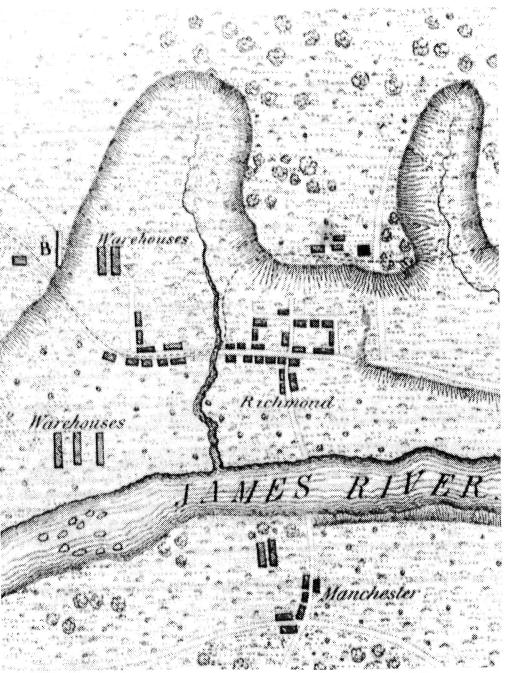

Map of Richmond, Virginia, drawn by a British officer in the raid of 1781.

the Maryland legislature, and make certain that any bill it considers is one in harmony with our own."

"Mr. Speaker!" cried a voice from the aisle. "I move that this Assembly give to General Washington, the savior of our liberty, anything he wants, as fast as he wants it, for the Potomac project!"

Applause, a ripple of approving laughter, and scattered "Hear! Hear!"

"Mr. Speaker!" The famous voice that all knew would speak for at least half the votes in the Assembly, quieted the room. The man it belonged to, Patrick Henry, was the only man in the room wearing a wig—to cover a bald head. Spare, medium height, he dressed in black clothes and a scarlet cloak, his hallmark. Standing with one hand on a hip, his shoulders drooped, his brow drawn into a frown on his long, thin, dark-skinned face, the talkingest man in America, "Son of Thunder," exuded drama as he awaited recognition.

"The Chair recognizes the Governor-Elect, the Honorable Patrick Henry!"

In the sudden, tautly anticipatory silence, the Voice, clear, strong, every syllable distinct, began in an attitude of respect. "Our great and beloved General Washington has a vision and a proposal that bodes good for the future of Virginia. (Murmurs of approval.) And for the nation. (Nods and glances of agreement.)

"He will, I feel certain, have our promise that this Assembly will take positive action before adjourning this session.("Hear, hear!")

"HOWEVER—"(The General's mouth tightened a little from the knowledge of this frontier land-owner's long, bitter rivalry with the tidewater aristocracy, and his intense antagonism for Madison and Jefferson)—"there are those of us who observe that our beloved river, the James, also reaches far to the west like the Potomac, and could easily— perhaps more easily—be connected to the Ohio!"

P.Henry (R.Beeman)

P.Henry (R.Beeman)

GW, Vol.6, p25 (Freeman) Members divided in support of James and Potomac. Patrick Henry (Beeman) Henry controlled at least half the Assembly, and was their spokesman. Henry lived near the James in western Virginia.

With every word (pronounced with a frontier country accent) his posture straightened. Erect, his sky-blue eyes shining with conviction, Henry cast his voice like magic through the room. Master of the spoken word, his mobile features expressing his strong emotions, his gestures eloquent and perfectly timed, he was known to have so enchanted one learned man, he unconsciously squirted tobacco juice from the gallery on members' heads.

"The James has fewer rapids," Henry cried. "It has this capital and the former capital, Williamsburg. It has the site of the first permanent English settlement on this continent at Jamestown. Next to it lies the Yorktown battlefield where our noble and illustrious General and his protegé the Marquis de LaFayette defeated the British army. Up and down the navigable miles of the broad and beautiful James, the high banks are lined with great plantations producing crops of great wealth. They already benefit from water transportation on the river. They have no need of canals and improved channels—but those above the falls, those to the west, those in the mountains and the far west have a GREAT need!" He paused exactly long enough for the thought to sink in.

In the cadence of the evangelical preacher he had regularly heard all his life, but with his own lightning flashes, he held his audience transfixed. "The James! has the potential as a great trade river no less than the Potomac! The James! so near the buildings of the old capital of Williamsburg it has the prospect to become quickly and easily the permanent capital of the United States!

"We are in good time to see it done. The Potomac has been pushed in Congress for the seat of government time after time. Our Virginia delegates deserve credit for that. But nothing can be DECIDED—until Congress has money. MONEY is what it takes to buy land and build buildings! When will that be? When CAN it be?! Our printed dollars have

less value than blank paper. Coinage is scarce and tightly held."

The voice tones, the severe but expressive face, the concentration of his thoughts and manner, intense with sincerity, the rhythm and increasing rapidity of his unhesitating sentences, penetrated all feelings, held minds enthralled.

"To hasten the day when Congress no longer roves between one borrowed building and another—to provide these newly united states with a centrally located seat of government—we in this Assembly passed a bill more than a year ago offering to Congress the entire town of Williamsburg!—all its historic buildings, and $100,000 for renovation! Our delegates to Congress should keep our James River offer before that august body as often as they do the Potomac! (Low murmurs) Likewise here, this Assembly should provide for the James as much western connection as it does for the Potomac!

"I propose that this Assembly add to the bill of General Washington a provision for the James! Put in as much survey MONEY to map a connection with the Ohio! Any map shows the Big Kanawha River, the Greenbriar, and the James are even better mated than the Little Kanawha, the Monongahela, and the Potomac as routes to the Ohio! Put in the bill also a James River COMPANY to sell stock and raise money for James canals and roads that will benefit our western Virginia farmers!

"We would not deny the Potomac and Georgetown on the Potomac the chance for a future such as our great and good Washington sees, but we must not deny the James and Williamsburg their chances. If we who love the James can graciously accept a plan to promote the Potomac, surely those who love the Potomac can bend to share with the James the opening of trade routes to the West!"

A high tension pause, and abruptly Henry sat down. Half the delegates sprang to their feet to

P.Henry Vol. 2,
(W.W.Henry) p241
(Tobacco juice)

The Transformation of
Virginia, 1740-1790
(R.Isaac) p267-8

P.Henry (R.Beeman)

P.Henry (W.W.Henry)

Journal of Cont.
Congress, May 1793

GW, Vol.6, p25
(D.Freeman)
P.Henry, Vol. 2, p421
(R.D.Meade)
Western Lands and the
Am. Revolution
(T.P.Abernathy)
P.Henry (R.Beeman)

cheer and clap their hands; the others applauded politely, whispering among themselves. "His land on the James—thousands of acres!" "I hear he's invested in Kentucky land by the Big Kanawha—" "And Ohio Company land as well!"

"So? The General owns thousands of acres over there in Ohio country, too!"

General Washington had risen quickly to his feet, moved forward, and begun to speak. Looking directly at Patrick Henry, he bowed, and said, "Honorable Sir, I welcome your promise to take action before this session adjourns. I also welcome the addition of the James River, which you have so eloquently described. It reaches deep into the western lands and could have as profitable a future as the Potomac."

Washington paused and turned his gaze from one side of the room to the other as he spoke. "No group should be discouraged from pursuing any plan that it considers beneficial to the whole country as well as to the state. The more communications we open to the West, the closer we bind that rising world—for that it truly is—to our interests, and the greater strength we acquire by it."

As he bowed and returned to his chair, the delegates, all of them, applauded mightily, some standing and crying out, "Hear, hear!"

The Speaker thanked "our most gracious General Washington," and added that the session could be expected to end in early January. "The statement of Honorable Patrick Henry, confirmed by the approving voices of the delegates, promises that in no more than six weeks hence, General, you shall have Assembly action to create two companies, Potomac and James, and money for surveys seeking other streams to link both to the Ohio!"

Amid the applause, a burst of cold air announced a new arrival. The doorkeeper stood open-mouthed but speechless beside a tall, slender, young man stylishly dressed, a large feathery plume trembling

in his hat with his every move. He was smiling broadly, and without a word strode toward the speaker's low platform.

The Governor's voice boomed, "GENERAL LA FAYETTE!! You have arrived at last!" A great bustle as all the delegates turned or rose to look, applauded, their voices buzzing. The boyish, lithe LaFayette removed his hat, and proceeding up the aisle, made slight bows left and right as he walked.

General Washington, his face aglow with smiles, met the 27-year-old Frenchman at the steps of the platform. He briefly grasped his shoulders in his huge hands, and looking intently in his eyes, said warmly, "Welcome back to Richmond, my boy. We have been looking for you for days! All is well?"

"Yes, mon Général, all is well with me. It is the weather that is not well."

Governor Harrison reached for Lafayette's hand, patted him on the shoulder, then listened avidly as the Marquis gestured toward the door. Raising his hand for attention, Harrison boomed, "GENTLEMEN! The Marquis has two companions we welcome and call forward to join us here—Count De Grandchain, commander of the naval frigate 'Nymphe' now anchored at Yorktown, and Chevalier Maurice Caraman!"

Greetings done, the Governor quieted the noisy Assembly once more. "Gentlemen, the Marquis we have been waiting for so impatiently has come back to us after a three-year absence. Many of you knew him during 1781 when he and his troops camped on the ropewalk and did their best to defend us from Lord Cornwallis's army. Here once again is our hero who played American mouse to the British cat, frustrating Cornwallis into settling down at Yorktown.

"The Marquis's letters to our valorous General Washington encamped in New York state brought our army and the French army and fleet to Virginia. You know the glorious end to that story. Now,

Lafayette Between Two
Revolutions
(L.Gottschalk) p125

GW Diary 1784

Patrick Henry

Lafayette (N.B.Gerson) p130

Lafayette (Gerson)31

Richmond During the Revolution (Ward/ Greer) p85-109

dear Marquis de LaFayette, this Assembly would drag me out to the lashing post if I did not beg you to speak!"

With a slight awkwardness that charmed his audience, the red-haired, lightly freckled young man faced them and began. "Dear friends," he said, "my heart is running wild with joy—I am once more in my beloved America! The journey I have just completed reaffirms that this is the most marvelous land on earth!

"Here in the capital of Virginia, I am among my esteemed comrades-in-arms, and near my adored adopted father, world-famous General Washington. I assure you his name is on every tongue in the royal courts and in the streets of Europe." (Applause)

The Marquis' English, studied since childhood, was fluent and near-perfect. His voice lilted and his sentences swayed to the beat of his native language. The effect was so appealing and lively, every delegate leaned forward, smiling, eyes fastened on the elegant, glamorous, romantic figure. Washington watched him with the smile of a doting father.

"I could not bear to return to France," LaFayette continued, "without seeing Richmond. Here in the heart of Virginia, I have deep memories of camps in the forests, camps beside villages, camps in cornfields. As you cannot avoid remembering, my small force and I could only dance through the wilderness holding General Cornwallis at arm's length. But at Yorktown, where my good friend Comte de Grandchain commanded one of the ships blocking Cornwallis' escape, we grappled and we won! (Applause)

"I will not take the time now to describe the many thrilling events during my five-month tour through this amazing country. But I must mention that I went with your great James Madison—whom I see sitting just there—to live three weeks with Iroquois Indians in the Mohawk Valley of New York. They had sent for me to come and advise them as a friend. I advised them to stay out of the quarrels of Europeans, be wiser than white men and keep peace among themselves. Do not give your land to the first comer for a barrel of rum, I said, but to the Americans on reasonable terms.

"With what fascination I observed their customs! We lived as they did, in huts and bathing in cold streams—an envigorating experience! (Laughter) A young Indian boy came away with me. I will take him to Paris and educate him—a most interesting experiment.

"As for the other towns and cities I visited, I thrilled to hear the cannon greeting me, the speeches, the music, the fireworks, the talks with old army comrades. Always I have marveled at the scenery in this grand country I love so dearly.

"Instead of more description, I will say only this to the Virginia Assembly as I have said to several other Assemblies: Preserve this wonderful country! Make strong arrangements for its future unity! A strong federation of all the states will insure eternal union, and, of course, their interior happiness, commercial wealth, and national consequence. I shall always be watching this land with a loving heart from afar, and dreaming of its golden future."

Applause went on long and loud. A voice shouted a resolution that the Assembly would present their affectionate respects next day. A hearty "Yea!" and the members surged forward to surround the fascinating Frenchman and General Washington.

Shortly, Governor Harrison's voice rose above the tumult. "Gentlemen! The Speaker bids me to announce a recess! The Governor invites you all to Galt's Tavern to drink a toast to our distinguished guests! Let us not delay, Gentlemen—our visitors must dine with the merchants at Trower's Tavern at three. Tonight at nine, in this room, we shall attend a grand ball. I assure you Gentlemen from France that you will dance with ladies more beautiful than any at the Versailles Court!"

Lafayette Between Two Revolutions (L.Gottschalk) p104 (quotes)

Marquis de Lafayette

Lafayette Between Two Revolutions (L.Gottschalk) p126 (quotes)

From John Marshall letter, 1783

From the front veranda of Mount Vernon, Virginia, the Washington family and many guests could view the Potomac from a high west bank of the river. In 1785, a wagon road behind the mansion led through the woods nine miles to the town of Alexandria. A little farther north, on the east bank (right), the Eastern Branch, or Anacostia River, flows into the Potomac. Just beyond, on the horizon, lies Georgetown, Maryland, often voted in the Congress as the South's choice for the location of the national capital.

54

CHAPTER 6

Mount Vernon Compact for Potomac

SCENE 1
WAITING FOR THE VIRGINIANS

PLACE: City Tavern, near the corner of Royal and Cameron Streets, Alexandria, Virginia, 10 miles from Mount Vernon, Washington's home.
TIME: Tuesday, March 22, 1785

CITY TAVERN-1785
Now Gadsby's Tavern
Museum and Restaurant,
Alexandria, Va.

City Tavern, Alexandria's depot for stage coaches traveling from Baltimore 40 miles northeast to Richmond 100 miles south, boasted excellent stables and a lively drinking and gaming room. Cooks and menus ranked high and the dormitory in the third floor attic could sleep 40 men in a pinch. A spacious room for meetings, banquets, and balls occupied most of the second floor.

In this room on the windy, damp, and wintry first day of Spring, three Maryland men and two Virginians—all commissioners appointed by their legislatures—were once more checking each other for news.

It was one o'clock. The men were annoyed, fretful, and uncertain what to do. They had been waiting since Sunday for the arrival of one more Virginia commissioner, either James Madison or Edmund Randolph.

They hesitated to begin their business meeting to work out an agreement concerning navigational rights, fishing and commerce regulations for the Potomac River, Maryland-owned boundary between the two states. These matters had to be decided before Washington's Potomac Company could begin its work.

But how long should they wait for Madison or Randolph? Should the meeting proceed? Or would someone object later if three Marylanders but only two Virginians made the decisions?

Stormy, querulous Samuel Chase from Annapolis fumed and almost stamped his very large foot. "Now dammit, I've rid ten hours through snow and hail and wild wind to get to this meeting, and here we sit doing nothing a second day, not knowing when, if ever, your Virginia men will show up!"

"We've done what we could," said short, plump Colonel George Mason of Gunston Hall on the Potomac, "dispatching the express horsemen yesterday with a letter to each man. But I can now inform you for certain that Mr. Randolph doesn't know about this meeting. As I came in the tavern, I was handed this letter, just arrived on the stage. It's from Randolph, written three days ago about another matter. He says not a word about our meeting. So, unless Mr. Madison knew about it and is on his way but mired in the mud a day or so down the road, it will take a week for either man to get our letter and two or three days more to ride here on our wretched roads."

"Then let's GO HOME!" exploded Mr. Chase.

Colonel Mason, the elder statesman, famous as the architect of Virginia's constitution—and bill of rights—both models for those later written and adopted in other states—began to speak quietly, sympathetically, trying to settle the impatient merchant, speculator, lawyer, and judge. Chase did not

G.Mason, Gentleman
(H.H.Milller)

settle.

"YOU tell ME, sir, how in the devil can the Virginia legislature be so slack and frivolous as to forget to send word of a serious meeting to the Virginia appointees themselves! I am disgusted—disappointed—mad as hell!" Chase's fiery complexion had become alarmingly brighter than its usual red, a condition that had won him a behind-his-back name, "Bacon-face Chase."

Mason drew back, not sure what Chase, the biggest man in the room, would do next. Riled, he had the harshest tongue and coarsest manners in 13 states. His immense size, his ungainly movements, aggressive voice, even the way his clothes hung on him, suggested the turmoil his behavior could excite.

"Where was the slip-up?!" he demanded. "Whose uncommon stupidity will make me lose a week's business for nothing?"

Alexander Henderson, whose presence had cost him but a short walk from his dry goods store in Alexandria, laughed and answered—knowing Sam's good humor would bound to the surface if coaxed a little—"Sam, you know how things go when TWO clerks work in the same office." He gave the answer in a gross exaggeration of his Scotch-burred accent. "Each mon figures the otherrr 'specially WANTS the job, and tactfully LEAVES it to him."

Sam guffawed and gave his friend's shoulder an appreciative bump. "Look, mon," added Henderson, "if Colonel Mason hadn't knocked on my door, I wouldn't be here to listen to you complain."

"And I myself wouldn't have known to knock," said Colonel Mason, "had I not received letters from Major Jenifer and Tom Stone here that they might stop by Gunston Hall on their way to the meeting—and that I was appointed to go also!" Major Jenifer picked up the story. "But as it turned out, I stopped instead at Mount Vernon and spent the night with General Washington—who hadn't heard

Story of the Declaration of Independence (D.Malone) p196

Life and Correspondence of G.Mason (K.M.Rowland) p84

a word about the when, where, nor who of this meeting! He immediately worried that Colonel Mason might not have received my letter mentioning that he was a delegate. To make sure, the General at once sent his coach to Gunston Hall to fetch the Colonel!"

Colonel Mason grimaced and shook his head. "The situation is a miracle of blunder and negligence," he said. "But even they yield to my amazing friend and neighbor George Washington! When he wants something as much as he wants this Potomac project, he extends his hands in all directions to get it moving."

The tallest, thinnest, quietest Marylander, Thomas Stone, dared to add a fact and a thought about Washington. "I wish he would raise a finger to beckon Congress to the Potomac. Every session, southern delegates try for Georgetown—but the Northeast men oppose it with Delaware Falls, and win. At Christmas-time, just before adjourning, Congress voted for Delaware Falls, either bank, for the second year running! And no Georgetown twin capital stuck to it this time. They think to make it final by directing three commissioners to lay out a district not less than two or three miles square, buy the land, and sign CONTRACTS with builders! They're to build SEVEN buildings—in an elegant manner—and $100,000 was voted! Georgetown has lost!" Stone stopped, a little flustered at having ventured so much.

"Did they name the commissioners?" asked Jenifer. Stone thought not. "Does Congress suddenly have $100,000 to spend on elegant buildings?" Sam Chase blew a loud guffaw. "Congress is half dead and stone broke! Tom Stone, you've been to Congress enough times to know that faces, and the interests behind them, change every session. Congressmen one year vote unanimously 'nay', Congressmen next year vote unanimously 'yea'. Every year, the western land scramble and locating the seat of govern-

Story/Dec. Independence (D.Malone) p.199

Journals of Continental Congress, Dec.24, 1784

ment get another going-over. Every year there's less money and more debt. Georgetown hasn't lost until Congress gets rich!

"I'm picked to sit in Congress again this year," Chase ranted on, "but you can see I'm putting it off as long as I can! The boredom didn't penetrate so deep while we were in Annapolis. But they took the session to Trenton last fall, and I can tell you, Trenton is no place to wait and wait for a quorum, or to listen for weeks to quibbling and quabbling.

Thomas Jefferson Papers (Burnett)1784

"The Jersey legislature decided to meet the same weeks Congress met, got to Trenton first and took all the best beds! After sleeping three to a bed a few weeks, we Maryland men gave up and left early in December.

Journ. Cont. Cong. Dec.20-23, 1784

"That's when the rest began working on where we'd meet, permanent and temporary. I heard all about it later from my friends in Philadelphia. They cast just about the only 'nay' votes against adjourning to New York after barely losing a move to adjourn to Philadelphia. Everybody except Elbridge Gerry wants big city comforts and entertainments— Trenton is no more fit to hold our meetings in than Princeton. How in heaven's name they could vote in the same day to build the PERMANENT capital in Trenton village I still cannot fathom—unless they figured that years away, when a capitol is ready in Trenton, they'll be comfortably dead and not obliged to go there!

"In the meantime, we southerners preferred Annapolis, except for the uncommonly jacked-up prices—but the uncommonly stern and strait-laced New Englanders, appalled and fatigued by the parties and extravagance of the social life (they said), garnered all the votes north of Maryland against returning to Annapolis.

"They wanted New York instead, and they won it. Half as far for Boston's men, but twice as far—or more—as Annapolis for me and all the Southern delegates. Trenton is not much better.

"Congress was to meet in mid-January in New York, but word comes that hardly anybody has shown up. I'm putting off as long as I can leaving family and business for six or so months—to sit around doing nothing in New York except wait for a capital to be built at Trenton! Going to Congress ain't worth a damn!"

His ranting was cut short by the tavern keeper. "Excuse me, Gentlemen!" he called as he stepped into the room from the staircase. "Gentlemen, his Excellency, General George Washington!" He stepped aside, bowing as the General, mounting the stairs behind him, walked past.

The beaming commissioners removed their hats and bowed. "General!" "Excellency!" "A fine surprise, Sir!"

Washington removed his hat, bowed, and said, "I overheard a remark about the Congress's decision to build the seat at the Falls of the Delaware. If I might be permitted to hazard an opinion, I would say that by the time the Federal buildings there are fit for the reception of Congress, it will be found that they are improperly placed for the seat of an Empire whose people are filling all the land east of the Mississippi. The seat of government will have to undergo a second edition in a more convenient place!"

GW Writings, Letter to Congress Pres. Lee, p70

"Hear, hear!"

The General smiled, his eyes crinkling in their peculiarly appealing way. The five commissioners laughed heartily, with Sam Chase whacking a fist against a palm in glee.

"I heard from the tavern keeper that you are still waiting for Mr. Madison and Mr. Randolph," said Washington.

"Yes, General, and we have just learned from a letter to me from Randolph that he is not aware of the meeting that he was supposed to attend," responded Mason. "Chances are, the same is true for Madison—as it was for Henderson and me."

Life and Correspondence G.Mason (K.Rowland)

"Very well," said Washington. "I concluded this might be the case, and decided to ride over to offer whatever assistance I could. I feel much responsibility for your coming here for this purpose. You know that immediately I returned home at the end of December from Annapolis, to which place I was requested by the Assembly to go—WITH my bosom friend, General Gates—" (he smiled faintly, the commissioners smiled broadly) I suggested Alexandria for the trade and commerce conference that both Assemblies desired.

GW Writings, Jan.10, 1785

"Now you five are here, and cannot act. Or can you? I have just received a copy of the Assembly's resolution to set up a conference with Pennsylvania on these river matters, and it specifies TWO Virginia delegates to attend. From this, we could infer that two Virginia delegates might prove adequate for the present conference," said Washington, meeting the gaze of each man.

G.Mason letter to Madison Aug 9, 1785. Mason Papers Vol. 2 (Rutland) describes these details.

"General, we THREE from Maryland's Assembly," said gray-haired Jenifer in his usual good-humored way, "have brought its great desire to form a fair and liberal compact as might prove a lasting cement of friendship between our states. We are highly disposed to do the business NOW, in the most amicable way, whether there be two, three, or four Virginia commissioners." ("Hear, hear," said Chase and Stone.)

"Very good," answered Washington. "However, if going ahead with only two Virginians does not strike the Virginia commissioners as advisable, perhaps they might consider another alternative."

The five commissioners studied the expression of Washington's face expectantly, hoping he was about to say what they wished for.

"Let us say that you wait here another day or two, and still Mr. Madison does not arrive. Were you then to move your meeting to Mount Vernon, and hold it in my presence, but without a vote, would the two legislatures accept this?"

He had said what they hoped for.

"My friend," Colonel Mason replied, "the whole country would berate us, and the Virginia Assembly especially, if we pretended that our hero could not advise, even replace any one—or all—of us."

"Hear, hear!" "Ah, General, you have saved this business!" "I shall feel deeply disappointed if Mr. Madison shows up now and we are obliged to stay in Alexandria." "Hear, hear!"

They made their plans. General Washington would send his carriage to City Tavern by three o'clock the day after tomorrow for Mason, more than somewhat ailing with gout, stomach trouble, and hemorrhoids. The others would come to Mount Vernon the following day, each in his own carriage, with Mr. Henderson leading the way.

GW Diary Tues.Mar. 22, Thurs. 23, Fri. 24

"I will expect the four of you in a caravan of carriages on Friday, in time for dinner," the General said. "I now invite you to dine with me at Lomax Tavern across the way. No stage coach arrivals crowd the place, and I have been assured that the lot of us will have the first shad of the season with all the trimmings for 10 shillings sixpence."

GW Expense Book, GW Diary Mar. 22, 1785

SCENE 2
FOUR DAYS AT MOUNT VERNON

PLACE: Mount Vernon, Washington's mansion.
TIME: Friday, March 25, about one o'clock, through Monday afternoon, March 28, 1785.

Cold mist and fog shaded the fields and curtained the woodlands even though it was midday. The tips of the tallest evergreens had vanished into clouds. Bare limbs of maple, pink with swollen buds, were beaded with water.

GW Diary, Fri. Mar. 25

Facing the river, the blurred outline of a long, white mansion, Mount Vernon, lay against the gray sky. In the opposite direction, along the road from Alexandria, four teams of horses pulling four carriages one behind the other, fast-stepped along a lane leading to that mansion. They slowed on entering its backyard, a 100-yard expanse of lawn, bell-shaped, bordered on each side by a wide, undulating driveway and a few tall trees.

The carriages rolled along the right-hand drive, past new-set young trees, some fallen over in the mud, some tied to stakes.

Through the mist, the men in the carriages saw a tall workman in floppy-brimmed hat, heavy work jacket, muddy boots, and rough trousers coming toward them. His easy, graceful stride and stately bearing suddenly betrayed his identity.

"My God, it's the General!" said the man in each of the carriages.

Washington removed his hat and walked to each carriage to shake hands. "Pray continue in your carriages along my new serpentine drive to the doorway and hurry inside to the fire. Colonel Mason is there keeping warm and dry, and Mrs. Washington will pour tea for you in minutes. I am pleased that you are early, Mr.Henderson having led you through woods and streams without getting lost or mired. Those miles do not improve with mild, wet weather—frozen mud makes for easier travel, as you know."

He then informed the drivers and postilions that stable hands would lead the horses to shelter and food, stow the carriages, and bring the men hot rum-tea and snacks. Turning back to the commissioners, he said, "Gentlemen, I will see you in the parlor shortly, and in more suitable attire. Today I have been a farmer planting pine trees, and staking shrubs and trees leaning badly from wind and thaw. Such tree-tending and laying out of drives and walks has become my amusement. Do proceed inside, Gentlemen!"

GW Diary, Mar. 25

GW Writings, Jan. 1785

That evening after dinner, and all day for the next three days, the six men sat together at a table in the study, taking up each item on the Maryland delegates' instruction papers, since the Virginians had nothing in hand. From time to time, they crossed the hall to the west parlor to drink tea with Mrs.Washington and to talk of families, home, and work.

G.Mason (K.Rowland)

In the great fireplaces of parlor, study, and dining room, pine knots snapped and crackled, oak logs burned long and hot. Outside, the temperature dropped and clouds thickened. Finally, Saturday at dusk, they poured inches of snow over the landscape. Servants brought candelabra to the conference table. Books and maps were drawn from the General's collection. From time to time, Colonel Mason's quill pen, scratching noisily, changed sheets of paper into historical documents.

GW Diary, Sat. Mar. 26

Dinner at two o'clock broke the conference into morning and evening sessions. Visitors—Mason's son and a friend, then a relative of Stone—dropped in, stayed for dinner. Washington remarked that every day one, two, three, even six guests came to his "National Hotel."

By suppertime at eight, the commissioners gladly put the Potomac out of their thoughts, enjoyed each other's stories, and climbed the stairs to third-floor bedrooms. In and out of the daytime scenes, short and pleasingly plump Mrs. Washington treaded quietly, spoke sweetly and often to her pretty, 18-year-old niece, Fanny Bassett, who was living there, to the servants, and to her two grandchildren. Running feet and the high-pitched voices of Nelly, six, and "Mr.Tub", four, flared out and were shushed. Black men-servants, slaves owned by the General or his wife, kept fires burning, brought refreshments, and served at the dining table.

GW Diary, Mar. 28, 1785

At the conference table, the five commissioners agreed that the River Potomac would henceforth be a toll-free, common highway for all Americans. They agreed on fishing rights, heard complaints

G.Mason (K.Rowland)

about landowners who claimed exclusive rights to "their" water, owners who lived on one bank but spread nets all the way to the other, fishermen who feuded with Virginians and scared away others from "Maryland's river."

All such actions would be outlawed. Both states would agree to share costs to build beacons and buoys, to cooperate in arresting and punishing criminals and pirates, and in collecting commercial debts.

G.Mason (Miller)

"Gentlemen," sighed merchant Sam Chase, "I wish we could keep a-going we're doing so well, and uproot a lot of other commercial snags between states. My business is battered and I am practically going broke because of the laws of Pennsylvania and New Jersey—Delaware, too—to say nothing of greedy New York. Did you know that New Jersey gets back at New York by punishing its own Jersey farmers if they're caught selling produce in New York?"

"Even worse," said merchant Henderson. "You should hear my company in Scotland complain about the Massachusetts port fees—high—very high. We have to bring our goods through Scot-free Connecticut ports."

GW Writings, Letter to J.McHenry Aug. 22, 1785

Washington cleared his throat, and all commissioners' eyes and attention turned to him. "Without giving Congress power to regulate commerce for ALL the states," he began, "we stand in a ridiculous point of view in the eyes of nations with whom we do business or attempt to enter into commercial treaties. We have no means to carry any treaty into effect. Other countries feel we behave as best suits our purpose—today as one Union, one Nation, and tomorrow as 13. Who will treat with us on such terms?"

He leaned back in his chair, folding his arms against his breast.

Sam Chase broke into the pause. "That's the sort of thing I've been saying to certain customers in neighboring states: 'Is there anybody left who will

treat with the likes of you?!' A merchant's blood is kept boiling with anger, and his purse shrinking in disappointment for all the regulating, chiseling, and underhanded cheating he meets out-of-state. Every MERCHANT, not just every state, sets a value to money!

G.Mason (Miller)

"If Congress could fix that one thing, I could make a profit! While they're at it, they ought to fix uniform duties and uniform interest rates on bills of exchange. Trade would boom! What we need is a meeting like this one—only bigger—with all our neighbors—all our STATES—to set things up so we could act as a unit since Congress can't speak or act for us."

"Well said, Sam Chase, well said!" the men agreed.

"Indeed, we need a unified commercial face to turn to the world," said Washington, speaking slowly, deliberately. "The spirit of trade which pervades these states must not be restrained. It behooves us, then, to establish unified, just principles. This any more than other matters of national concern, cannot be done by 13 heads differently constructed and organized. The necessity of a controlling power is obvious. Why it should be withheld is beyond my comprehension."

GW Writings, Letter to J.Warren Oct. 7, 1785

Colonel Mason nodded in agreement. "Yes, General. I have changed my mind on that issue during the past year. My son has been looking into taking up a mercantile career. It is very difficult, very risky. I can see that a strong central government must replace the league of states. To obtain unanimous consent of 13 state Assemblies on every action Congress proposes is, as we see, virtually impossible.

G.Mason (Miller)

"That famous 'nay' vote from little Rhode Island outweighed 12 others voting 'yea' in regard to a tax to support Congress—so Congress remains in poverty. Such vetoes stop most proposals of Congress, so all is at a standstill.

G.Mason (Miller)

"BUT," Mason said in the same breath, "I must

G.Mason (Miller)

In the study at Mount Vernon, three Marylanders—Samuel Chase, Thomas Stone, and Daniel of St. Thomas Jenifer—and two Virginians—Colonel George Mason, and Alexander Henderson—sign the Potomac Navigation and Trade Compact under the benevolent eyes of Washington. This compact and suggestions for further trade agreements led in two years to the Constitutional Convention in Philadelphia.

George Mason

add that I am very apprehensive that, soured and disgusted with these unexpected evils, we might run toward the opposite extreme. The times, the spirit today, is not the same as it was 10 years ago when we were signing the Declaration of Independence!

"The revolt from Great Britain, and the formations of our new state governments at that time—" ("actions in which you, Colonel, played a most significant role!" interjected Jenifer) "—those events," continued Mason, acknowledging Jenifer with a smile and nod, "stirred a certain degree of enthusiasm which inspired and supported the mind. We seemed at times to be walking on enchanted ground!"

Colonel Mason paused, his round, plump face flushed, his eyes misty.

GW Writings Letter to John Jay May 18, 1786

The General carried on the mood. "From the high ground we stood upon, from the plain path which invited our footsteps, to be now so fallen—so lost—it is really mortifying."

Elbow propped, chin and jaw cupped in his hand, he slowly shook his head. "The wheels of government are clogged, and our brightest prospects and that high expectation which was entertained of us by the wondering world, are turned into astonishment—and contempt." He leaned back, stared out the window, his lips pressed hard together.

GW letter to J. Warren Oct. 7, 1785

Mason said the words: "What we need to do, Gentlemen, is get our neighbors and our neighbors' neighbors together and make a general overhauling of our Articles of Confederation!"

Chase slapped his hand on the table. "To start things off, we need to get some action from the commercial interests. If we merchants make enough noise, the states, and Congress will both have to pay attention. We could start by sending resolutions to the state assemblies, pressing them to press Congress!"

Stone's mild voice ventured, "The Congress are often at a standstill for want of delegates (he paused, looking at Chase) to attend the sessions."

Defensively, Chase shot back, "What good does it do to attend and pass laws? Nobody pays any attention to them."

"Furthermore," added Jenifer, sympathetically, "Congress has no means of enforcing any law."

Washington was not so sympathetic. "When the representation of a great country is so—THIN—as not to be able to execute the functions of government, be the causes what they may, it is shameful and—disgusting. It hurts us. Our character as a nation is dwindling, and what it must come to if a change should not soon take place, our enemies have foretold, for in truth we seem either not capable or not willing to govern ourselves."

GW Writings, Letter to W. Grayson July 26, 1786

Sam Chase's mouth drooped, but he gave no other sign of discomfort. Colonel Mason broke the tension. "I move that we put on paper these observations about our worst commercial evils, offer our cures as 'suggestions,' and send them to the Virginia and Maryland governors and assemblies."

The letter was written. After the specifics of uniform money value, duties, and interest rates, the commissioners worded a call for broader action for the states through a conference every year.

G. Mason (Rowland)

"We'd best stick to saying 'commercial matters', lest we ask for too much and get nothing," growled Chase.

On Monday morning, Colonel Mason copied the "suggestions" letter four times, one for each governor and assembly, while Stone made four "Mount Vernon Compact" copies. In addition, Mason penned a letter to the Pennsylvania Council, as the Virginia Assembly had directed him to do, asking for cooperation in the plan to join the Potomac to rivers, including some in Pennsylvania, leading to the Ohio.

G. Mason (Rowland)

Dinner odors tantalized their appetites before all the copies were ready to sign. With General Washington standing beside his chair watching the little ceremony, Colonel Mason, then each of the others, moved around the table, dipping their quills and signing the various documents.

"Although your name will not appear on these documents," Colonel Mason remarked to Washington, "it will be evident that you were part of the conference from the name of the place where we held our meeting."

The General shook the hand of each man as he completed the signing, and directed him to a tray of long-stemmed glasses filled with rosy-red wine.

"Gentlemen," he said when the work was done, "I offer a toast to five men whose vision and labor will be far-reaching, affecting the national union and prosperity! I believe with all my heart that this compact, and this letter will start a series of actions that will preserve and strengthen our union.

"Good sense prevailing elsewhere as it has here, these actions will encompass other mutually advantageous subjects. If we do not act to preserve our union, we will find ourselves fulfilling the predictions of our detractors: that a people governing themselves cannot keep order or prosper, and are bound to fall asunder in chaos, violence, and economic ruin. Pray the states act in time to give long life to the United States of America!"

When at the dinner table the soup plates had been emptied and a servant was taking them away, Colonel Mason asked a question of considerable interest to all. "General," he said, "have you heard anything new about how much the price of land in the west has advanced in the three months since our state assemblies approved your Potomac plan?"

GW Writings, March 1785

"I have only heard that prices are rising every day. If the plan is effected, of which I have no doubt, the price will increase much faster. Your investment in the Ohio Company, Colonel Mason, should pay off well one day, but in the meantime, yield will be scarcely enough to justify recording

GW, Vol.6 (D.Freeman) p. 33

it—at least that is the case with my Ohio and Kanawha acres," Washington replied.

Sam Chase caught Washington's eye and with a quizzical smile remarked, "Land prices have gone up fast on the Delaware River, I've heard. In fact, I've heard that Robert Morris is buying land by Lamberton at Trenton—hundreds of acres, a ferry, and a tavern on the road to New York. Elbridge Gerry may be having second thoughts about how long the 'virtue' of a Delaware Falls capital will last!" Chase guffawed.

Without a flicker of change in his expression, the General answered, "Without money to buy land or build, Congress is in the same position with choosing a seat of government as with everything else: Nothing can or will happen."

"Not even if New Jersey or Pennsylvania—or even a rich merchant—gives land and $100,000?" smirked Chase.

Seeing the General's expression change, Henderson quickly spoke up. "That amount of money won't last two weeks! Congress won't get more since Maryland, Virginia, states to the south, and delegates who hate Robert Morris presumably will vote against appropriations for Falls of the Delaware!"

Through the rest of dinner, opinions and speculations passed back and forth about the Potomac's chances of capturing the capital. "Potomac Company's canal project and linkage to the Ohio should make all the difference!"

"Inevitably, the seat must come to Georgetown, the most central location between north and south."

"Potomac will get the seat as new faces and forces enter the Congress. All we need is time."

"While we're waiting, Madison will carry on, fighting the Northeastern men in Congress—he's in his prime, only 36."

"Right now we're buying time through the money Congress does NOT have!"

Washington, who had paid strict attention to his

Land survey map of Trenton, 1789, shows ferry, land, and "Morris Tavern" by Lamberton, adjacent to Trenton, and a "Morrisville" label on land opposite, on the Pennsylvania side, all indicating ownership of some time. (Trenton Public Library archives)

plate of roast mutton and rutabagas, joined the laughter at this remark of Colonel Mason. Immediately, Sam Chase was ready to poke more fun at Congress and its votes to choose a permanent place for its meetings.

"You all know Francis Hopkinson in Philadelphia (nods and smiles) and how he can make a joke out of anything—except a flag: The flag he designed for the United States is the best thing he ever did! ("Hear, hear!") So last year, while Congress held on to having TWO seats, one at Delaware Falls, one at Georgetown, Hopkinson kept coming up with explanations of how that would work exactly.

"At first, he said Congress was setting up a machine of cogged wheels in the sky. Then, Congress were regulating the machine—great mechanics that they are—by attaching a giant pendulum to swing back and forth between the Delaware and the Potomac. (Smiles, chortles)

"Later, Hopkinson said he'd been inspired by Cyrano de Bergerac's *Voyage to the Moon and the Sun,* and decided that Congress House, President's House, and other official houses would be made of very light wood and fitted with large sails. Delegates atop each house would pump giant bellows creating enough wind to fly Congress and buildings between Potomac and Delaware in four days!" Chase could hardly push the last words through his laughter. The others laughed loud and long, but they had barely calmed when Chase began again.

"General, our friend Hopkinson had another inspiration, intended as a compliment to you. I trust you will see it that way. Instead of making all the government buildings in the usual shape of boats to float from one river to the other, Hopkinson said Congress House would be a boat in the shape of a rocking horse. It would be surmounted by a statue of the hero of the Republic in a pose remindful of

his valorous leadership at the Battle of Trenton—"

Washington's burst of laughter, followed by five other whoops, held up the story for some seconds. Chase continued, "The rocking horse and hero would be big enough for all the members of Congress to ride INSIDE—(new convulsions of laughter)—as it floated back and forth between the Potomac and the Delaware!"

When the men had composed themselves and wiped their eyes, Colonel Mason rose and held up his wine glass. "To our hero and host, whose presence on battlefield and legislative field are essential for victory!" Washington responded, "To inspired commissioners, and government by the governed!"

Glasses drained, the General invited the men into the west parlor—"not for tea, but to pay our respects to Mrs. Washington who is presiding over the children's dining table. Our little folks are pretty Nelly and lovable Mr. Tub, or Wash, Mrs. Washington's—and my—grandchildren. There is also Mrs. Washington's niece, Fanny Bassett, who will help us out as long as she will consent. You've seen the children staying out of the way, heard them bumping about upstairs. I have promised them that, before they go to their rooms, they may say goodbye to 'the Gentlemen', since you will all be gone before breakfast." He led the way out.

"All, except me," smiled George Mason. "I trust you will feed me a tittle if I rise later, and perhaps loan me your carriage to go home."

GW Diary March 1785

"If you promise to send back some of your young shoots of Persian jasmine and guilder rose. Tomorrow I return to digging holes and shoveling manure—the farmer's gold," Washington said.

GW, Vol.6
(D.Freeman) p.56

"And now, Mrs. Washington, Fanny, Nelly, and Tub, may I introduce to you the Mount Vernon Compact commissioners. You must always remember these far-sighted men! Their practical common sense may lead us on a path that will regain respect and glory for our beloved country."

Mount Vernon on the Potomac.

Meeting in late September 1786 on the second floor of New York's City Hall on Wall Street but facing Broad Street (above), Congress heard an urgent call for a Constitutional Convention the next May. The call came from delegates who had met in Annapolis to consider trade obstacles—and worsening economic and civil disorders. Congress 18 months before had moved from Trenton to await construction of a permanent capital at the Falls of the Delaware. Moneyless, it built nothing; powerless, it only talked.

66

CHAPTER 7

Call for a Constitutional Convention

SCENE: New York City Hall on Wall Street facing Broad Street. Second floor room used by the State Assembly from time to time, but presently loaned to the Continental Congress.
TIME: September 19, 1786, about 4 p.m.

Hamilton, who lived a block from Congress in NY City Hall, most likely delivered the Annapolis Convention Report, rather than Convention President Dickinson, who lived in Delaware. According to Madison, Hamilton wrote the work draft, and copied the final document.

A Closer Look at the Annapolis Convention (S.V.Baltz) p9

Alexander Hamilton, just off the ferry from New Jersey at the end of the long road from Annapolis, Maryland, suddenly felt fatigue drop away. Home again! And with a piece of paper in his inside coat pocket that could possibly turn all America around!

His highest hopes—and worst anxieties—were riding on the power of the words he had drafted a few days ago at Mann's Tavern on the main street of Maryland's capital, words that he and the little group of delegates had agreed upon after much debate and revision.

"But will all the states concur as we hope and appoint men to meet at Philadelphia on the second Monday in May next as we propose?" he mused. "They responded poorly to Virginia's call to the trade convention in Annapolis. Well, thank heavens ALL the five-state gathering of delegates at the convention—much too big a word for a dozen men!—felt as strongly as Madison, Randolph, Tenche Cox, Abe Clark, Dickinson, and myself, that this country MUST have a strong CENTRAL government! We failed for lack of delegates to work on trade barriers as the Mount Vernon Compact bid us, but our disappointment released our true feelings—that we must have a whole NEW framework of government!

"This week, our call for a constitutional convention will arrive in all the state capitals. Tomorrow

(he patted his coat pocket) it will confront the Continental Congress."

The coach turned the corner onto Broad Street. Leaning out the window, Hamilton could see the clumsy old City Hall at the end of Broad where it joined Wall Street. Two stories of red brick, unornamented except for projecting wings, a trio of arches fronting the entrance, a skimpy iron balcony, and a green copper roof. In the attic facade, miniature dormers appeared like a row of tiny heads in pointed hats. Crowning the edifice, a slender cupola, faintly Turkish with its open, arched supports and onion-shaped, green copper cap, was topped with an out-size weathercock.

Hamilton looked at it and laughed. Yet he felt an affection for the 80-year-old clump, for he had pleaded many a case in its court room behind the little balcony, and sat many a day in the Assembly room in the right wing next to the court.

He would stop by, leave the paper in his pocket with Charles Thomson, secretary to the Continental Congress now occupying the Assembly room, then go home just steps away on Wall Street.

The horses clopped steadily along the dirt street toward City Hall. Hamilton, quite alert, even excited at being in a big city again, smiled as he gazed at each familiar store and house on the way, looked for faces he knew among the people on the side-

Details from "Elevations of Old City Hall", as it was before 1789. (Collection of Independence Natl. Historical Park, Philadelphia, Pa.)

walks, and congratulated himself that he did not live in a village of 2,500 but a metropolis of 25,000 —almost as large as Philadelphia.

He found Thomson in his office at the head of the stairs and adjacent to the meeting room of the Continental Congress. White-haired at 55, a little hump-shouldered after 12 years of clerking for Congress, he was bent over his desk, his quill rushing its scratches across paper. He dropped his pen to grab Hamilton's hand in greeting.

"Oh Lord yes, I'm still here writing letters. When Congress has enough delegates on hand to have a meeting—not often enough—I live in this building, my wife says. She must go alone to the theater or parties in your fair city. Feasting and every kind of extravagance go on, though everyone complains of poverty, and areas burned out 10 years ago lie neglected still.

"Congress ends the workday at 3, dinnertime. My deputy and two clerks go out to eat—did you know our civil servants now number 50 ? I stay and write, write, write. My clerks help in the evening. They live in the attic here—a jail for debtors before Congress came.

"So, we'll get everything done by the time Congress convenes in the morning—the journal, approved bills, letters. Look at this one. In the midst of writing bankers, begging them to lend Congress $500,000 (we cannot recruit soldiers to guard the arsenal in Springfield, Massachusetts, unless they know we can pay them), I must stop and write the New York city fathers again, asking them to put up chains across Wall Street to divert traffic. Noise of passing carriages, almost unceasing, causes daily interruptions to discussions. Delegates can't hear each other's arguments!"

"Do they ever?" Hamilton said, and both men burst out laughing.

Then Hamilton hastened to hand to talkative Thomson the paper he had brought from Annapo-

lis. "I have brought to Congress on behalf of John Dickinson, trade convention president, his letter of submission for the report and suggestion adopted by the convention. We believe the suggestion, if accepted by the states, will result in a solution to this now floundering nation's problems. It is a call for a convention next May to revise, amend, rewrite our constitution to provide a strong central government."

Smiling, Thomson took the paper, read it quickly, and reached out to shake Hamilton's hand. "At last! A special convention is better than leaving the job to Congress. They voted last May that THEY should revise the Articles of Confederation. Young Charles Pinckney brought up the matter, and they finally agreed to let him and a committee write out some amendments. Pinckney is only 26, a South Carolinian with more drive and energy than any of the others. Knows much about everything. But so far, Congress has not acted. I know Pinckney and his committee look to the Annapolis trade conference as a source of hope.

"A convention led by our best men—Washington, Franklin, Morris, yourself, Mr. Hamilton—can quickly remedy the weaknesses now dragging us into anarchy. But next year may be too late. This minute, New England is moving toward fullblown civil war, and a break from the Union."

In shock and despair, Hamilton covered his face with his hands and groaned. He looked then at Thomson and said, "Your mention of $500,000 to pay for protection of our arsenal in western Massachusetts is a measure of how much the situation has worsened while I was on the Annapolis trip. Is it still Mr. Shays who gathers the army, plans the arsenal attack, and looks to wage full-scale warfare? (Thomson nodded.) Has Congress sent anyone to Springfield to assess defenses and make a plan of action?"

As he answered, Thomson beckoned Hamilton

Continental Congress in N.Y. City Hall (J.Platt) p16

City of New York in the year of Washington's Inauguration (T.E.V. Smith) p5

Platt. p9

Continental Congress (E.Burnett) p663

Cont.Congress in N.Y. City Hall p663 (J.Platt)

Constitutional Convention (Warren) p21

Journ. Cont. Congress, Vol.31.

Charles Thomson

Cont. Congress
(E.Burnett) p672

Platt p5, 6, 7, 8

Power of the Purse
(E.J.Ferguson) p250

to accompany him into the adjoining room where Congress held its meetings. Annapolis Report in hand, Thomson walked slowly toward the door while relating the news.

"General Knox will go to Springfield in a few days. But without money to pay soldiers—for I expect nothing will come of our begging letters—Congress cannot recruit an army.

"In the event that Shays' farmers succeed in capturing the cannon, muskets, and ammunition at the federal arsenal in Springfield, who knows what will happen in, or to, the state of Massachusetts."

They stepped through the door onto a handsome dark green carpet, and proceeded toward the President's platform. Its canopy of red damask, the red damask window curtains on either side, the red leather upholstery of 36 chairs arranged with their fine mahogany desks in rows, gave the room an air of richness and dignity. Life-size portraits—royal gifts—of the French King and his Queen Marie Antoinette, hung side by side in elaborately carved, gold-leafed frames next to a full-length painting of General Washington. They faced on the opposite wall smaller portraits of American Revolution generals who also helped to defeat the English King. Thomson and Hamilton, absorbed in the story they feared was the opening of a drama of civil war and the death of the Union, scarcely gave a glance to the room they were walking through.

"When I left for Annapolis at the end of August," Hamilton said, "we had just had news from western Massachusetts that Shays' army of farmers, well armed, had attacked courthouses in Worcester, Berkshire, and Hampshire, closing down the courts. Local militia did nothing to hold them back. Some even joined the mob." Hamilton shuddered. "It reminds me of the mutinying soldiers in Philadelphia in '83."

All New England was in turmoil, it seemed to Thomson, with mobs in nearly every state taking the law in their hands. Insurrection was said to be brewing in Vermont, and troops were called out in New Hampshire when unruly crowds beseiged the legislature. "I understand that the farmers particularly are hard hit by high taxes to pay state war debts, and by having to pay in coin, not paper. Judges jail those who don't pay, and confiscate their property. Rhode Island on the other hand is printing paper money by the millions, which keeps farmers and debtors quiet, but ruins everybody else. So the distressed parties are fighting their governments. Congress, weak, poor, unattended, indecisive, can help no one."

Thomson, agitated, his expression grim, his voice heavy, added, "All of this is bad, but it is not the worst. Some days ago, James Monroe, our foreign affairs secretary, informed Congress that several secession committees had met in New York. They want to take the states east of the Hudson out of the Union and form a separate government. You know Theodore Sedgwick of Massachusetts—well, he was heard to ask, 'What can the Southern States give us? Nothing!' The middle states held a meeting, too, and also talked of breaking away from the Southern states."

Hamilton was rubbing his brow in dismay. "We are at the edge of a precipice. We can possibly survive a Shays' rebellion. We cannot survive separate confederations. If the states do not agree to a constitutional convention, or send no one, as Rufus King predicted when I passed through Philadelphia, and if Congress hangs back, insisting on tinkering with the Articles of Confederation, we are doomed. Congress delegates come to meetings or not as they please, and those who come can decide nothing, being absorbed in the game of wearing each other down with argument. They are so jealous of the little power they have, they stand in the way of getting more. What have they made up their minds about since coming to New York 18

Cont. Congress
(E.Burnett) p657

Continental Congress in New York City Hall 2nd. floor 1786. Tracing of the floor plan from collection of Independence National Historical Park, Philadelphia.

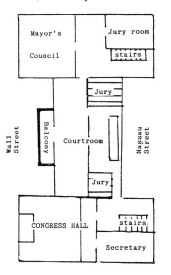

Cont.Cong.in N.Y. City Hall (J.Platt) p10, 11, 12

months ago? That the President is to wear a black robe during sessions, and be called 'Excellency'. That members will be called 'the Honorable' and rank above every state officer except the Governor! Augh! I cannot think of a single good thing to say about Congress!"

With a tiny smile and a raised eyebrow, the secretary of Congress for 12 years—since its beginning—declared there was one good thing he could credit them with since they moved to New York. "For more than a year, they have spent little time arguing about where to locate the seat of government. I am so grateful."

Cont. Congress (E.Burnett) p616-620

Hamilton, amused, observed that the creature comforts of New York after the miseries of the villages of Princeton and Trenton, had no doubt diminished the delegates' enthusiasm for building a permanent village capital at the Falls of the Delaware as Congress had last voted. Thomson, with a little shrug, answered, "Umm-hh. Well, it's true that in Trenton in late '84 when Congress was voting for Delaware Falls, the members were talking outside their meetings in French Arms Tavern about nothing else but settling in a big city during the building years of a permanent capital. Villages have little of interest to drink or eat, too few beds and diversions.

Hist.Trenton, p192 Trenton Hist.Soc.

"Philadelphia was still on the rejected list of most delegates who happened to be on hand for the votes, so New York City won the temporary seat. Soon after Congress had a quorum in New York— it took a month—Delaware Falls had its death blow.

"Richard Henry Lee, Congress President then, had a letter from General Washington at Mount Vernon saying something like, 'By the time buildings on the banks of the Delaware are ready for Congress, it will be found that they are improperly placed— and others in a more convenient place will have to be built.'

Writings of Washington, IX (Sparks) p95

"Word got around. Some months later when Congress took up appropriating $100,000 to start construction at the Falls—Gerry's motion—only his state, Massachusetts, and New Jersey voted for it.

"Since Congress has hardly enough money to stay in business, with such opposition what's the use of bringing up the location question again? So they haven't. BUT—with terms ending and new men coming in each session, it's risky to predict how long this enjoyable calm and peace will last. Congress is best known for undoing this year the very thing it fought hardest to do last year."

"Charles Thomson," Hamilton said, "I marvel at your stamina—listening to, writing down all the arguments of all the sessions of the Continental Congress for 12 years! You are its continuity, the constant through all the changes of delegates, meeting places, and disputes. It was a lucky day for this country when your enemies blocked your appointment as a delegate to the Congress in 1774, for the Congress could then call you—the most fiery Son of Liberty in Philadelphia—for its secretary. All these years, the confidence that Congress has had in you, in your integrity, has had no limits. You have been its reliable source of undoctored history, its discreet adviser, its respected sage. I salute you, honorable Secretary."

The aging man laid his hand on the shoulder of young Hamilton, gazed at his pink cheeks and flashing eyes, blinked back tears, and nodded his thanks. After a pause, he reminded Hamilton that last year his enemies—Arthur Lee, John Adams, Sam Otis— tried to push him out. "'Nosey', they called me (he touched his long, pointed nose) meaning I know too much. But despite their hard work of conniving, I am still here."

The two men had mounted the few steps to the top of the President's platform. Thomson proceeded to President Nathaniel Gorham's desk to add the Annapolis Report to a small collection of papers.

"Tomorrow's business," he said. "Your report will

History of Trenton, p195 (Trenton Hist. Society); and Journ. Cont. Cong., Sept.22 1785

GW Writings Vol.28, p172 (Fitzpatrick), letter to Grayson, June 22, 1785

Cont. Congress, Vol.8, p119, 225 (Burnett), Grayson letter to GW, Oct. 1785.

Cont. Cong.in N.Y.City Hall.(Platt) p15

Dict.Am.Biog.

Charles Thomson (J.Hendricks) p140, 153n

be on top—but Gorham brings them up as he deems best, you know."

To leave the platform, Hamilton pushed aside the damask curtain loosely furled with a silk cord, and hanging in front of the steps. "These fine decorations—in fact, all the furnishings of this chamber must have cost someone a pretty penny," Hamilton remarked.

Cont. Cong. in N.Y.
City Hall (Platt) p5n

"Congress paid for them. Something over a thousand dollars, practically their last penny," confided Thomson. "But this is the first time Congressmen have sat in their own seats at their own desks instead of those loaned them by others."

Cont. Cong. (Burnett)
p16

"I am reminded by your mention of Congress's poverty," said Hamilton as they proceeded along the aisle between the two groups of desks and chairs, "to inquire if any part of the law passed by Congress ordering a land survey at Delaware Falls, and contracts entered for construction, was ever carried out?"

Jour. Cont. Congress,
Dec. 23, 1784

Thomson, with a little shrug and sidelong glance at Hamilton, replied, "Surveyors and building contractors, Mr. Hamilton, don't do business with clients known to all the world as verging on bankruptcy. Besides, word circulated around Trenton that the South was going to block any move to appropriate money. No contractor needed to wait for the effect of Washington's disapproving letter to Congress."

"I will wager," Hamilton replied, "that New York is so much to the taste of Congress, they secretly hope no one will mention the villages by Delaware Falls again. With Potomac men probably resigned to failure after so many defeats, and few voting for Philadelphia as temporary capital, New York will keep Congress indefinitely!"

Wm. Pierce of Georgia
description 1787

Thomson walked with Hamilton to the head of the stairs just in time to see President Nathaniel Gorham coming up. Gorham, 45, wore as always a cheerful, pleasant expression on his long oval, plump face. A poor boy from Charlestown across the bay from Boston, he had become rich through trade and commerce.

"President Gorham!" Hamilton greeted him. "I have brought from Annapolis, where men from several states met to consider the problems of commerce, a report for the consideration of Congress. It contains our earnest call for a convention next May to remedy the weaknesses of our Constitutional form of government. Reports of disorders in your own state of Massachusetts tell us we must make haste!"

"I need no convincing," Gorham answered, nodding his head vigorously. "I will do my best to nudge this Congress into giving its blessing to such a convention. However, it may take a Shays victory at the arsenal to lever the delegates into supporting drastic changes—drastic is what we need."

"Thank you, Excellency!" exclaimed Hamilton. "Drastic alterations will come—by agreement or by FORCE!"

Congress action:
Sept. 20, Annapolis
Report read.
Oct. 11, Report sent to
committee.
Feb. 12, committee
renewed.
Feb. 21, call for
Constitutional
Convention accepted.

On August 22, 1787, most of the 35 Constitutional Convention delegates crowd the dock at the foot of Market Street to look at, and consider riding on, the first passenger steamboat in the world. Even this startling invention of John Fitch would not throttle discreet arguments among the delegates, or lobbying for items not yet included in the plan of government they have worked on all summer. One such stalled item concerned a requirement for a 10-mile square of land, under the control of Congress, for the national capital.

72

CHAPTER 8

Ten-Mile Square in the Constitution

SCENE: Market Street Wharf, Philadelphia.
TIME: Wednesday, August 22, 1787, a very hot day, about 4:30 in the afternoon.

The 10-mile square conversation aboard Fitch's boat is not a matter of record. That such a conversation took place in some location is very likely. Records show Pinckney first, then Madison, then both, in Aug/Sept pressed the committees to include the federal district in the Constitution.

Poor John Fitch
(T.Boyd)

Recessed for the day at four o'clock, most of the 35 delegates still attending the Constitutional Convention's summer-long session walked the block from the Independence room of the State House on Chestnut Street to High (Market) Street. There, they turned right for a few blocks' stroll to the river wharf.

Curiosity had moved them to accept the invitation of the eccentric mechanic, John Fitch, to see, even to take a ride on, a new kind of boat he had invented. His boat moved against the current without sails or oarsmen, he said, and he once had it going five miles an hour downstream! John Fitch, a long-chinned, bony-faced, very tall, gaunt, talkative Connecticut man of little schooling, called his invention a "steamboat."

Two years ago he had the idea of hitching to boat oars the piston rod of a steam engine, invented in England some years before to pump water from coal mines. The steam force behind a piston would be strong enough to push oars against river current, he thought. Obsessed, he scrounged money, and with mechanic Harry Voight, toiled stubbornly to hammer out the parts and create a workable steam engine to power a set of oars.

Now (he had announced in his invitation to delegates of the Constitutional Convention), this very day, he would formally demonstrate his steamboat "Perseverance". Its success would prove he was not a crazy man as quite a few people thought.

Blocks away from the Market Street wharf, delegates in their silks, satins, tricorns, and ruffles could see a black column of smoke rising from a tall stackpipe on the boat. Closer, they heard the babbling and laughter of a fair-size crowd eager for entertainment, expecting disaster. A slow, rhythmic ch-ch-ch reached their ears.

They saw tall posts of a large box-like frame standing on the boat's deck. "No sails!" "So noisy!" "All that smoke!"commented voices in the crowd behind a chain blocking the pier entrance. Many of the shopkeepers, stall tenders from the roofed-over market in the center of the street, dockmen and workmen, sailors, and artisans who lived and worked in nearby houses, had seen the boat slowly moving up and down the river during the past month of tests. Most still expected it to explode.

"It don't go no faster than I can walk, so what good is it?" they said to each other.

Even to some learned convention delegates, a steamboat seemed of questionable value.

"I see a row of oars hanging along the sides of the high frame, so it's apparent this boat will move by the old way of paddling," Charles Pinckney told his fellow South Carolinian, Pierce Butler. That ex-British army major, who had married into plantation money, replied that Fitch might be making the mistake of some convention delegates who had tried to inject new power into old Articles of Confederation. "Both frame and oars fell down," Butler observed.

"Even so," replied Pinckney, fast-striding to keep up, "some delegates still show signs of resistance towards making provisions for a few basic needs as we build a new framework for our government."

"You are referring to our own esteemed Carolinian, Judge Rutledge, I presume?" said Major Butler.

Pinckney grimaced and nodded. "As chairman of the Committee on Detail to organize three months of Convention actions—and proposals for action—into a coherent draft, he should have persuaded the other four members to include my seat-of-government paragraph for the Convention to debate. But he didn't—even though I had been invited to submit it to them.

"Instead (the phrasing still makes me grind my teeth!)—instead, they included two sentences that seemed to say Congress could adjourn only to the place at which they had been sitting! That's New York! We MUST get rid of those words! My paragraph would clarify everything!"

Pinckney, out of breath from trying to keep up with Butler's long legs, as well as from the agitation his talking had stirred, motioned Butler to pause for him to speak his most important words. "Congress has moved again and again since the war because the delegates deplored village housing, food, and boredom—or Philadelphia's mobs. They like New York's comforts and entertainment! They will hang onto them—you will see—making New York in time the capital, unofficially permanent. We must not let that happen! A paragraph in the Constitution would force them to build an independent, permanent capital, and to move there.

"Somehow, Madison and I must convert three of the five Committee members—Rutledge, Wilson, Randolph, Ellsworth, Gorham—convince them of

the importance of our 10-mile square paragraph!"

As they sauntered on, Butler declared that Pinckney's paragraph was too timid. "This Convention should decide upon, and include in the Constitution, the NAME of the place for the capital. With this distinguished, reasonable group of men, we could expect a more CENTRAL location than the Falls of the Delaware, which Congress has voted for during the past few years."

"So you told the Convention the other day," answered Pinckney, "and you know how everyone groaned and headed you off. 'Location' is the fighting word. But my paragraph would go through without a fuss, I'm sure. It simply states what Congress has written into every move it has made to locate the capital—that Congress will have a permanent capital, and total control over the district it occupies."

"Oh, but you put in something new—the big size of this district!" Butler reminded him. "I think a two or three-mile square, such as Congress talks about, is big enough."

Young Pinckney, his cheeks pink and soft brown eyes glinting, half whispered, "But think of it: A TEN-mile square will forever eliminate our two biggest cities—both in the North—as likely locations for the seat of government. Pennsylvania law now excludes Philadelphia, but a newer local law is easy to come by."

Butler's heavy black eyebrows rose. "Ahh I see. A 10-mile square swallowing those cities would deprive local politicians of power when Congress took control. New York and Philadelphia wouldn't like having Congress set their tax rates, make their laws, and command their militia. But Potomac farmers won't mind at all!"

They were just past the market, mostly deserted, for even the butchers had closed their stalls to join the audience of the steamboat show. "Most—perhaps all five of the Committee of Detail will come

Charles Pinckney

to see Fitch's boat, and my aim is to corner at least two of them," confided Pinckney. "Madison has already been working with Governor Randolph—but Madison was too ailing today to come here even though he's a strong supporter of Fitch. Oh—there—look to the right. There's Judge Ellsworth. I'll start with him. He sees us—he's beckoning. Well, Major, I am starting out lucky, as usual."

Connecticut's Contribution to the Development of the Steamboat (P.Hoopes)

Alone at the edge of the noisy crowd, Judge Oliver Ellsworth of Connecticut, his broad face lit with pleasure at having gentleman company, greeted the Carolinians warmly. "I'm waiting for Governor Randolph," he said. "He insisted that I witness this steamboat event, especially since the inventor is a Connecticut man. Randolph says the steam-powered boat will prove to be as important as today's Convention debate about the slave trade. So, I may faint with hunger and parbroil in the sun, but I will see history made.

"Think of it! Steam pressure doing the work of many men! And faster than men could move a boat this big against the current. Such power—ah! Governor Randolph! I was just saying that steam power may change the world!"

GW Diary Aug22, 1787

Handsome Edmund Randolph, noted for his impeccable manners, tilted his head in agreement, greeted the three delegates, and said, "I am truly amazed that General Washington has shown no interest in this demonstration. He and Gouverneur Morris—both are staying with Robert Morris, you know—have gone with Morris to his country place, 'The Hills', instead of coming here.

"I suppose I shouldn't be surprised. After all, the General has sided with James Rumsey who is telling everybody that Fitch stole from him the steamboat idea. Rumsey claims he made a steamboat before Fitch—I doubt he did. Even the General says Rumsey's boat—the one the General saw—was a small model, and that it moved by a mechanical device, not steam."

GW Diary Sept.1784

Judge Ellsworth thought it just as likely that Washington did not come to the wharf for a more personal reason. "The poor man can go nowhere without people flocking to look at him—'their darling hero' as the newspapers say.

George Washington (D.Freeman)

"With this crowd here, and the General's rheumatism little improved since he arrived in May with his arm in a sling, a rest in the country will do him more good than enlightenment about Fitch's boat."

Randolph dabbed at his sweaty brow with a lace handkerchief. "All true! All true! But I know how much trouble the General will go to just to have a look when he hears of a new device someone has invented. However, I know, too, that his impression of Fitch, who went to Mount Vernon to get the General's support, was of a braggart, rude and ill-mannered. He pressed the General hard, thus annoying, even offending him. I well know from Fitch's visits to the Virginia legislature how many rough edges he shows—shabby workman's clothes, bushy hair, leathery complexion, unschooled speech. He's an aggressive, arrogant, fast talker with a lightning temper.

Poor John Fitch (T.Boyd)

Annals of Philadelphia (Watson)

Poor John Fitch (T.Boyd)

"Besides not liking Fitch, the General may believe Rumsey is the true inventor of the steamboat, as he swears he is, assailing Fitch at every turn. The General called Rumsey a genius mechanic, and the Potomac Company hired him to superintend the canal work. He displeased some directors (though not the General) by digging river channels instead of canals. Rumsey resigned at the end of a year, ostensibly because of a feud with his assistant, whom the company officials liked.

"Potomac Route to the West" (Bacon-Foster) *Columbia Hist. Society, Vol.15*

"During the past year, work on canals has recommenced. Our best argument for a Potomac capital is that canals bypassing the falls will make possible water transport from the west!"

Pinckney saw his opening, and in his mellow Southern drawl began. "But, Governor Randolph, we have nothing to guarantee that the seat will

Madison Papers, Vol.5,
p378 and 409
(Convention record)
(Elliot)

Signers of Constitution
(Ferris/Charleton)

Making of Const.
(Warren) p512n

ever get out of New York! On the contrary! Your committee draft of the Constitution contained phrasing that delegates interpreted as limiting adjournments of Congress to the place where it has been sitting—which at the moment is NEW YORK! What we NEED in the Constitution is a paragraph that REQUIRES a PERMANENT seat in a district not attached to a state!"

"Permanent seat! Long-suffering words!" said a voice familiar to all delegates by the frequency of hearing it more times a day than any other, except Gouverneur Morris's. Attorney James Wilson of Philadelphia, a scholar of political theory like James Madison, had much influenced the convention in shaping bitterly argued features of the new government structure. His companion, Hugh Williamson of North Carolina, an older man whose nose was longer even than Charles Thomson's, had stood out in Convention debates for his sharp wit and insights. He was also known for working on scientific experiments with Benjamin Franklin, a convention delegate who looked askance at Fitch and his steamboat.

"What a mercy you Southerners waited until last week to bring the words 'seat of government' to the convention floor!" Wilson breezily exclaimed. "I can think of no other subject with equal power to divert politicians from a critical issue into a tedious, exasperating, stubborn, long-drawn-out argumentation—and a decision that won't stay final! Had Madison included in the Virginia Plan—our invaluable basis for work at this convention—a mention of 'seat of government', we would have spent this hot, hot summer hammering that phrase to senselessness instead of hammering out a Federal government!"

Pinckney laughed with the others, then, glancing quickly at Wilson and Randolph as he spoke, reminded them that it was THEIR Committee report that prompted the utterance of the words 'seat

Hugh Williamson

of government' on the Floor, and a New Englander, Rufus King, not a Southerner, who launched the debate. "A big surprise to me, hearing Mr. King calling for as 'strong a cure as we can devise'—to direct Congress to settle in a permanent place."

Mr. Williamson wagged a forefinger while recalling that King was as disturbed as the southerners by the word "adjourn" in the Committee's sentence about sessions of Congress. "My fellow Carolinian, Mr. Spaight, denounced it on the Floor as a back door way to fix the permanent seat in New York! How did that alarming and abominable sentence get into the Committee's draft?"

Ellsworth answered, "No, no, that's not what we meant—you gentlemen misread it—a matter of punctuation!"

"But that is what the words said, and when Mr. Madison tried to alter it—"

"—he made it worse by adding that the First Congress MUST fix the PLACE for the seat—"

"—his entire amendment was struck down!"

"With good reason—the First Congress would debate, debate, debate, never agree on a place, and nothing else would get done!"

"Mr. Williamson! Mr. Ellsworth!" exclaimed Governor Randolph in his most authoritative tones. "Gentlemen! You are speaking louder than the steam engine! Remember our pledge of secrecy regarding Convention actions!

"Come! Let us make our way around the crowd to the pier. I was told by Dr. Johnson who brought us the invitation from inventor Fitch, that the pier has been reserved for convention delegates."

Governor Randolph took the lead of the half-dozen gentlemen, his gracious manner and splendid attire causing the multitude to part for them. At the chain across the pier entrance, a dockman let them through, and they proceeded toward Fitch's boat to join a number of other delegates already eyeing the vessel.

Madison Papers, Vol.5
p409-410 (Convention
record) (Elliot)

Fitch Autobiog./Hist.
Steamboating (Prager)
p178

Fitch Autobiog./Hist.
Steamboating
(F. Prager)

Oliver Ellsworth

Madison Papers, Vol. 5
(Elliot)

"Strange looking boat," murmured Pinckney, staring at its 45-foot length, caged, he thought, in long oars attached six to a side of a tall frame. Above its height, smoke poured from a pipe, the chimney of a brick furnace sitting on the floor of the boat. Fire roared in the furnace, heating water to steam inside a boiler. Spurts of the steam entering a cylinder pushed a piston up, condensation let it down. Ch-ch-ch-ch went the spurts of steam, a dozen times a minute, then more as boiler pressure increased. John Fitch and his partner, Harry Voight, absorbed in doctoring an ailing part, made no move to greet their distinguished guests.

The 30 or so delegates stood in pairs or small groups, leaning their ears toward each other to hear above the engine noise. Ellsworth had gravitated to young Rufus King, whose oratorical gifts and intellect promised a brilliant career Ellsworth was certain. "Ah, Rufus! I have just escaped a hot tangle with North and South Carolina. Your name was mentioned—that it was you who untied the evil bag marked 'seat of government.' We hoped to keep it closed until the Convention had completed its critical work."

Sweating profusely, he pushed his hat above his brow, and mopped with a handkerchief. "I am still a-wonder that you took such a risk, Rufus."

King, his pleasant face beaming below his dark curls, patted Ellsworth on the shoulder. "I'm still a-wonder that your Committee included such a confusing, pointless adjournment item, one the Southerners immediately suspected was intended to keep the capital in New York by hook or crook. All I was asking for was clear phrasing committing us to build a PERMANENT capital—no more roaming!

"I thought we had clarified the wording, and it would pass—when all of a sudden Madison added that the First Congress MUST decide on the location. Down it went. We are left with your 'adjourn' phrase, which will spark hours of argument, and

end with nothing in the Constitution.

"On the road again! Congress will remain 'the Ramblers', losing respect, records, good clerks—our faithful secretary Charles Thomson excepted—the good will of foreign diplomats, and time spent on endless voting to name the place where we will next sit. So amateurish! Too, too embarrassing!"

Ellsworth grimaced. "Madison and Pinckney want a 10-mile square of land, which Congress will control. That will exclude New York and Philadelphia, but make Georgetown, Maryland, a certainty."

"You forget the Falls of the Delaware," answered King, wagging a finger.

"No one can forget that it belongs more and more to Robert Morris! Have you heard he's just bought 400 acres on the Pennsylvania side? You know, of course that he and a partner also own Lamberton land next to Trenton. It smells of profiteering and domineering. The Southerners are dead-set against the Falls. When George Mason of Virginia declared war on Trenton as national capital the other day in Convention, he may have been aiming underhandedly at Morris.

"July 26—remember? Late afternoon. Just about everybody was on his feet, ready to leave for a 10-day recess. Only the Committee on Detail would stay and work. Suddenly, I heard Colonel Mason proclaiming that he had a motion. 'It would be proper,' he said, 'to make some provision in the Constitution against choosing for the permanent seat a town used as a state capital!'"

"Oh, I remember well the loud moan that arose," King said with a laugh, "and how impatiently we listened to his speech. We could see our 10-day recess evaporating!

"What a relief to hear Gouverneur Morris tapping the floor with his wooden leg and saying very loudly that if the Constitution excluded specific places for the seat, it might make enemies of Philadelphia and New York against the WHOLE

Bucks Co., Pa., Land
Records, Nixon to
R.Morris, Mar.8, 1787.
Bought at Sept. 1786
auction. (Betty Huber,
research)

Madison Papers, Vol.5
(Elliot) July 26, 1787,
p374 (Convention
record)

Rufus King

Constitution! 'They have expectations of winning the seat!' he said. We were so afraid of losing our 10-day recess, we cheered the half-dozen delegates from North and South who stood and repeated Gouverneur Morris's words."

Ellsworth's laughter and description of Mason's agitation was interrupted by the brisk voice of Dr. Samuel Johnson, recently chosen to head Columbia College in New York. "Gentlemen! Your laughter is too appealing—may I join?"

In a moment, he was adding to the story. "Did you see Mason's hand rubbing the air as if he were erasing a slate? 'I didn't mean to excite hostile passions against the federal system!' he said, and withdrew his motion. But that's not quite the end of the story. We were waiting for Washington to gavel us to our recess, when all at once, Pierce Butler, standing by General Pinckney near me, shouted, 'I'm for fixing, by the Constitution, THE PLACE!—a CENTRAL one—for the federal seat!' General Pinckney glared at him, and, I think, pulled his coattail. Butler said no more, the gavel fell, and we got our recess."

Just then, the energetic voice of John Fitch in his boat rose above engine, delegate, and crowd noise. "Gentlemen!" he shouted, his sun-burned, bony face beaming. "This steamboat is raring to take as many as 20 of you UP the Delaware to Petty's Island—an hour's ride—and back with the current in half that time. Nothing to fear, taking this ride. Me and Harry Voight here have navigated miles and miles in this river and the Schuylkill, too, to test our new furnace and boiler. Everything is working perfect—or was yesterday! I see my friend Dr. Johnson, and I want to thank him for spreading my invitation amongst you convention delegates, who—we hope—are inventing a government that will run as sweet as this steamboat did yesterday!

"Now step over here on to the deck and take a seat! You'll be safe as a flea in a featherbed—and

the canopy will save you from falling soot! Come one, come 20 !"

Without hesitating, Dr. Johnson and Rufus King, who was on the committee of Congress to consider Fitch's petition for bounty lands in the west, took the step from pier to boat deck and called to Ellsworth and Randolph to join them. Other delegates asked each other, "Are you going?" "Can we be sure it won't blow up?" "Suppose the engine quits and we're stranded in the middle of the river!" "The convention would have to adjourn if Fitch's boat trip came to a bad end!"

John Fitch called, "I would offer you a ride all the way to Trenton if we had a little more time. It's 40 twisting river miles, and might take from noon 'til dusk—but next year or the next one—when we get the money to build a bigger engine, we'll be making the trip in five hours!"

A voice called out, "On our straight post road, a horse WALKS 30 miles to Trenton in five!"

"With you being rattled and jostled all the way!" Fitch countered. "And five hours back, whilst this boat speeded by the current will make the trip in half that time!"

"Gentlemen, I am boarding!" announced Mr. Ellsworth. "Connecticut men know how to make safe boats—also I see that small vessels will follow us, life boats so to speak. Come, Mr. Rutledge, keep me company. Mr. Pinckney, Governor Randolph, Mr. Williamson! I truly believe this may turn out to be a historic hour!"

Pinckney followed. He turned and beckoned his Carolina colleague, Judge Rutledge, who slowly, judiciously nodded and went. Williamson said to Wilson, "As a matter of scientific interest, I shall go. Come with me, I believe it's a significant event, and quite safe. Perhaps you would like to hear about a letter I received from Washington describing the MECHANICAL Rumsey boat he saw—no steam." Wilson climbed the steps after Williamson.

Signers of Constitution (Ferris/ Charleton)

Madison (Elliott) Vol.5, p374 (Convention Record)

Fitch Autobiog./Hist. Steamboating (F. Prager)

Which delegates took the trip is not recorded. Almost all the delegates went to the wharf on this occasion.

Poor John Fitch (T.Boyd) p201

Governor Randolph declared he and the other Virginians would come on board to take a close look at the engine and oar-working apparatus, but could not take time for the trip.

"Yes sir," they heard Fitch saying to Randolph above the fast and noisy throbbing of the engine, "I've had this boat going up to five miles an hour—downstream. With a bigger engine, it would go faster, say, 20 miles an hour, and that against the current, too!"

"Twenty! It hardly seems possible!"

"I can't believe it!"

"It's true!" exclaimed Fitch, smiling broadly, his black eyes glittering with excitement. "I'm planning on such an engine, but it takes money to buy the materials and shape them into cylinders, pistons, shafts, and wheels. If you gentlemen in politics will help me with the money, I can do regular ferry trips to Trenton within a year! No more bumpy rides on rough roads! I first thought to put a steam engine on a coach, but then I thought of the trouncing my bones and the engine would take, riding so fast on our cursed roads! Water gives a sweet and soothing journey!"

After a quick tour of the cranks and paddles and chugging engine, Governor Randolph assured Fitch he would give the inventor and invention "every continance" he could, then led his Virginians back onto the pier.

"There's plenty seats!" Fitch cried. "If no more of you gentlemen will go, I'll call to the crowd." Fitch paused. Turning to the crowd behind the pier chain, he shouted an invitation. A dozen men hurried to the boat, followed by an eager nine-year-old.

"That's one of Charles Peale's boys," said Thomas Mifflin. "Which one are you, son?"

"Rembrandt, sir. My daddy is painting General Washington's portrait."

"Yes, we know! Does your daddy know you are taking this ride on the steamboat?"

"Oh, yes sir! He likes this boat. He, me, and Mr. Fulton have watched it every day."

Fitch's voice rang out, "We're raising the anchor! Heave off the lines! Get ready to engage, Harry! Gentlemen, this partner of mine, Harry Voight, is the best mechanic, clock maker, and engine builder this side of Hell!"

The inventor rushed from the canopied deck to the rudder. The piston in its steam pressure chamber was at last bouncing up and down 30 times a minute, and Voight engaged the rods between the pistons and the axlewheel. Its crankshafts began to lower the front racks on each side of the frame, until the "duck feet" paddles of their oars dipped into the river. Smoothly, they pulled through the water.

The boat shot forward six feet! As the forward racks began to rise, aft racks on both sides of the frame were moving down. When their oars cleaved the water and drew a stroke, the boat surged forward another six feet! Excited cries rose from people on the dock, the pier, and the the boat's passenger deck beneath the canopy.

"Gentlemen, this is unbelievable!" shouted Wilson to Williamson on one side and to young Pinckney on the other. Pinckney had managed to seat himself between Wilson and Rutledge, hoping for a chance to talk about their Committee and his paragraph. All the gentlemen were nodding, smiling, and keeping their eyes on the racks of oars now moving rhythmically and energetically up and down in tandem.

"It looks as if we're moving very fast—and so smooth and even!" Pinckney exclaimed above the engine's pounding noise.

"It's a little eerie, don't you agree?" shouted Williamson. "No sails, a phantom crew pulling the oars! Only two sailors in sight—one throwing hickory wood into a furnace, the other at the rudder. If Washington and Franklin could only be sitting here

Fitch Autobiog./Hist. Steamboating (F. Prager)

Autobiog. Fitch, p179 (Randolph letter)

Rembrandt Peale account of riding on the boat.

Artist Fulton lived at 2nd and Walnut (Phil. City Directory 1787) 4 blocks away

Poor John Fitch (Boyd) p184

John Fitch

with us!"

"It's a lot cooler out here, too—in spite of the furnace!" Wilson said. For some minutes, the passengers were too occupied with the motion of the boat, the fast ch-ch-ch-ch of the engine, the creaking of oars and racks, the rumblings of the wheel and axletrees, to converse.

In a half-hour, the gentlemen under the canopy had become so accustomed to speed, noise, and automatic oars they began to talk about other matters.

"I'm glad to have the chance to compliment you, young man," Wilson said close to Pinckney's ear, "on your contributions to the new Constitution. The Convention and our Committee have taken many items—about 20—from the draft you brought in May when we began. A useful document!" Wilson leaned around Pinckney to address the last remark to Rutledge.

"South Carolina has much reason for pride in its delegation!" Wilson added, his large, slightly protruding eyes shining through spectacles under bushy eyebrows.

"Indeed," Rutledge said, leaning toward Wilson, "it was astute of the convention to instruct our committee to include in the draft for debate worthy items from all the propositions, drafts, submissions, and Articles of Confederation, as well as the Convention resolves of the past three months.

"You, Mr. Wilson, showed a most adroit skill in organizing dozens of items into a masterly draft. We gave the Convention an orderly, harmonious document, I believe. As some astonished delegates observed, it was not a revised Articles of Confederation, but a new form of government!"

"If I may speak frankly, Gentlemen," Pinckney said, turning from one to the other to ensure that each heard, "there is still one important item that ought to be included. It concerns the seat of government paragraph—"

"Oh yes, Mr. Pinckney," Wilson said, "and you have resubmitted it—Madison too. But do you think it wise to bring this up? Is it really necessary for it to be included in our Constitution?" Wilson inquired. "We are all tired, all anxious to be at home looking after our affairs. General Washington says the sheriff is about to sell some of his land to get money for taxes. Mr. Madison is over-fatigued to the point of illness—the poor man is lying in bed now, worn out, but copying the notes he made of today's debates. Colonel Mason's nerves are frazzled. The seat of government is a most irritating and devisive subject. It can only delay our going home, and will put the delegates in a bad mood!"

"I agree with Mr. Wilson!" Rutledge declared, straining to be heard over the engine noise.

"But I want you to understand," the judge added, "that I am not opposed to your paragraph—and neither is anyone else on the committee. Mr. Wilson here, Ellsworth, and I were all present in the Independence Room four years ago when the mutinying soldiers threatened us!"

Pinckney nodded vigorously. "I do remember, sir! Which surprises me the more, that my simple paragraph is left out. It only says what you have just told me no one opposes—Congress's power to fix and control a permanant seat in a district separate from any state! Who will argue about that! Arguments flare about WHERE—not whether! Is it not wise to include the 'whether' in the Constitution to give a strong legal foundation for the creation of a non-state territory, and the power of Congress over it?"

The two older men had turned in their seats to look at Pinckney as he talked. In the strange setting of engine noises, the bumping and scrunching of the mechanical devices, their steady, relentless movement, Pinckney waited for a response.

Judge Rutledge shook his head. "It is not wise for us to open the subject. I think it not even nec-

Convention of 1787
(J.F.Jameson)

Making of Constitution
(Warren) p391n

"Pinckney and the
Constitution"
(McLaughlin)
Am.Hist.Review 1903-4

Making of the
Constitution (Warren)
p384-7

James Wilson

Madison Papers Vol.5
Aug.18 (Elliot)

GWWritings, Letters to
Mercer, Sept.9, Feb.15,
1787; Jan.11, 1788

J.Madison (Brant)
p154

essary." Wilson nodded. "The debate could destroy both Convention and Constitution."

Pinckney made his verbal bows to his powerful companions. "Truly, good sirs, I am flattered that you have already accepted so many of my submissions and included them in the Constitution. I am honored that you, Mr. Wilson, whom we all rank among the foremost in legal and political knowledge, speak so well of my work. Judge—Governor—Rutledge, you know how much I value your good opinion and your valuable support, here and in Charleston.

Madison Papers, Vol.5 (Elliot) Aug.18, p439-40

"Mr. Madison's paragraph is slightly different from mine, but only slightly. Even should you prefer and accept his, I shall be pleased, very pleased! Mr. Madison is a scholar, a profound politician with broad knowledge on every point in our debates. He is a great man and I am honored to work so closely with him on this matter. 'Closely' should be taken literally," he laughed. "Too many of us are crowded into Mrs. House's rooms! Madison and I have one writing table between us!"

Making of Const. (Warren) p.116-7

Mr. Wilson and Judge Rutledge were settling back on the bench with a good laugh when Fitch turned from the rudder, his expression triumphant. "Petty's Island, Gentlemen! We've bucked the current three miles in a little less than one hour!" he shouted.

Dr. Johnson exclaimed enthusiastically, "Mr. Fitch, this is a most impressive, noble exhibition! You deserve every continance and encouragement for such ingenuity and industry to invent this amazing transport!"

Autobiography of J.Fitch, Johnson's letter to Fitch

A great smile lit Fitch's rugged face. "Will you put that on paper, sir?!" he shouted.

On the pier by Market Street wharf, when the steamboat had moved out of sight, General Mifflin, dapper and handsome, remarked to Governor Randolph that, with the Falls of the Delaware only five—or was it three?—hours from Philadelphia by steamboat, Southerners might shift their votes for the seat of government to Lamberton by the Falls—just for the ride.

Randolph answered that Madison might then regret trying to help Fitch's boat succeed. "Madison asked the Virginia Assembly to grant money. But not even Patrick Henry could persuade the delegates that this rough, uneducated Fitch could build anything. He has now proved he can. I shall give him all the encouragement I can."

Poor John Fitch (T.Boyd)

Mifflin laughed. "I'll stick with a horse that knows to pick up speed when I crack the whip."

The crowd on the wharf quickly dispersed. Delegates, their dinner hour long past, lingered little, leaving in pairs and small groups for taverns and boarding houses.

Governor Randolph suggested to Mr. Gorham that they dine together at the Indian Queen, review the items left in their Committee of Detail Report, and think about what to do with those put aside for lack of agreement after debate. Gorham accepted. In step, the aristocratic Virginia governor and the Boston merchant, son of a packetboat operator, began their walk up Market Street.

Gorham's long oval face sank with gloom into his double chin. Usually he wore a congenial expression, but today he looked anxious, fatigued, even irritable. "We'll never get finished with this job," he said.

"Look at the number of big, important items that have been haggled and left lie." He counted them off on his fingers—electing the President, treaty-making, impeachments, money bills. "And there are at least 50 new submissions! Maybe a hundred! Madison has 20, Pinckney has 20, Gouverneur Morris a handful, Mason, Gerry—"

"Even Rutledge and I have some," laughed Governor Randolph. "I am aware we are inundated, clogged, stuck. I think we should tell the delegates

Signers of Constitution (Ferris/ Charleton) p 75

that it is time to set up ANOTHER committee to ponder the big matters, invent solutions for them, and to sort out the smaller swarm to see how many can be discarded. At other standstill points in this convention, special committees have devised breakthrough compromises."

Brightening, Gorham, who served as Chairman of the Convention when it met as a Committee of the Whole for discussions, exclaimed, "How soon can we suggest this? Tomorrow, perhaps?"

"We most certainly can begin planning for it right now. We can think about who should sit on that committee," answered Randolph.

"Inventors! One from each state," said Gorham. "Twelve's as big as a committee should be. And no longwinds, a-hemmers and a-hawers."

"I'd pick Madison for Virginia," said Randolph.

"From Massachusetts...how about Gerry?" said Gorham. "No, no, I take that back. He can analyze acutely, but when he speaks, you begin counting the stumbles and lose the thought!"

"No, not Gerry. He's a Grumbletonian, and against anything he didn't think of first."

Gorham's chortle turned into a giggle. "Did you hear what Washington said about one of Gerry's ideas? One day when the debate about having an army had heated up, Gerry made a motion to put a limit of 3,000 men for a Federal Army. I happened to be bringing a paper to the General at that moment. He whispered to me, 'You should move to amend the motion to say, 'No foreign enemy may invade the United States with more than 3,000 troops!'"

Governor Randolph had to stop and hold his sides his laugh went on so long. They had passed the noisy corner of Front Street—much of the steamboat audience seemed to be there having refreshments—and gone beyond the gatehouse leading to Benjamin's Franklin's house just after Third Street. Randolph dabbed at his eyes and nose, composing

himself.

"Do excuse me, my friend," he said. "It's not often we get such a good laugh out of a Washington remark. Now—where were we in the list of prospective members for postponed and last-minute submissions? Ah, yes. Massachusetts. Rufus King seems a good choice. But for chairman: Who's best at inventing compromises?"

"I think everyone would agree it's either Gouverneur Morris of Pennsylvania, or David Brearley of New Jersey."

"Let's have BOTH!" exclaimed Randolph. "Then I'd pick Williamson for North Carolina, Butler for South Carolina, and Daniel Carroll for Maryland. They'll know what to do with Madison's 20, Pinckney's 20, and everybody else's 60 submissions. Oh my, I'm hungry! I hope the Indian Queen has plenty of dinner left—we're almost two hours late! I usually sit at Mrs. House's table, but her bowls and platters are empty by four-thirty!"

Before turning at Fourth Street to the Indian Queen, they paused to gaze toward Sixth Street where Robert Morris lived and the General was a guest, and to note that the State House was barely visible over the treetops although only two blocks away.

As they entered the familiar doors of The Queen, Gorham exclaimed, "Philadelphia! Always interesting and stimulating! I would not for a minute regret seeing the seat of government permanently located here. Even those desperate, awful hours in the State House when mutinying soldiers outside were pointing their muskets at us, did not sour me on the city. It's the best in the country for meetings. Lodgings are cheap and comfortable, food is cheap and cooks very accomplished. Almost every night there's a sociable at a mansion, or a play at a theater. It's too bad the Delaware isn't Washington's favorite river!"

They had sat down at a freshly-clothed dining table, ordered a roast goose dinner, and had just

Making of the Constitution (Warren) p247n

Dict. of Am. Biog.

Making of Const. (Warren) p483

received plates heaped with food when Mr. Gorham said, "One last question. How do you propose we deal with Madison and Pinckney's seat of government paragraph? Let it die in our committee? Or bring it out—if beforehand the delegates will solemnly promise not to argue from now until Christmas?"

"Why Mr. Gorham!" replied Randolph, breathing in the exquisite aromas of roast goose with dressing and gravy. "We'll just let the new Committee on Postponed Matters decide that!"

August 31. The Convention appointed a Committee on Postponed Matters: Chairman, Brearley; Sherman, Dickinson, Baldwin, Carroll, King, Gilman, Williamson, G. Morris, Butler, Madison. It approved the Madison-Pinckney paragraph for Convention debate:

"(The Congress shall have power) To exercise exclusive Legislation in all cases whatsoever over such District (not exceeding ten Miles square) as may, by Cession of particular states, and the Acceptance of Congress, become the Seat of the Government of the United States."

September 5. The Convention took up, and with no debate, agreed to the paragraph, including it as Article 1, Section 8, in the Constitution.

September 15. The Convention voted to approve the Constitution.

Madison Papers, Vol.5, *p511 (Elliot)*

Stump speaker Willie ("Wi'lie") Jones reminds his 183 followers at North Carolina's convention of 1788 that they were elected to delay the state's ratification of the Constitution "until it contains our rights." For more than a year, this large state and small Rhode Island were "foreign countries" among the other 11 United States. With no Carolina delegates in the first session of the First Congress, the South almost lost to Pennsylvania the location of the national capital.

CHAPTER 9

Carolina Balks: No Rights, No Ratification

SCENE: Hillsborough, North Carolina, Saint Matthew's Church, used as school and free meeting house, corner of Tryon and Churton Streets.
TIME: Saturday, August 2, 1788. Early morning, about 5:45.

"We were elected to hold off ratifying this Federal Constitution until it includes a bill of rights, and that, gentlemen, is what we are going to do this morning!" Willie Jones of Halifax (whose name was pronounced 'Wi'lie') shouted the last sentence of his speech. About 200 men clustering around the tree stump on which Jones stood, yelled "Yay, Wi'lie!" clapped their hands, and war-whooped like Indians. As Jones stepped down, his arm was grabbed by a sunburnt, snaggled-toothed, bare-legged delegate in homespun shirt, knee pants, and home-cobbled shoes.

"It ain't goin' take long this morning, Mr. Jones! The vote yistiddy—to amend first, ratify later—told us what today's final vote will be—all OURS!" With a loud cackle, he slapped Jones on the arm and declared he'd force himself, as an Assembly delegate, to stay for an Assembly meeting in the afternoon, then right off he'd be saying gitty-up to the horses and heading for the western hills.

He kept on talking even after Wi'lie started the crowd moving across the yard towards the church door: "Ain't no delegate itchier to leave Hillsborough than me! Five days on the trail—13 days of sittin' down listenin' to foolishness across the aisle—and 13 nights sleeping with 10 head in a wagon in them campgrounds—man, I'm iller'n ary rattlesnake! So Guv'ner Johnston, watch out!"

The 60 families living in the Piedmont junction of Carolina postroads coming from coastal Edenton and New Bern 100 miles east had welcomed the state Assembly in several other years. For this special session to take up the question of ratifying the new, proposed Constitution sent down from Philadelphia, they had put into service every available bed, made pallets on the floors, and cleaned up the campground by the Eno river.

For two weeks, the town's few taverns had been jammed. The camp was crowded with dozens of covered wagons of delegates, some of whom had brought their womenfolk to cook, and children that couldn't be left at home. The large, handsome houses of planters, judges, lawyers, and merchants were rearranged inside to accommodate the Governor, former Governor, well-known Assembly leaders, and a few delegates who had been Revolutionary Army officers.

Inside a rundown church converted to meeting house in the village by Eno River and three Occoneechee hills, 84 pro-Constitution delegates had been listening to the shouting outside, bursts of laughter, and cries of "Wi'lie! Wi'lie!"

At the front of the church, stalwart Governor Samuel Johnston in gentleman's silk, silver buckles, and three-cornered hat, was standing by the first pews among solemn, long-faced gentlemen

Hillsborough's History of the Town of Hillsborough (A./P. Lloyd) p12

planters, lawyers, bankers, and merchants. Another smaller group of delegates—lesser land owners, merchants, artisans, tradesmen—had taken seats in the pew behind him and quietly talked among themselves.

Noises in the balcony over the entrance attracted attention. Heads turned to see who had come in, although everyone knew it would be the same two sets of five men from the Kinston area who, sitting as far apart as possible, had watched the convention since the first day. Governor Johnston lifting his hat toward the balcony, loudly called, "Governor Caswell, sir!" and bowed.

To the men around him, Johnston said, "In that balcony is one of the most disgraceful results of the anti-federalist election campaign—the exclusion of Richard Caswell of Kingston (pardon, KINston—I still forget the Assembly threw out 'King' for 'Kin') from this convention. I have greatly needed his help here. His prestige and speeches as well as Dobbs County's five votes, would have done us much good against Wi'lie Jones."

"Well, that's what comes from letting his supporters riot at the election poll," said Richard Spaight. "On the other hand," he added quickly, "the antis would otherwise have won that election at Kinston's courthouse, and five more delegates would be here yelling in the churchyard for Wi'lie. It's better they're sitting to themselves in the balcony, rejected by the Convention, like Caswell and his men."

"Sometimes," sighed merchant John Steele, "pinching the candle flames, whacking the opposition in the dark, and running off with the ballot box seems to be the only way to win anything in Kinston."

Governor Johnston frowned. "But Governor Caswell and his men won overwhelmingly in the special election I permitted after the riot! If the antis were so sure THEY were 'way ahead in the first

election before the riot began, why didn't they take part in the second election instead of staying away? What a spectacle on the first day of this convention to have both sets of Dobbs County delegates walk in here. What a worse spectacle to see a committee dominated by antis refuse to seat our seven-times-elected Governor Caswell!"

"But the committee didn't seat the ANTIS from Dobbs County either," John Steele reminded him.

"Yes, but I don't miss THEM," said Governor Johnston.

Laughter broke the tension and gloom. But almost immediately, Wi'lie Jones's voice outside, with the accompanying whooping and hollering, brought them back.

"Confound Wi'lie Jones!" exploded Archibald Maclaine. Sharp-tongued and impulsive, he had helped distinguished attorney Iredell, young attorney Davie, and Constitution signer Spaight present arguments for ratifying the document. "I say again, confound Wi'lie Jones! What he is about to do is turn this state of North Carolina into a foreign country as far as the rest of the United States is concerned! In about 30 minutes, we won't be a part of the United States any more! What's worse, Wi'lie Jones is enjoying himself doing this far reaching, foolhardy damage!"

Iredell with dismay in his voice noted that Jones had done better in Carolina than his friend, Patrick Henry, did in Virginia. "James Madison out-talked Henry and turned the Virginia Assembly to ratify. But I doubt even Madison could've swayed the Wi'lie Jones crowd. Jones had twice the number of delegates he needed to stop ratification—all of them elected by men fooled into believing the Federal Constitution means nothing good, just more taxes and less liberty."

"No, not Madison, nor anybody, could change a mountain man's mind any more than Madison changed Henry's," declared Colonel Davie. "Wi'lie

Hist.Town/
Hillsborough (Lloyd)
p16

Drawing of interior shows left and right staircases, presumably to a balcony.

Proceedings and Debates of the Convention of North Carolina 1788 (verbatim) p18-19

N.C.Hist.Rev. July 1946, p309/311 (C.Alexander)

The Anti-Federalists, p244 (J.T.Main)

N.C.History, Geography, and Gov't. (H.T.Lefler) p539

N.C.History as Told By Contemporaries (H.T. Lefler) Apr.30, 1788, Norfolk Jour.

Ratification of the Federal Constitution in N.C. (L.I.Trenholme)

N.C.Historical Review Oct.1940/Jan.1941

N.C. Hist. Rev. (A.R. Newsome) Oct.1940/ Jan.1941

Proceed.and Debates/ N.C. Convention 1788, p20

N.C. Hist. Rev. Jan./Apr. 1941 "Willie Jones of Halifax" (B.P. Robinson)

Dict. Am. Biog. Vol.10 (D.Malone)

said on the third day here, 'Let's vote right this minute! We've talked Constitution for a year and we all know how we're going to vote now and later—it's a waste of time to talk any more.' He was right. Nearly two weeks later, not one vote has changed—on either side, I might add."

Just then, the crowd noise outside burst through the open church door. Jones, vigorous 47-year-old tobacco planter, owner of the best race track and most elegant house in the northeastern corner of the state, marched in at the head of 183 noisy, happy supporters. He stood as regal as a prince, walking with calm dignity at the head of his excited planters from east and west Carolina, some of them frontier men from a county 400 miles west—less than a hundred from the Mississippi. They were still talking loud, and their heavy boots thumped hard on the wooden floorboards.

Hist./Town of Hillsborough (Lloyd) p41, 160

As the town clock at Market House gonged six times, Wi'lie Jones took his usual seat on the first pew in the choir stall, seats in front at right-angle to the regular pews. Everyone could easily see his dark hair, wide-spaced eyes, and fine aristocratic nose. His athletic figure reminded them of his love of outdoor life—horses, racing, fox hunting—and his poise recalled his youthful title of "wildest gambler" in Carolina, as well as his long and distinguished career in state politics.

Portrait (NC Div.Arch. and History)

N.C. Hist. Rev. Jan./ Apr. 1941 (Robinson)

His delegates could also easily see the nods of Wi'lie's head to direct his spokesmen—he spoke little in public, but exerted his power in private conversation. He could silence his followers by raising a finger, raise derisive catcalls for an opposition speaker by sneering.

Iredell (McRee) Vol. 2 p232

Calmly, he took from a pocket of his fashionable but plain grey silk coat a carved briar pipe. He filled it with shredded tobacco from a pouch, and lighted it with a flaming candle brought earlier from the inn of Mr. King by his attendant slave. Smoke curled above his head while his men slowly, rau-

cously, squeezed into their pews and extra chairs in the aisles.

Governor Johnston's gavel brought the voices down to a low buzz. He called for a report of the Committee of the Whole.

"The Committee of the Whole Convention voted to send Congress all 20 resolves adopted by the Virginia Assembly for amending the Constitution, and to add 26 more," read the clerk in a monotone. He then began to read all 46. By the time he had finished, his voice was lost among those of the delegates.

Proceed. and Debates/ N.C. Convention 1788, p 219

Wi'lie Jones puffing smoke, gave a nod to Thomas Person, who immediately shouted a motion that the Convention concur with the report.

"I object!" All heads turned. The passionate voice belonged to Archibald Maclaine, standing fist on his hip, face defiant. Wi'lie Jones knew him well for saying that Jones condemned the Constitution after catching a glimpse of half of it—over the shoulder of another person.

History of a Southern State: N.C. (H.T. Lefler) p281

A rumbling growl began. Feet stomped the floor, and there were cries of "Out of order! Sit him down, Guv'ner!" "Vote! Vote!"

Bang! Bang! went the gavel. "Gentlemen! Gentlemen! Let us not repeat yesterday's warm altercation, replete with ugly insinuations when we took up the motion to ratify now, amend later—"

Proceed. and Debates/ N.C. Convention 1788, p 215

The shouting and stomping increased. The Governor's voice boomed over the noise. "The question before the convention is, Will the delegates concur with the report and vote of the Committee of the Whole to reject ratifying now, amending later? (Shouts of approval) All in favor say 'Yea'!"

p219

The "Yeas" could have been heard down in the river camp, but the "Nays" demanded a rollcall vote of the nearly 285 delegates. Wi'lie's men applauded, yelled, and stomped when their victory was announced, and increased the volume when Wi'lie himself rose to present a motion. He raised a finger for silence.

He noted first that 10 states of the 13 had ratified the Constitution—so the new plan of government was already in effect. Since North Carolina from the moment of the vote just taken was not a part of the federal union, Congress would probably lay a tax on North Carolina goods imported by other states.

"I move," he said, "that we recommend to the State Assembly—which is us—that, in that case, it enact a law for collecting a similar tax on goods imported into our state (yells and applause) AND appropriate the money collected to the USE OF CONGRESS!" (Low, questioning murmur on both sides of the aisle)

The vote was called for, and the "Yeas" made a mighty chorus.

The Convention adjourned as the town clock bonged seven times. Jubilant Jones forces pressed toward the door, their hero patted on the back, shaken by the hand, and hugged all the way. When the waiting families of the delegates, the towns-people, and visitors from miles around saw Wi'lie coming out the door, they shouted, "There he is!" "We heerd all the votes, Wi'lie! We knowed who'd won!" "Your name ain't Wi'lie for nothing!"

The 84 losers, with Caswell and his Kinston, Dobbs County, friends from the balcony, gathered by the church door around the Governor, Davie, Iredell, and other leaders. Davie, who attended the Constitutional Convention in Philadelphia but had to leave before the signing, spoke with intense feeling, his fists clinched. "How could anyone in his right mind interpret the Federal Constitution as silly as Wi'lie Jones has!" he said. Davie, a Halifax neighbor and in-law of Wi'lie's, had been angry ever since he'd heard that Wi'lie called the writers of the new Constitution "scoundrels—particularly General Washington and Colonel Davie!"

Even after Wi'lie denied he ever said such a thing,

Davie suspected he had. It felt worse to him than wild-talking General Thomas Persons' words— "George Washington is a damn rascal and traitor for putting his name to such an infamous document as this new Constitution!"

Davie, his young face flushed with wrath, added, "Wi'lie and his puppets are saying what they think Patrick Henry said in Virginia —they all point out the most dire threats in the least likely places. Even level-headed General Lenoir of the militia has been repeating absurdities! You all heard him say in this Convention, 'Look at the power Congress will have in the seat of government! Ten-square-mile state! EXCLUSIVE power! It will control the MILITIA! Men could be drafted and carried thither, and KEPT there for LIFE! If any soldier dared complain, he would be deemed a traitor! He would be tried without a jury in that terrible 10-mile square!'"

Davie threw up his hands. "Where on earth could he—could Wi'lie's men—get such ideas?"

"From preacher Lem Burkitt of Hertford County," Governor Johnston said. "He told his people the 10-mile square would be walled in, fortified with 100,000 men, who will sally forth, enslave the people, and disarm them!"

Richard Spaight of New Bern, who, like Davie, had recently turned 30, and had signed the Constitution in Philadelphia, said with a bit of an Irish accent, left-over from a youth spent abroad, "Patrick Henry preaches damnation on this EXCLU-SIVE POWER phrase. Preacher Burkitt amplified that with hellfire and won election to this convention. Not only would Congress's army sally forth and enslave us—General Washington and John Adams would take over as kings and turn the country over to France, which would force all Americans to be-come Roman Catholics!"

Lawyer Iredell, shaking his head in wonder, spoke of talking to Will Lenoir, reminding him of mutiny-ing soldiers threatening unprotected Congress in

Willie (Wi'lie) Jones

Signers of the Const. (R.G. Ferris/G.H. Charleton)

"N.C. Ratification" *N.C. Hist. Rev.* Oct.1940, p291 (A.R.Newsome)

Ratification of Fed. Const. (L.Trenholme) p283

Lenoir County Heritage, p21

Proceed. and Debates/ N.C. Convention 1788, p 183

Newsome, p290

Signers of the Constitution (R. Ferris/ J. Charlton)

Biog. Const. of U.S. (B./ L. Mitchell)

N.C.: First 200 Years (J. Young) p141

Philadelphia, and the decision then—five years ago—to provide Congress a meeting place where it could protect itself. "But I was talking to the wind," Iredell said with a shrug. "He came back at me with a harangue in which Congress was a gang of devils, all secretly plotting to turn 10 square miles of this country into a hellhole of tyranny. He kept emphasizing '10 SQUARE miles,' so perhaps we should offer an amendment to change that to 10 ROUND miles."

With a laugh, the group of delegates began to make a move to break up and get on toward breakfast. But Governor Johnston began to speak, and they stopped to listen. "The antis used, and exaggerated, anything to win votes. Then they were obliged to include all those absurdities in their Bill of Rights. One of their 46 proposed amendments spells out limitations on Congress in the 10-mile square—it can only make regulations about police, and 'good government' as defined, you can be sure, by Wi'lie Jones."

Proceed. and Debates/
N.C. Convention 1788,
p 214

Spaight declared that the Federal Congress elected this winter in the 11 ratifying states— "North Carolina of course won't have an election"—could be expected to ignore that particular amendment. "Then we will hear the antis here telling bigger and wilder stories about EXCLUSIVE power and square capitals. What a weapon to use against the entire Constitution!"

"Next year is bound to be different," said the Governor. "When our voters see George Washington working again for the whole country, EXCEPT for peculiar little Rhode Island and cranky North Carolina, they will turn from Wi'lie Jones. Then WE will have the votes when we walk into the inevitable Second Convention on Ratification—and WE will win! I do not believe that our voters will hold out for remaining a foreign country within the United States for six years, as Wi'lie Jones recommends."

Through the applause and cries of "Hear, hear!" the old aristocrat's voice rang out. "At that Convention, Dobbs County delegates, headed by our great governor Richard Caswell, will be there—seated and voting!"

The group broke up with applause and a rumble of cheerful voices. Mingled together were affectionate greetings for the aging and ailing Caswell—Revolutionary War hero, the state's first American governor, the main writer of the state's Constitution—buoyant exclamations about the future, and details of travel plans.

Dict. Am. Biography
(D. Malone)

As the Governor and his half-dozen distinguished companions crossed the churchyard toward Tryon Street, they fell silent and slowed to listen to the words of Wi'lie Jones standing on his stump and shouting his speech to the crowd. One hand chopped the air as Wi'lie's voice took on the cadences of his hero Patrick Henry, and revival-meeting preachers.

"In this convention," Jones cried, "Matthew Locke from Rowan told how all the tax money squeezed out of you good people will be swept away by the courtly parade of high and mighty officials! They'll spend money like the King of France and bankrupt the states! In this convention, Will Goudy from Guilford warned about giving a central government all the states' power. 'If we give more than we ought to,' he said, 'we put ourselves in the situation of a man who clamps on an iron glove which he can never take off until he breaks his arm!'"

Proceed. and Debates/
N.C. Convention 1788,
p 207

p24

Jones looked over the crowd clapping and calling out its approval, and took notice of the defeated Gentlemen walking very slowly across the churchyard. He held up his finger for silence, and raised louder his voice.

p197

"Since famous names have been mentioned as approving this Constitution as it stands, I will mention Mr. Thomas Jefferson, whose great abilities are well known. When the Virginia convention met in

"Rights first, ratify later," a delegate explains to his family in the Hillsborough campground. For a two-week stay in the village, the surest bed and board for some of the 270 delegates were their own wagons, provisions, and cooks. Bill-of-Rights anti-ratifiers also wanted to change parts of the Constitution—the 10-mile-square paragraph in particular. Exclusive power over a federal district meant Congress intended to draft 100,000 men and send this army out "to enslave us all" they said.

Richmond last month, Mr. Madison received a letter from Mr. Jefferson, who is in Paris, France, taking over where Dr. Franklin left off. In that letter, Mr. Jefferson said he wished the required nine states would adopt the Constitution as it stood—not because it deserved adoption, but to preserve the Union. HOWEVER—he wished that the other four states would REJECT it so there might be a certainty of obtaining amendments—a Bill of Rights! (Rumbles of pleasure)

"This information came to me from one who knows Mr. Madison well!" Wi'lie shouted.

Across the yard, Colonel Davie muttered to the Governor, "Probably a spy for Patrick Henry. Thomas Jefferson would spit fire if he knew that remark—he's changed his mind now—went from Henry to Wi'lie Jones. Jefferson hates Henry so much he once said he was devoutly praying for his death. It was Henry who sicced the Virginia Assembly into investigating Governor Jefferson for cowardice when Benedict Arnold and his British army raided Richmond during the War."

Jones had moved deeper into his subject—"and so there are only two states that have not ratified! But people in the western lands see it the way we do! Kentucky's Territorial Assembly unanimously rejected this Constitution! New York, I predict, is going to reject it, too! Alexander Hamilton, known as a bastard Scot from the West Indies, has harangued the New York Assembly for weeks to ratify. Still, most members REJECT ratifying! They call their delegates rats and anti-rats! (Laughter and hoots)

"Nevertheless the Federal plan is in effect, elections will soon be held, a President will reign, and Congress will meet. But I predict that our holding back, combined with the complaints of ratifying states about the lack of a statement of rights, will result in nothing of importance getting done in Congress until our amendments are taken up and

added to the Constitution! (Applause)

"It may take 18 months—or 48 months—to amend. I'd rather be 18 years out of the Union than have a Constitution without our Rights spelled out!"

Over a wave of applause and cheering, Jones pushed on, his voice riding over the noise. "Those educated, wealthy, aristocratic planters, lawyers, and merchants in the eastern part of this state think you and I are childish to insist on listing our rights—speech, religion, trial by jury, and all the liberties we fought a war to secure—in any plan of government that men devise! But you and I are the ones who suffer when rulers deny we have these rights! I say make our laws before we sign up!

"We're not in a big hurry, thinking of political jobs and pay like some we know, are we?" (NO!!) I'm a high-living, high-standing, much educated planter—BUT—my friends, I am on the side of the poor, hard-working, democratic small farmers and skilled craftsmen, east and west in this state. There are a lot of you—and I am going to help you keep political power in your voting hands!" (Applause, cries of "Wi'lie! Wi'lie run for Governor! Wi'lie for President!")

Jones jumped down from the stump into the adoring crowd.

Governor Johnston and his companions walked away in silence. In front of the closeby house of William Hooper, noted lawyer, signer of the Declaration of Independence, and a Convention candidate who suffered two black eyes as well as defeat on election day, the men were greeted by Hooper himself. Johnston and Caswell, his house guests, were mounting the porch steps with their host when they heard a frantic, distant shout.

"Governor! Governor!"

Caswell spoke up. "It's Francis Child. He brought the state records from Kinston, where the last Assembly was held."

Child ran up, red-faced and out of breath. He

Jeff. Ency. (J.Boyd) *Letter May '88*

Man From Monticello (T. Fleming) *Jeff. letter to Madison*

Patrick Henry (R. Beeman) p133

Odd Destiny: A. Hamilton (M. Hecht) p152

Proceed. and Debates/ N.C. Convention 1788, p 197

Hist. Southern State: N.C. (Lefler) p283

AntiFederalists (J.Main)

Ratification Fed. Const. (L.Trenholme)

Historic Map of Hillsborough

For History's Sake (H.Jones)

Odd Destiny: A. Hamilton (Hecht)

handed the Governor a letter. "Excuse me, sir, and Governor Caswell, and Colonel Iredell, and—everybody—but news has just arrived from Richmond that New York ratified the Constitution by eight votes on July 25!"

"Thank the Lord! Hamilton did it!" cried Spaight, clapping his hands together. "He somehow, finally, turned some delegates around, for he was losing badly two weeks ago! Does the letter name any names?"

Governor Johnston shook his head. "No, but it says a letter with details follows."

For History's Sake (H.G. Jones) p65

Mr. Child coughed. "Governor, there's another very important matter, sir. It's about bringing the records. Governor Caswell, you saw us loading in Kinston, and that it took six wagons and horse teams to bring those papers. We come better than 100 miles, there to here. With the loading, the roads so bad, two rainstorms, the heat, and a broken axle, it took us two weeks to get here—and we have to take the wagons, team, and men back to Kinston. The men want to leave now, and they are after me for their pay. I need your signature on this bill so the treasurer can disburse the money, sir."

Jones p62

Johnston said, taking the paper, "Mr. Child, I hope you have allowed a discount for not bringing the records to last year's Assembly at all."

"Then the state should add something," Child said, "for waiting a year to pay me in '86 after I hauled a hogshead and barrel of Continental paper money from Kinston to New Bern. I was trusted with the Treasury of the state, and given none of it for 12 months!"

Jones p 60

Johnston frowned and exclaimed, "Look here! A bill for nine pounds for six men, plus nine shillings in coin and a quart of rum for the seventh! I doubt the Treasurer has that much, especially the rum!"

Proceed. and Debates/ N.C. Convention 1788

"Well, sir, it's one expense you will rid the state of soon, what with the talk yesterday, and an Assembly vote this afternoon about putting our permanent capital near Isaac Hunter's place in Wake County," Childs said.

All the men laughed. "I'll make a prediction," said Spaight. "The Congress of the United States will pick a place and build a capital 10 years BEFORE North Carolina stops its Assembly from wandering hither and yon. Now that's TRUE contentiousness—when any bunch of men can keep up an argument 10 years longer than the old or new Congress of the United States!"

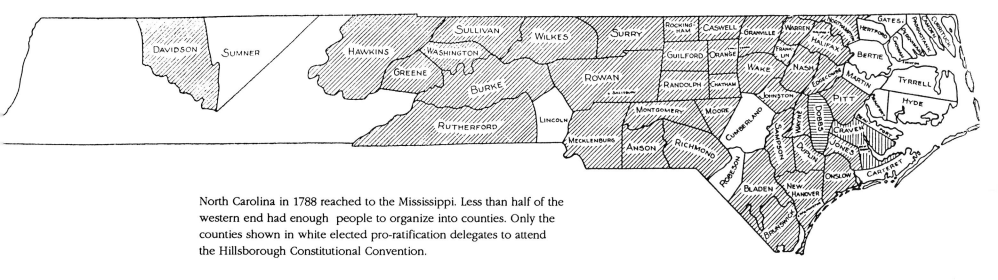

North Carolina in 1788 reached to the Mississippi. Less than half of the western end had enough people to organize into counties. Only the counties shown in white elected pro-ratification delegates to attend the Hillsborough Constitutional Convention.

Eligible voters—men owning property—announce to the sheriff at the courthouse polling table the name of the candidate they favor in the 1789 election, the first under the new Constitution. Candidates and voters stay on to keep score, talk politics, socialize, and enjoy free liquor. At the Orange County, Virginia, poll, James Madison promised a Bill of Rights if elected to the House of Representatives, and ceaseless efforts to win the 10-mile square capital district for the Potomac.

CHAPTER 10

First Federal Election: Madison in Virginia

SCENE: Orange, Virginia, County Courthouse.
TIME: February 2, 1789, a cold, wet day.

J.Madison (I. Brant)

James Madison, suddenly famous in all Virginia for doing the impossible—out-talking Patrick Henry in the Convention—was, eight months after winning ratification of the Constitution, running for a seat in the First Federal Congress.

Patrick Henry (R. Beeman)

His opponent was Henry's choice, James Monroe. Madison had wanted a Senate seat, but Henry's backstage power and Assembly oratory—"with unworthy Madison in the Senate, rivulets of blood will flow throughout the land!"—saw to it that the legislature did not appoint him.

Madison's papers Vol. 5 (Elliott)

Polling day in the eight-county district began with a mix of rain and mushy snow. It settled in by noon as cold showers alternating with near-freezing drizzle. Thick dark clouds hung over the village of Orange, Madison's hometown, the county seat and voting place.

Gentlemen Freeholders (C. S. Sydnor)

Virginia's polling day routine was quite familiar to Madison and Monroe—and to Washington, Jefferson, and Henry. Madison had already stood for election to the state legislature six times, beginning 12 years ago when he was in his mid-twenties. He knew that in each county seat, the sheriff picked the date, usually a monthly court day. The eligible voters—men owning a house on 25 or more acres or owning a house and lot in town—might come miles on horseback or wagon to do business on court day. They bought or sold land or slaves, registered complaints, answered a court summons, paid a debt, bought supplies, and socialized.

When an election was added to the day, they went by the courthouse to drink cups of spirits from a barrelful paid for by the candidates. Full of bumbo (rum, sugar, and water) and opinions, they went inside to the courtroom and lined up in front of the sheriff sitting behind a long table.

The Candidates (Robert Munford). A play of 1770

The sheriff knew them all, knew who was eligible to vote and who was not. He checked each name in the polling book, then put the question: "What man do you vote for?"

Almost all the replies today had been "James Madison for Congress!" The clerk by the sheriff's side kept score, name by name.

Gentlemen Freeholders (Sydnor)

Madison kept score, too. He sat with his own clerk at one end of a table. The law required candidates to attend the polling, face the voters, and answer any questions they might ask. Several justices of the peace kept watch, ready to subdue rowdiness or fisticuffs.

All through the day, the crowd keeping warm in the courtroom between bumboes, knew who was winning. Some kept their own score boards, or looked over the shoulders of the clerks, or asked the candidates themselves.

J.Madison (Brant)

Today's election day scene had a slightly different look from the usual. The opposition candidate,

James Monroe, who ordinarily would have been present, was a day's ride away in his own county seat, Spotsylvania, some 30 miles east, counting his votes at the poll there. The empty chair at the end of his, and Madison's, polling tables was visible evidence that the day's winner represented not just one county but a district of eight.

These eight counties had been carefully picked by Patrick Henry. Six of them had chosen anti-Constitution delegates last year for the ratifying convention. In today's election, Henry counted on them to hold to last year's opinions and vote against Federalist Madison.

Gentlemen Freeholders (Sydnor)

To win, Madison needed a majority of the 2,000 or so votes that would be cast.

To get them, Madison had resorted to "electioneering" and to "appearing in the flesh," both of which he disliked. But it was made necessary by the preachers and the newspapers who were spreading Henry's slanders and falsehoods.

J. Madison (Brant)

For a few weeks, Madison had traveled alone through the district. So had Monroe. Then they teamed up, being long-term friends, traveled together and debated the issues at public gatherings in churches and courthouses.

Today, Madison in his own county courthouse was busy greeting, shaking hands with, and catching up on the news about old friends, neighbors, and acquaintances. In late afternoon, he had known for hours that almost all of them had given him their votes.

About an hour before dark, the cold rain stopped. In the courtroom, a black man refilled the fireplace with logs. Another brought in candelabra, their lighted candles flickering away the courtroom's deepening shadows.

The low-pitched mixture of a hundred male voices rose and quieted and rose again. Men in wigs and silk stockings, men in fur hats and leatherstockings, old men leaning on canes, young men play-

fully shadow boxing, came and went, sat and lounged on long benches, changed conversation partners, walked to the door for more bumbo, talked and talked.

At the polling table, no one had faced the sheriff for a half hour. He rose from his chair, stretched, and walked to the end of the table where Madison was talking earnestly to three men. They, being taller, bent toward him.

"Those four hours in Independence Hall," Madison was saying, "the soldiers in the yard, the sounds, the anxiety—they're as clear to me now as if it all happened yesterday, not almost six years ago. Congress encircled! And a state government saying it would do nothing to protect us, the national government! Think of it! Is it not symbolic of the country's need for a strong central government not dependent on any state's generosity or judgment?"

The men glanced at each other, straightened up, and spoke all at the same time, "Well—". Two of them relinquished the floor to the Mayor of Orange. "As much as I love Virginia, I see from our desperate money and trade conflicts that we must have CENTRAL direction with some uniformity. To drift any longer as 13—or more as the western settlers organize—independent countries means disaster for all." (Nods and murmurs of "That's right" from his companions.)

The Mayor frowned, and added, "My wonder is that Mr. Monroe, a good, sensible man, can take the side of Mr. Patrick Henry to condemn this federal government. They've done their best to scare us out of supporting it. One of their most peculiar warnings concerns Congress's 10-mile square of land, which you put in the Constitution, and which you were just explaining to us. They insist that this government square will become the sanctuary of the blackest crimes! For one thing, any man acting contrary to the commands of Congress will be dragged there and hanged—and, even worse, with-

J. Madison (Brant)

Biog. of the Constitution (B. Mitchell)

out benefit of clergy!"

With a little laugh of disbelief and a shake of his wigged head, the town's most prosperous merchant added, "I just can't understand how your opponent, Mr. Monroe, could travel around with you for two whole weeks, listen to your sensible straightening out of his and Mr. Henry's pronouncements, and not succumb to your fine logic!"

"To hear good sense only forces him to twist it more in answer!" declared an elderly Colonel who lived on the plantation next to the Madison estate, Montpelier, four miles beyond the town. "One night when I happened to be in Culpepper County, I heard your debate at Hebron Lutheran Church, and Monroe twisted something you had just said until it was unrecognizable—except that all of us listening recognized that was what he was doing."

"Hebron Lutheran!" exclaimed Madison. "That was the night I got my one scar of battle!" He touched the end of his nose on the left side. "Mr. Monroe and I attended the church service, then listened to a lengthy program of music by two fiddlers. They're Germans, you know, and remarkably fond of music. They also vote together for the same candidate, which often swings that county for or against you.

"Finally, we spoke and debated and then answered some questions. After about an hour, when the fire had gone out, we went outside. The discussion went on, all of us standing in the snow. They stood patiently listening to us argue constitutional subjects. They seemed to consider it a sort of fight, and they were required to be spectators.

"We then had to ride in the night 12 miles—three hours—to quarters. In the coldest cold I ever endured, my nose was frost-bitten! You can still see the mark."

The sheriff, who had waited and listened before breaking into the conversation, leaned with the others to peer at Mr. Madison's nose.

After their inspecting and exclaiming, the sheriff said, "Mr. Madison, it seems to me highly unlikely that enough more voters will appear in the next hour to affect the result. I feel like making the call to close the poll. In no time, it will be dark. The weather is bad, and those who need to go home tonight had best be leaving soon."

Madison made the sheriff a small bow and said, "The opening and closing times of the polls, sir, are entirely your decision."

As the sheriff started toward the door, a ragged cheer from the crowd ran about the room. Talk groups broke up, clearing the aisle for him. The doors to the vestibule swung open, the outside door was pulled ajar, but only enough for the sheriff to put his head out, look about the yard, and make the call required by law.

"Gentlemen freeholders! Come into court and give your votes, or the poll will be closed!"

"We've all voted!" a voice in the courtroom shouted, evoking a titter.

The sheriff, not answering, stared outside. "I think I see some voters arriving," he said, drawing himself inside. "Six men are tying up their horses. They're all soaking wet. After wrassling through this weather and over god-awful roads to vote, nobody better tell them the polls have just closed."

He looked out again. "Hurry up!" he called. "You're just before coming into an empty room!" Drawing his head inside, he informed all, "Oh, that's the Davidsons and the Crombies from Raccoon Ford. They've got to get across so many swampy stretches and cricks to go anywhere, we hardly ever see them. They must be right mad at some candidate to do all they've had to do to get here."

Pulling the door shut against the cold, he waited until, one short bumbo later, the latch snapped, and six wet men, breath a-smoke, entered.

"Get yourself a snort of bumbo to warm you a little," the sheriff greeted them, "and come on in to name your Congressman. Right there in the aisle

Montpelier Mansion now open for guided tours. Route 20 West, 4 miles beyond Orange, Va. Last tour 4 p.m.

J. Madison (Brant)

Gentlemen Freeholders (Sydnor)

97

stands Mr. Madison, the candidate with the most votes here—though Lord knows how well he's doing in the other seven polls."

The six newcomers, all small farmers like most of the county's voters, gulped their rum, saluted friends, and walked single file to the polling table.

"Who do you vote for?" said the sheriff, and all six men answered together, "MR. MADISON!"

J. Madison (Brant)

"That makes 216 votes for Mr. Madison!" the sheriff announced. (Cheers and applause) "Mr. Monroe, his opponent, got only 9 votes! I declare the poll closed, and our Mr. Madison the winner!"

The crowd surged toward Madison. Laughing and shouting men pulled him into a chair, lifted it ("Hold on!") and marched in a procession out the door, across the yard, and into the tavern of Bell's Orange Hotel. Madison on his perch, looking smaller than ever, his dome-shaped hat slightly askew, pulled at his heavy cloak, gamely waved and smiled at his enthusiastic supporters.

Gentlemen Freeholders
(Sydnor)

Inside the tavern, the hundred or so men crowded into the bar room, gaming room, hallways, and entrance. Noisily cheerful, they pressed toward the bar to claim the mugs of beer that candidate Madison was paying for.

The sheriff, squeezing through the crowd with a beer mug foaming over, bumped into one of the last voters of the day, Mr. Crombie.

He stopped, a question on his mind. "Mr. Crombie," he said, "we were glad to see you freeholders ride in and vote, no matter the weather or the bad traveling you had to put up with. But I was right surprised, right surprised. You gentlemen must have some kind of strong reason for risking pneumonia to come vote for Mr. Madison. How many hours were you on the trail?"

"We coulda got here in six hours," Crombie replied, "but the crick was a-flood and we must press on upstream through thick woods some miles to find a fit place to ford. So it took us 10 hours and

we can't go back tonight—we must find a fire to dry us and a floor for sleeping."

"Oh, we'll find you some families to put you up—certainly we will for anybody as BENT as you on giving Mr. Madison a vote!"

Mr. Crombie answered the implied question. "Well, you see, we was afeared the weather was too bad for most of the voters to come out. We knowed no weather was too bad to hold back us living in Raccoon Ford. Mr. Madison mustn't lose his own county, we said, and who knows? our six votes in a poor turn-out could tip the total in his favor. He's had mighty opposition! Only lately some folks our way have turned toward him after seeing him talk in our church."

J. Madison (Brant)

The sheriff nodded. "We got a good sign last month when we had the election for Presidential electors. All the candidates were for General Washington, of course, but the winners were mostly Federalists. That showed that most voters support the Constitution."

Brant

"'Nother thing, sheriff. At church, the preacher told how Mr. Madison writ letters to all of them, saying he was NOT agin putting our rights into the Constitution—which knocks down another lie Mr. Henry's Jemmy Monroe has spread around.

Brant

"Besides that—" Mr. Crombie's eyes narrowed, studying the sheriff's gaze for a few seconds—"besides that," he proceeded, "I hear Mr. Madison will keep on pushing hard to get the federal capital built on our Potomac River. OUR and George Washington's river. With one sitting in the President's chair, and the other sitting in Congress—" Mr. Crombie raised his eyebrows knowingly.

"I heard it said a few days ago," the sheriff answered, "that the stage carries a letter from Madison to Mount Vernon every day and he gets an answer right back. So they're already working hand-in-glove."

Madison Papers, Vol.5
(Elliott)

"That's interesting, interesting, more than a little.

You see, back a few years, I bought some western land way up the Potomac between Harper's Ferry and Charles Town. There 're a lot of General Washington's kinfolks in those parts—his brother Charles the town is named after, another brother. Sam, and nephews and cousins, quite a bunch. Good things are likely to happen to land up there. I bought a hundred acres on the rebound after Patrick Henry beat me out of a thousand acres of cheap land in Kentucky. Wouldn't it suit me fine to see my Potomac land outvalue his Kentucky grab!—which it should if the President and the Congressman bring the capital where they want it!"

P. Henry (R. Beeman)

At that moment, the barkeeper lifted a big brass tray and struck it hard with his fist. "Quiet! Quiet! Our friend the Colonel here will toast our Congressman!" The Colonel, standing on a chair, raised his beer mug, and called out in a high, strained voice, "To our friend and neighbor, our honored Congressman who will straighten out the world for us, Mr. James Madison! Hip, hip—"

"HOORAY!" chorused the crowd.

"Speech! Speech!"

Taking the Colonel's place on the massive oak chair, Madison beamed at his applauding audience, said his thanks, and reminded them that he had a good chance NOT to bear the title of Congressman longer than tonight. "You have given me 216 votes. Each of the other seven counties must give me even more to make a win. The Virginian we should be toasting was elected last month in 11 states—the illustrious General of the Revolution, George Washington! (Cheers) May the electors abide by the decision of the voters and unanimously elect him President of the United States! To General Washington—President Washington! Our first President under the Constitution!"

"WASHINGTON!" The shout filled the tavern, glasses clinked. A pause to drink, a burst of excited talk, exclamations, and laughter.

Madison stepped down from the chair, and immediately his place was taken by a muscular young man with curly red hair. Everyone knew him as the Irish coachman, and many had heard him singing as he drove the stagecoach along the road south to Richmond and north to Baltimore by Fredericksburg.

"Therre's a new song people in the cities are a-singing," he said loudly. "It's easy to catch the tune, and the worrds will sound very familiar. So join in wheneverr you hearr this line—'Grreat Washington shall rrule the land!'"

G.W., Vol.6 (D. Freeman) p147

With the Irish tenor's voice leading the way—"We've ratified our federal plan!"—the voters sang out loudly in tuneless harmony and high feeling, "GREAT WASH-ING-TON SHALL RULE THE LAND!"

"While Franklin's counsel aids his hand—" "GREAT WASH-ING-TON SHALL RULE THE LAND!"

Odd Destiny: A. Hamilton (M. Hecht) p168

Part Two
First Federal Congress, First Session
April-September 1789

Rapturous approval, love, and joy resound from the crowds of New Yorkers and visitors lining the inaugural parade route of George Washington, first President. In his coach, he raised his hat again and again. Then laying it aside, he wiped his teary eyes, and placing a hand over his heart, he waved the other yellow-gloved hand, smiled and nodded at the crowds. On Broad Street near Federal Hall, he stepped out of the coach to a "clap of thunder" greeting—the voice of thousands. In a few minutes, the crowd roared again when Washington reappeared on the Hall's balcony to take his oath of office.

CHAPTER 11

Washington's Inaugural Day

SCENE 1
CAPITAL QUESTIONS

PLACE: New York City, a town of 25,000. Presidential mansion at 3 Cherry Street.
TIME: Thursday, April 30, 1789, at 6 a.m.

GW Letter to dentist,
Mount Vernon Annual
Report 1983

By candlelight, George Washington in his nightshirt and spectacles was striking and drawing a long razor blade on a taut leather strap. Back and forth with quick strokes he sharpened the razor to finish his shaving. His mouth and cheeks were sunken, for he would wait until the last minute to put in his uncomfortable false teeth.

Reidar Sognnaes DDS,
Professor, UCLA (GW
dental problems)

Peering into the mirror, he stretched his pale, well suds'd skin, and drew the blade carefully across it. He rubbed the area; no stubble. He touched the deep scar blemish in the hollow of his left cheek, reminder of the worst abcessed tooth he ever had, and passed his glance over the smallpox scars on his cheekbones and nose.

Quietly he drew a long breath and put his attention to washing the blade in a bowl of hot water. As he wiped it dry, he gave his shoulder joints a twist or two, and bent his hip joints left and right. After two years of rheumatism in his arm, the stiffness and soreness appeared to be moving into his legs, he feared.

Private Affairs of GW
(Tobias Lear/Stephen
Decatur, Jr.)

"Christopher?" he said in a low, quiet voice. Immediately, a young black man opened the door and entered.

"Mornin', General President!" The President's face lit up, a little amused at this new valet de chambre. He was standing in for old Billy Lee, Washington's body servant and friend for almost 40 years. With

GW (Freeman)

both knee caps lame now, Billy had to be left in Philadelphia to have them looked after.

"I am late rising this morning, Chris, after so many long days of travel, receptions, visitors, and visiting. Nor does the weather favor us today ("No, sir.") being both damp and chilly. With the new brown suit only light-weight broadcloth, I had best wear heavy underwear. ("Yes, sir.") The swearing-in ceremony will take place outside—on a balcony that we have waited an extra week for the Frenchman to complete.

NY City in the Year of
Washington's
Inauguration, 1789
(Thomas E. V. Smith)

"Then, unless it rains , I expect to walk six blocks on Broadway—as well as the two from Federal Hall—to the church service at Saint Paul's. In this changeable weather, I must be careful not to take cold on my first day in office." ("No, sir!")

J. Madison (Brant)
p255

Suddenly, outside, a loud BOOM! The house, and even their bones vibrated. "OHhh! That's the right way"—BOOM!—"to start this day!" Chris giggled. BOOM! the cannons roared again—and again—until he counted 13.

NY City in 1789
(Smith)

"The guns at the Battery are giving credit to Rhode Island and North Carolina where none is due," murmured Washington.

Dawn's light struggled through heavy clouds as the President proceeded with his toilet and dressing. At 6:45, Washington was sitting on a chair, his long hair, more white than reddish light brown,

Private Affairs GW
(Lear/Decatur) p163.

now well-brushed and hanging loose.

Dictionary of Hairdressing and Wigmaking (J. S. Cox)

Chris rearranged the cover about the President's shoulders before squeezing the powder-bellows. A light fragrance spread through the air as he deftly whitened all his master's hair with the starchy powder. Expertly, he plaited it into a foot-long queue, securing the end with a small, neat bow of brown ribbon. He then drew up over the queue a black silk tube—"bag"—the shape and almost the length of the queue, and held in place by a narrow ribbon around the President's neck. No curls about his ears, or waves in his long, straight hair—he did not own wigs, though artists kept suggesting he ought to by clothing his head in the latest wig style.

Mount Vernon research: No wig purchase in GW accounts.

Mount Vernon paper quoting eyewitness descriptions.

GW's America (John W. Tebbel)

GW (Douglas Freeman)

During this morning hair-dressing ritual, Washington had gazed out the windows. Across a small park sloping toward the East River, he could see Long Island on the far bank. On that shore a dozen years before, when he was only 45, he had labored through a terrible night of fog, directing the many loadings of his soldiers into dozens of small boats. The fog and darkness had hidden them while oarsmen silently rowed to Manhattan's wharves, and returned for more. In the morning, when the British General sprang his trap, he caught no one.

Washington smiled to himself.

Chris was removing the covercloth when the President suddenly remarked, "I may not be able to visit the livery stables this morning as I ordinarily do. Did the stableboys coat the whites with paste and wrap on their body cloths last night? Do you know for certain?"

Private Affairs GW (Lear/Decatur) *p215*

"Yes SUH! Jacobus was polishing up EVERYthing on the coach, and when he finished, he took Fides and James over to the stables. I'm sure as I can be they're this minute brushing the whites 'til they look like satin and silk! By breakfast time, they'll have the hooves blackened, the mouths washed, the teeth picked and cleaned. Jacobus, he's a little bit lazy, but he knows how partic'lar you are about your horses, General President."

The President rose from his chair saying, "It's time to move. People are already arriving to look at me. Oh—they've seen me through the window. A little group of men. They're waving." He made a little bow and backed away.

In a few minutes, he was fully dressed and brushed, his teeth in place, his waistcoat watch showing one minute before seven. "You know our superb cook Sam Fraunces always says he never asks have the diners arrived, but only has the hour arrived." Down the stairs, he walked quickly, looking with interest at the colorful, scenic wallpaper where full-size ladies and lords walked, played the lute, or sailed on a lake.

GW's America (J. Tebbel) *p256*

He admired again the dark, carved wainscoting of the staircase in this house where he had now lived one week, frowned at the small vestibule and low ceilings. The clock struck seven as he walked through the door into the family dining room behind the stairs.

(Lear/Decatur)

"This house is far too small for the job!" he declared after greeting his two secretaries and all had sat down. "An uncommodious room for receptions AND dining. Across from it, an office only half large enough, and this small family dining room. That's all there is on this floor. Upstairs, half enough bedrooms on two floors, all cramped. When Mrs. Washington, two children, and servants arrive next month—plus two additional secretaries we must house—we may be camping in the reception room instead of entertaining Congressmen there!"

His two secretaries laughed politely but said nothing. Tobias Lear, young, reliable, and eager to please, had been living at Mount Vernon for two years as tutor to Washington's step-grandchildren, "Nelly" and "Wash" Custis, and as aide to Washington. Colonel David Humphreys, a war-time aide to Washington, had also spent the past two years at Mount Vernon. He had been collecting material for

GW (G. W. Custis)

a biography of Washington, which he had never had time to write.

When word arrived that the electoral college had unanimously voted Washington president, he pressed Lear and Humphreys into service as his secretaries.

Breakfast was served—the usual Indian corn hoecakes and coffee—and eaten in silence. Washington then asked about mail and messages. Lear replied that all of them were congratulations.

GW Writings Apr. 30, 1789

"Condolences would better fit my view of the situation. I greatly apprehend that my countrymen will expect too much from me. I fear if the issue of public measures should not correspond with their sanguine expectations, they will turn the extravagant praises which they are heaping upon me at this moment into equally extravagant censures."

Colonel Humphreys leaned forward to say, "How many times have I heard it said, General, that people were supporting the Constitution provided General Washington would be the President!"

(While there is no record L'Enfant voiced at this time his wish to design the city to be built in the 10-mile square, it is likely he would have tried. As the much-praised engineer-artist in charge of Federal Hall's renovation, and as an army officer known to Washington, he no doubt had opportunity to approach him. Accent: L'Enfant later refused a teaching job citing "my bad accent." Talkative L'Enfant: Senator Wm. Maclay's Journal, p32.)

"Your Excellency," began Lear in the little silence that followed, "there was one message told to me that I was asked to repeat to you, and which looked far beyond your election and inauguration.

"The Frenchman who planned and supervised the work on Federal Hall, Major Pierre Charles L'Enfant, expressed at length his great admiration for you and requested to speak to you on a matter of greatest importance to the whole country, he said. It concerns the 10-mile square and the city to be built for the seat of government."

Washington looked up, eyes lighted with interest. "Did he elucidate?"

"Only to say that he would put his heart and soul in the work, and that the result would make history, world-wide."

Washington smiled. "He is quite a talker. I regret he has such an accent, for I have much difficulty in understanding what he says, particularly since my hearing has dulled. The situation is not helped by his long, winding sentences, or their number and the speed at which he speaks them. He was one of the many Frenchmen who came about the same time as Lafayette and spent their first winter in America at Valley Forge."

Lear had nodded and smiled all the way through Washington's description of L'Enfant. "He mentioned Valley Forge to me. He said he drew the pictures for General Von Steuben's training manual that winter, and painted a portrait of you."

"Only a sketch," corrected Washington. "But he is an excellent artist. The eagle he designed for the Order of the Cincinnati is in every way elegant, although the perfection he demanded of the Paris jewelers who made a quantity resulted in an amazing bill, as yet not completely paid. He seems not to have much practical sense about money and costs, a flaw that disturbs me in anyone.

GW (D.Freeman)

"A present example is his work transforming New York City Hall from shabbiness and awkwardness to magnificence as Federal Hall. But few speak as much about magnificence as they do about cost—twice the $32,000 allotted. A lottery must pay the debts. Yet, who else in America could have produced such ideas and performed such perfect work?" The President's expression became pensive, and his gaze turned to the flowering springtime scene outside the window.

NY City in 1789 (Smith)

Colonel Humphreys remarked that city officials were saying L'Enfant refused to alter any detail of his plans, ignored expense, had fits of temper to do everything his own big and grand way. "He talked incessantly, they say, quarreling with masons, carpenters, plasterers, everybody. He hired only foreigners as upholsterers, saying no one in the local guild could properly do the work he wanted."

L'Enfant and Washington (E.S.Kite)

Washington looked at the Colonel and said, "Yet, he transformed the building inside and out in six

Life of Pierre.L'Enfant (Hans Paul Caemmerer)

months. On my plantation, to get men to work quickly and to a high standard, someone must constantly press them, critique them, and make demands upon them. That is how the Frenchman managed the Federal Hall renovation—or the recent almost-overnight construction in Philadelphia of a festival building when the French minister celebrated the birth of a royal heir—or the Ratification parade and outdoor banquet for 6,000 people in New York last year. The Federal ship "Hamilton," saved from the parade and displayed in the Bowling Green, still reminds people of the unprecedented public spectacles the Frenchman produced for that day.

A.Hamilton: Odd Destiny (Marie Hecht)

"This week, I heard from Mr. Hamilton nothing but praise for the man and the work he has done on Hamilton's house just down Wall Street from Federal Hall. Numerous others whose houses he has altered and decorated also lavish praise on him. While I have observed that he is over-proud, temperish, a perfectionist, and unconcerned about costs, I think with tactful instructions and guidance, he would be able to contribute many fine works to the architecture and artistry of our future capital.

"But it is too early to speak about this to him or anyone. When you next see him, tell him so, but invite him to write me a letter setting forth his purpose."

The President had begun rising with his last words. Lear and Humphreys jumped to their feet. "Thank you, gentlemen. Since there is time before the Committee of Congress arrives at 10 or soon afterwards, I will walk to the livery stable and inspect the horses—unless I am not able to escape the house without attracting the crowd. In that case I will retreat to my bedroom upstairs to write my journal and a letter or two."

In a few minutes, he was retreating to his bedroom and saying to Lear, "It only confirms that I must lay down a rule about visitors. If I am to at-tend to any business whatsoever, visitors who have no public business with me but who desire only to pay their respects or simply look at me, must call at a specified hour on one or two days of the week. And none on Sunday! Ask the newspapers to print an announcement to that effect, Mr.Lear."

Private Affairs GW (Lear/Decatur)

GW, Vol. 6, (Freeman) p187

SCENE 2
THE INAUGURAL PARADE

PLACE: Mansion on Cherry Street and a mile or so along Queen, Dock, and Broad Streets to Federal Hall on Wall Street. (N.Y. City 1789 map, p145)
TIME: Same day, until a little past 1 p.m.

At 9 o'clock, bells began to ring in all the churches of the town, calling people to prayer. As if in response, the sun suddenly broke through a small opening among the gray clouds.

Newspaper accounts, Apr. 30, 1789

In the little park and on the walkways beside and near the President's house, crowds lost no one to the prayer meetings but drew new watchers instead. At 10 o'clock, they heard, applauded, and cheered a company of marching militia tramping on Queen Street toward Cherry. Less welcome were soldiers taking positions in front of the crowd, and lining both sides of Cherry Street to the President's front door.

An hour passed. Another hour. Noon came, but the Committee of Congress did not. The skies hung gray again and the crowd sat down on the damp ground, cloaks drawn against a chill sea breeze. Why all this delay? Congress had been in session since 10—what could they be doing that was important enough to keep thousands of people and their hero waiting more than two hours?

At half past noon, the sound of cheering crowds in the distance brought the people on Cherry Street

This Was New York in 1789 (Frank Monaghan/Marvin Lowenthal)

scrambling to their feet. They pressed close to the line of soldiers and stared down Queen Street. Soon they were cheering cavalry clopping past, two carriages behind them bearing Congressmen, followed by a large, empty carriage, splendid with flower garlands and cupids painted on its doors, that would soon return with the President.

A parade of carriages, some open, some enclosed, followed. Men in their finest velvets, silks, beaver tricorns, and brilliant regalias, waved and bowed to the crowds. So did a dozen well-dressed gentlemen on horseback, and a jaunty company of citizens on foot.

Annals of Philadelphia (J. Watson)

Twenty minutes later, Washington in the great coach was gracefully bending his neck to the right, to the left, his expression beaming yet dignified, saluting the wildly cheering crowds of people.

GW (Freeman)

For Washington, this was the fourteenth day of such a sight. It had begun on the morning he began the trip from Mount Vernon to New York.

Crowds had flocked to the roadsides to see him pass, shout his name, sing to him, throw hats into the air. The journey took a week and ended with a thrilling barge ride from New Jersey's shore to cheering crowds on the dock at the foot of Wall Street in New York. For another week, he had bowed to crowds watching his house, crowds gathering wherever he went.

GW's America (Tebbel)

NY City in 1789 (Smith)

Now he bowed and lifted yellow-gloved hands to tens of thousands of men, women, and children screaming their joy and excitement. To the ladies in second-floor windows who fluttered handkerchiefs and threw flowers while shedding tears of happiness, Washington lifted his hat, and smiled with lips pressed against his teeth.

In front of and behind the President's coach, the parade had lengthened with artillery, grenadiers in plumed hats and gold-trimmed blue and white uniforms, officials on horseback and in carriages. Just behind the President's carriage came his personal canary-colored coach drawn by six satin-and-silk white horses. They had waited with the others—soldiers, cannon, and carriages—assembled during the morning on Queen Street. Inside the coach rode Lear and Humphreys. Outside rode coachman Jacobus, the footmen, and postilions in red and white uniforms.

"What did you find out about the cause of the delay?" Lear was asking Humphreys. The Colonel laughed. "Plenty! I spoke to Colonel David Franks who was waiting at Federal Hall while we were waiting with the President.

Recollections and Private Memoirs of Washington (G. W. Custis)

"Franks and I have known each other since I was an aide to General Washington, and he was an aide to General Benedict Arnold just before Arnold turned traitor. Franks said the Senators and Representatives had a joint meeting at Federal Hall and became tangled in a debate about what the President's title should be, how he should be addressed! They fussed and fumed and argued on and on and on. They still haven't decided! So we may hear some of them saying 'Your Excellency,' others calling him 'Your Mightiness,' or 'His Highness,' or even 'Worshipful President!'"

"Good glory!" groaned Lear. "He hates all such titles as much as John Adams loves them! But if the Congress never decides, then people will be able to go on saying, 'Mr. President.'"

Maclay's Journal Senator William Maclay Apr. 30, 1789

GW (Freeman)

As the Inaugural parade proceeded along Queen Street, passed Wall Street, bent west at Dock Street approaching Broad, the long, sustained cheering, wild agitation of acres of arms, hands, and hats, the tension of rapturous emotion brought thousands to tears.

The President wiped his eyes. Laying his hat aside, he placed his hand over his heart to bow and bow to the great general public, his countrymen whose approval, joy, and love thundered about him, embracing him.

At the junction of Dock Street with Broad, George

GW (Freeman)

Washington leaned forward and gazed briefly at a square brick building three stories high on the corner of Broad and Pearl, a continuation of Dock. He saw the sign, "Fraunces Tavern." How many times he had entered that door for many memorable occasions—a dinner intended to poison him, another to celebrate Evacuation Day of the British Army, and a dinner he and his officers could not eat as they tearfully bade each other farewell.

N.Y. City in 1789
(Smith)

The great coach turned right, into Broad. Six blocks straight ahead loomed Federal Hall. Surely all of the town's 25,000 residents and thousands of visitors were here and shouting! Even to a hard-of-hearing President, the roaring voice of the crowd was overwhelming.

Broad Street ended at Federal Hall's front arches on Wall Street. High above them hung a huge eagle, carved spreadwing, and brightly painted. Behind the building, 13 years before, Washington's army had formed ranks beside their tents to hear read the Declaration of Independence, just arrived from Philadelphia. Behind the building now a large, two-and-a-half storied extension was the meeting place of the new federal government's elected House of Representatives.

A long block before reaching the Federal Hall, the President's coach stopped behind a line-up of soldiers, cavalry, and artillery reaching to the Hall entrance. As Washington stepped out of his coach, the sudden roar of crowd voices sounded like a clap of thunder.

He stopped, placed his hat over his breast, nodded and smiled as he looked intently at the thousands on the sidewalks, the hundreds hanging out of windows, and hundreds more looking down from the roofs of buildings.

N. Y. City in 1789
(Smith)

So thrilling was the scene, so beatific Washington's smile, the people's voice rose in wave after wave of joyful chorus.

Just then, the escorts from Congress surrounded the President. In his graceful, rhythmic manner, he strode with them along the corridor formed by soldiers, horses, and big guns. At the Wall Street entrance of the temporary national capitol, George Washington vanished from sight through arches supporting a spacious new balcony.

SCENE 3
OATH-TAKING SEEN FROM A ROOF

PLACE: The flat roof of Alexander Hamilton's law office on Wall Street, next door to his home, and in sight of Federal Hall.
TIME: Same day, to the end of the swearing-in.

Friends, neighbors, and drop-ins had joined Alexander Hamilton, his wife Betsy, and five-year-old Angelina, the oldest of their three children, on the roof of Hamilton's office. Sitting on hassocks, footstools, and pillows, they had watched the crowds for hours, heard its faint, distant roar gradually grow into a thunderous shouting as Washington's coach progressed along the route toward Federal Hall. Finally, they had seen the President and his escorts walk between the lines of soldiers into the Hall.

*A.Hamilton: Odd
Destiny (M.Hecht)*

"Ahhhh!" sighed a white-haired neighbor, wiping his eyes. "Ahh! Now I can die content. I need nothing more to complete my happiness! I have seen that great good man who saved our country!"

"My God, what misplaced sentimentality!" grumbled a handsome young man about the same size and age as Hamilton. Aaron Burr, rival and associate in politics and law practice, had unexpectedly dropped in with his wife, Theodosia, and his daughter, Theodosia, a rosy, bumptious nine-year-old. They lived in a nearby mansion on the wrong side of the Hall for seeing the inauguration. "Doesn't that old man know that French generals

*Aaron Burr: Great
American Rascal (Veil)*

and soldiers, money, cannon, and fleet freed our country?!" Burr had continued. "George Washington was a losing general—and without the French, who decided to come after the successes of General GATES, the 'great, good' Washington would have LOST our country!"

Hamilton laughed at Burr's outburst."That kind of talk today will elicit only a fist in the nose, Mr. Burr. It's probably providential that you are out of sight and hearing of the crowd since everyone knows you've kept to the contrary side when it came to admiring General Washington—"

"With good reason!" interrupted Burr.

"—for your own reasons! I'm surprised you came out for this joyful occasion when you're outnumbered 40,000 to one. I suggest you will find it safer to stick to talk of money and law, about which you can speak with more respect."

Aaron Burr (Veil)

"Can I?" rebutted Burr. "Money is contemptible! BUT—truly attractive and important as a means of gratifying those I love." He glanced at his two Theodosias. "As for the law," he said with a shrug, "the law is whatever one boldly asserts and plausibly maintains!" Amused by his own wit, Burr laughed loud and long. Seeing Hamilton's disapproving frown, Burr said, "Oh well, of course YOU are cheering today. So would I if I were as eager as you apparently are for a high position in this new federal government.

A. Hamilton: Odd Destiny (Hecht)

"You'll probably get one," he raced on. "Robert Morris is passing the word that you're the best man for running the national finances—and the Morrises have a special 'in' with the Washingtons. I hear that Lady Washington—is that what we call her now?—will stop with Mrs. Morris in Philadelphia on her way here, and Mrs. Morris and her daughters will follow Lady Washington's carriage to Elizabeth Town wharf—AND, that Senator Morris and President Washington will meet them with the Presidential barge, the singing barge men, and

Inaugural scene from Hamilton's Wall Street roof top on April 30, 1789, about half past one o'clock: Repeating the words of New York's Chancellor at the end of the oath-taking ceremony, the crowd shouted, "Long live George Washington! President of the United States! God bless our President!"

109

other fol-de-rol!" Burr's voice had a tinge of contempt.

Hamilton stood up. "My, you're full of news today, Mr. Burr. Excuse me, but I see we have a friend climbing through the roof door."

He was glad for a reason to hurry away, especially after seeing the close-set eyes and prominent nose of Pierre L'Enfant, the architect, rising under the tall, rounded, black beaver hat through the opening. "Major L'Enfant! What are you doing HERE?!! The architect should have a special seat inside the Hall he transformed from dingy meeting house to Congressional palace!"

The tall, well-dressed gentleman lifted his hat in greeting and resettled it on his French wig, flat on top, curls in front and above his ears in the style long known as "L'Enfant."

"Colonel! Madame Hamilton!" he responded, holding open the roof door for another ascending man. "May I introduce my young friend Duncan Fife who is soon moving to New York from Albany. He is a furniture maker of great artistic talent. Yes, the Congress put me out on the street—directing traffic! Humiliating." His last words were half muttered.

"What?!" exclaimed both Hamiltons. "Unimaginable! Directing traffic?!"

"Exactement. Seven of us were to select some militia and constables, then assist them in keeping the center passages to the Hall open on both Broad and Wall Streets. I declined this 'honor', this insulting crumb of recognition for my work, which all agree is magnificent beyond anything ever seen in America. Have you been inside it? The great skylight in the lobby of the House of Representatives ornamented with a profusion of stained glass in the richest taste! The octagonal white and blue hall for the representatives—Ionic columns and pilasters! And the Senate! My inspired design of the ceiling medallion: a sun with thirteen stars! The

accent of strong color against the white of the walls—patterned crimson rug, crimson draperies and canopy of the presiding officer—very dramatic!"

Suddenly the heavy hum of crowd talk erupted into a massive roar.

"Look! Look!" called Mrs. Hamilton. "The President has come out on the balcony! Angelina! Look this way! Lift her, Alexander, so she can see!"

L'Enfant hurried forward to join the others tensely watching Washington bow and bow, his hand on his heart, his face animated though firmly controlled. From a crowd so dense one could have walked the length of Broad Street on the heads of people, roaring cries sounded wave upon wave.

Washington, deeply moved, backed away from the balcony railing, then sat down on a chair near a small table where a Bible lay on a crimson pillow. The crowd, appearing to understand his feelings, hushed into a profound quiet.

"I can't see anybody in the balcony now!" young Theodosia Burr said in a strong voice. "Shh!" cautioned her mother and Betsy Hamilton simultaneously, then smiled at each other. In a voice as loud as the nine-year-old's, her father remarked, "We're too far away to see much that is going on in that balcony, my darling. What we can't see are 85 politicians and God knows how many specially favored friends squeezing into the space. While Mr. Washington is now out of sight, he will soon be back at the rail, looking for more adulation. Be sure to shout loud and admiringly, or else he will glare at you!" Burr bugged his eyes at her. They laughed and laughed.

Twenty-year-old Fife, the cabinet-maker (who in a year or so would spell his name Phyfe) stared with wide-eyed curiosity at the two attorneys. He had read about them in the newspapers, heard about them in grog shop politicking. He noted that they were not tall—L'Enfant stood a head higher than either—that they were slender, handsome,

L'Enfant: W. W. Corcoran eye-witness description (Columbia Historical Society Records)

Dictionary of Hairdressing and Wigmaking (J. S. Cox)

Life of L'Enfant (Caemmerer)

N. Y. City in 1789 (Smith)

Aaron Burr (Samuel Wandell)

Dict. of Am. Biog. p553

about 35—the same age as L'Enfant. Red-headed, dark-blue-eyed Hamilton had quite a straight, pointed, long nose. L'Enfant's profile showed a slightly humped nose and heavy lips, in contrast to Burr's delicate features. Burr's dark, almost glittery eyes, very high forehead with receding dark hair, wide mouth, and finely shaped nose, gave him a fascinatingly mischievous look.

When Burr began to laugh, the Frenchman's face, which had tightened at the slur on Washington, now wore a stormy scowl of angry indignation. "SIR!" he thundered. Out poured a heavy drenching of L'Enfant's peculiarly accented English, admonishing Burr, chastising Burr, for his "insulting, untruthful, disgusting remarks about that great and good man, General Washington, the President of the United States, the most honorable, modest, trustworthy, intelligent—"

"SHHH! Shh! Quiet! They've started!"

Everyone on the roof, even young Theodosia, stared at Washington's tall figure standing by the iron railing of the balcony, his right arm outstretched, his hand on the pillowed Bible. They heard faintly the familiar tones of his voice repeating the oath, but made out no words. They saw him bow, leaning low to kiss the Bible. The man who had administered the oath, New York's Chancellor Livingston, raised his arm toward the crowd and shouted, "Long live George Washington, President of the United States! God bless our President!"

Thousands of voices amplified the salute: "LONG LIVE GEORGE WASHINGTON, PRESIDENT OF THE UNITED STATES!! GOD BLESS OUR PRESIDENT!" A great agitation of raised arms and hands, waving hats, and handkerchiefs sent out waves of energy and emotion.

"HUZZAH! HUZZAH! HUZZAH!"

BOOM!! BOOM!! Cannon firing at the Battery orchestrated the huzzahs, the bows of the President to the left, to the right, his final bow to all, his turn to leave.

The scene on the balcony folded inward. The crowd, humming with talk, shifted, stirred, continually fraying around the edges as groups broke away to move toward the next scene of action. Within an hour, the speech inside Federal Hall became history, the ceremonies completed, and the new government of the United States was walking the half-mile along Wall Street and Broadway to pray at Saint Paul's.

On Hamilton's office roof, Pierre L'Enfant put his hat on and looked around for Burr. He had thought of better reprimands for him. But Burr and his two Theodosias had departed with the first huzzah of the crowd.

"Perhaps he rushed off to attend the church service," suggested Hamilton with a teasing smile.

"I hope NOT!" exclaimed L'Enfant. "I dislike the thought of his looking at, sneering at, my beautiful 'glory' over the altar, especially designed and created for Saint Paul's. I hope even more that he will not have an appointment in the American government!"

"Not much chance," replied Hamilton. "The President dislikes him. Burr lasted two weeks as a military aide to Washington during the war—until the day the General caught him rifling through the General's private papers. He was already exasperated with Burr's impertinent retorts, his obvious contempt for the General's military knowledge, and his too freely offering the General advice on all subjects. Later Burr took the side of the Conway plotters trying to oust Washington for Gates. He even defended the stupidity, perhaps the treachery of that unbearable man, General Charles Lee, when he almost handed over our army to the enemy at Monmouth, New Jersey. No, Burr won't be appointed. Heaven help us if he is ever elected to any office!"

"But YOU will be appointed," said L'Enfant, and

Aaron Burr (Wandell)

N. Y. City in 1789 (Smith)

Pierre L'Enfant silhouette scissored by DeHart about 1785, the only known portrait of L'Enfant

N. Y. City in 1789 (Smith)

Aaron Burr (Wandell)

Aaron Burr (Veil)

I hope very much that I, too, will receive the appointment I wish for."

"Oh? What position do you have in mind, Major? Not renovating a hall in Philadelphia for the Congress, I hope. I'd like to see the capital stay here in Federal Hall, New York!"

"No, no, my friend," answered L'Enfant. "Not Philadelphia, not New York. Your Constitution says the new capital city must be in a 10-mile square detached from any state. That would exclude both cities, for neither will give itself and so much land around it to be ruled by Congress. No—only an unoccupied 10-mile square will have the space and freedom to be developed into a great national capital for the future as well as the present. Such a city should not be built without a plan. It is my dream, my heartfelt desire to create that plan. It offers a great occasion for acquiring reputation.

L'Enfant Letter to GW, Sept. 1789

"Think of it, Colonel Hamilton! No nation has ever before had the opportunity offered it for deliberately deciding on the spot where its Capital City should be fixed! Obviously the plan for it should be drawn on such a scale as to leave room for aggrandizing and embellishing in the future! Nothing will be wanting in my happiness if I gain the appointment for this work!"

"Hmm," murmured Hamilton. "Well. That interesting ambition, Peter, pertains only to the PERMANENT capital. But during its construction, we will have a temporary seat—here, I hope. Come downstairs and stay a while—bring your friend—"

"Fife. Duncan Fife. He is soon finishing his apprenticeship in Albany and setting up a shop in New York. Please tell all your friends who need chairs and tables, my dear Colonel, that Mr. Fife designs furniture of distinguished style."

SCENE 4
INAUGURAL NIGHT FIREWORKS

PLACE: Broadway from the Battery to Wall Street, and Wall Street to East River.
TIME: Inauguration night.

Red, white, and blue fiery blossoms expanded magically in the sky above the old Dutch fort at the tip of Manhattan Island.

N. Y. City in 1789 (Smith)

As the crowd responded with ahhh's! and applause, the grand finale of bangs, pops, and shrieks sent exploding colors rocketing, wheeling, cascading, spraying, and wriggling across the dark sky. The crowd, seated on the ground for the two hours of pyrotechnics, rose to cheer the beautiful and exciting display, to applaud the evening at its end, and to begin the move toward home.

Diary of Tobias Lear

At the entrance of General Knox's house, third in a row of Broadway houses on Bowling Green's west side, President Washington was saying his thanks and goodbyes. Knox, his close friend, responded, "Next year, you will have only a few steps to walk from here to your presidential mansion. Believe me, the city fathers are serious about tearing down the old fort and putting in its place a splendid house for the use of the President of the United States."

N. Y. City in 1789 (Smith)

The President's answer was lost in the great shout of the crowd as it saw him in the light of lanterns held by his military escort. Soldiers on horseback had escorted his coach to Chancellor Livingston's house next door at four o'clock for dinner. Now soldiers on foot would walk him home. Even the President's experienced horses would not be trusted to behave calmly in streets noisy with fireworks, shouting people, and crowds pressing close to the President. He had insisted that his horses and coach be excluded, as all others had, for the safety of everyone.

N. Y. City in 1789 (Smith)

Emblazoning the night sky over Old Dutch Fort (left), spectacular red, white, and blue fireworks top off President Washington's Inaugural Day. He watched from the house of General Henry Knox (right), on Broadway at Bowling Green Park. He then walked more than a mile home, admiring along the way huge, back-lit, transparent paintings on cloth.

Before leaving General Knox's portico, the President admired the lavish illumination of the first house in the row, the home of the Spanish Minister. Hundreds of lamps and candles outlined the facade, its arched windows and door, and all the great urns of flowers along the house front. Inside the windows, pictures painted on scrolls of thin cloth and backlit by the candles of great chandeliers, moved across the windows, and held Washington's rapt attention for several minutes. The Minister suddenly came out to bow and bow, and voice many congratulations.

This Was N. Y. in 1789
(Monaghan/
Lowenthal)

Then, with Lear on one side, Humphreys on the other, soldiers behind them and others leading the way, Washington walked through applauding crowds opening a path for him along Broadway's uphill slope to Wall Street.

At the French Minister's tall, spacious house midway the next block, the President stopped in the midst of the enthusiastic crowd to admire the fine transparencies sitting in its shallow garden.

N. Y. City in 1789
(Smith)

Lantern light shining through three great sheets of thin cloth framed in wood, illuminated colorful paintings of American scenes. One showed settlers, Indians, forests—the past. The second displayed George Washington's portrait, the Constitution, and the flags of America and France entwined—the present. The third predicted a future of radiant glory, cornucopia, merchant ships, money, and liberty.

A man as tall as the President moved close to the soldiers near Washington. He caught the President's eye. Washington smiled and bowed. "Good evening, Major L'Enfant."

L'Enfant made a deep bow. "A spectacular evening and day, Your Excellency! I hope there was a moment when Mr. Lear could tell you the message I gave him for you."

Washington nodded and answered, "My reply was that it is too early to discuss this matter, but that I would welcome a letter from you. I am well dis-posed to your style and taste having examined the distinguished work you carried out in Federal Hall. I compliment you wholeheartedly."

"Mr. President, I wish for no greater honor than praise from your lips and opportunity from your hand."

"Goodnight, Major," the President said, and pro-ceeded on his homeward walk. A block or so later where Trinity Church sat at the crest of the slope, he and his escorts and the surrounding crowd turned right into Wall Street. Amid applause and huzzahs, they approached the brilliantly illuminated Federal Hall on the left, and across from it a mammoth portrait of Washington on thin cloth, back lit, hang-ing over Broad Street. Far ahead on the river, lan-terns outlining the masts and riggings of the ship "North Carolina" glowed like a pyramid of stars.

L'Enfant wrote GW in
Sept. 1789

N. Y. City in 1789
(Smith)

New York's Federal Hall of 1789, first United States Capitol, had for 80 years served as City Hall when architect-engineer Pierre L'Enfant began its renovation. His workmen built a back addition about 60 feet square and 46 feet high for the House of Representatives (right) with offices around the outside. At the front of the building, he converted a second floor courtroom into the Senate chamber, and extended its balcony over an arcade created below. "The finest building in America" cost double the expected, requiring a lottery to pay the bills.

CHAPTER 12

Morris Deals for the Capital

SCENE 1
MACLAY'S CHALLENGE—SUSQUEHANNA

PLACE: Senate Chamber, second floor of Federal Hall, Wall Street at Broad, New York City.
TIME: Monday, August 24th, 1789, after Congress has worked five months on the Bill of Rights, import taxes, creation of Departments.

Maclay's Journal,
Aug.24, 1789

Two dozen Senators gazed silently after the tall, stately figure of President George Washington walking with easy grace out the door of the Senate Chamber in Federal Hall. Beside him, bewigged John Adams, his long, sheathed sword thumping his thigh, looked more than usual the plump, short, pot-bellied Vice President. Behind them strode Tobias Lear, trim, sharp-nosed young secretary to the President.

N.Y.City in 1789
(Smith)

With the President's departure, most of the Senators turned to each other to comment on his visit, or to stroll about the Chamber, or converse in a walkway between the crimson canopy of the Vice President's platform and a great arched window. Their backs to the canopy, the whisperers looked out at multicolored light falling upon the elaborate iron balcony that encircled the vast lightwell.

At one end of the Senate Chamber, the two Pennsylvania Senators glared at each other and openly quarreled by their adjacent desks.

Senator William Maclay of the Harrisburg area on the Susquehanna River spoke in a low, intense tone to Senator Robert Morris of Philadelphia.

Maclay's Journal
Aug.24

"You kept silent! You even looked shamefaced in his presence! Everybody except me simply stared at the man, saying nothing, letting ALL go as he wanted. My objecting motion dangled in dead air while I waited for your second. You didn't open

your mouth! This morning, you told me over and over you thought the same as I did about buying land from the Indians in Georgia—but with the President sitting under the canopy, and asking for the exactly opposite policy, you lost your tongue!

"Last Saturday when he came with General Knox to the Senate and I balked at giving him then and there what he wanted, you backed me up! So did the Senate! Mr. President stalked out, angry and grim. Today, you were scared he'd do that again?"

Morris fluttered his fingers at Maclay. "Not so loud, Senator. We must present some semblance of unity if we are to get anything done for our state."

"Nobody will be fooled by semblance," muttered Maclay, flicking the air with a hand. "They know you're slippery and I'm roughbarked—opposites. Over and over we get together to talk, talk, agree, agree. We take our seats in this chamber. Comes the vote. You go snipsnap and contradiction!

"You are doing that with the capital business! After months of sticking to votes on titles, proper ceremony, raising the vice president's pay—AND waiting for the New York and New Jersey Senators to take their seats—we at last can bring up the matter of the permanent seat! I sought your agreement to put forward ALL the places in Pennsylvania that had sent in their bid. You nodded consent.

"NOW you're telling me the only name you'll

"Morrisville" name appears by Falls of the Delaware on 1789 map (Trenton Public Library archives). In addition, on Sept. 4, 1789, Morris said he had just exchanged Lancaster land for land near Falls of the Delaware.

Quotes drawn from or based on various Maclay journal entries.

William Maclay

mention tomorrow is Falls of the Delaware already known as 'Morrisville,' on the Pennsylvania side, while Morris Ferry and Morris Tavern on the Jersey side flank Trenton and Lamberton!"

"Why not?" shrugged Senator Morris, his hands, fingers laced, lying across his prominent belly. "The Falls has the best chance to win the permanent seat—the Old Congress three times chose it and twice ordered surveys! Since our Pennsylvania members have agreed to vote for ANY Pennsylvania place that ANYBODY offers—"

Through gritted teeth, Maclay contended that the present Congress would not vote like the Old Congress. "Two houses to persuade! Three times as many men! All present to vote! The South much stronger! Virginians, from the President—Madison speaking for him—on down the list, are leading the Potomac crowd. They know you own Lamberton land, and Morrisville—both sides of Delaware Falls, Delaware Works and all! Alexander White, who represents a Virginia district upriver from Georgetown, told me he'd vote to remain in New York before he'd agree to Falls of the Delaware!"

Morris had been shaking his head and trying to interrupt with, "Senator—Senator—", and now broke in. "Virginians vote only for their Potomac, no matter what else is offered! New Yorkers and New Englanders vote only for their convenience—which does not include a 10-day coach ride to attend Congress in a slave state! They have voted for, WILL support my river! Their convenience—my—Pennsylvania's prize!"

Maclay wagged his head hard. "Yes, yes, our state is the right place for the capital but other towns are just as central as Morrisville, and are not dominated by one owner."

"Susquehanna towns like Maclayville or your father-in-law's Harrisburg, days away from anybody's convenience but yours?" said Morris, adding the mocking smile he knew infuriated Maclay.

"Harrisburg has been mentioned very favorably by the Marylanders," answered Maclay not looking at his antagonist while striking a palm with a fist. "I have said little myself in favor of it—except to assure them that if Congress chooses that place, I will make a gift of half my 200 acres there."

"So! Each for his own, Senator!" gaily sang Morris. "Let me repeat what I told you on Saturday. I said, 'Let those fond of this place or that place bring them forward for the federal city—and I will bring forward the Falls of the Delaware!'"

Maclay's voice and brows went up together as he glared and said, "Very well! Tomorrow I shall present a motion for Harrisburg! AND for Wright's Ferry, and Lancaster, and Carlisle, and Yorktown, Germantown, and Philadelphia!"

Vice President Adams' gavel tapped upon his desk. Maclay sat down, turning his back on Morris, whose little smile had relaxed into a smirk. Adams on his velvet sofa behind his small table under the elaborate canopy called the Senate to order.

Suddenly, a loud commotion started up outside the open doors to the balcony. On Wall Street, horses neighed, voices shouted, wood and metal crunched, carriage doors slammed. Maclay turned towards the noise—and Morris. At the sight of him, Maclay hissed in a loud whisper, "Northeast men want to stay in New York, permanent or temporary. So, don't count on them to vote for Morrisville! The POTOMAC crowd can offer New York the temporary seat—and maybe for a lot of years.

"Then, if for lack of money, a Potomac city isn't built, the seat will have become so entrenched in New York, it will stay forever! That's what Northeast men are counting on—they vote for convenience and money, not for the best interest of the country as I do!"

"We're all thinking of convenience and money, aren't we?" Morris asked serenely. "A hundred thousand dollars a year in trade! We can have it

Maclay's Journal Aug. 25

Street noise incident from another day, Maclay's Journal

Senators of the First Congress meeting in Federal Hall, New York, face Vice President John Adams seated under a crimson canopy. Crimson curtains, seats and probably rug against light-colored wainscoting and plaster enlivened the chamber. Architect L'Enfant designed the capitals of the pilasters and the ceiling's sun and stars. The glass doors (left) lead to the Inaugural Balcony.

119

permanently at the Falls if we middle states and the Northeast can stick together for Delaware Falls and New York City. We can beat the Potomac crowd! We should move quickly—NOW!"

They had talked oblivious to the commotion of balcony doors banging shut against the street noise, or calls to order from Mr. Adams. Only when a rough Southern voice from the row of desks and chairs in front of them called, "Gentlemen!" did their thoughts break away from their fascinating subject. "Gentlemen," repeated James Jackson of Georgia, "we are about to call for adjournment. Leave your quarrel for a minute and vote! Then carry on as long as you like while the rest of us depart for a cool, quiet place to dine."

After adjournment, Maclay grumbled that Jackson must have overheard them. "Yes," said Morris, "YOU were talking very loud."

SCENE 2
DELAWARE FALLS-NEW YORK DEAL

PLACE: Private dining room, City Tavern, west side of Broadway, just north of Trinity Church.
TIME: Two days later, Wednesday, August 26.

Despite the absence of Senator Morris at the weekly meeting of the Pennsylvania delegation, Speaker of the House Frederick Augustus Muhlenberg, big in height, girth, and voice, rose and called the group to order.

He recognized Senator Maclay. Standing a regal six-feet-three, gray-haired Maclay, his face fierce and grim, snapped, "Since we are to talk about the permanent residence, I will get the subject off to an irritable start.

"It's this: I wish there were some way to reprimand Mr. Otis, the Senate secretary, for leaving out

Maclay's Journal
Aug. 26

of the minutes my nomination of Harrisburg, Wright's Ferry, Germantown, Yorktown, Carlisle, and Reading for the federal city. His behavior showed it was deliberate!

"When I rose and asked Mr. Otis why he had not inserted the petitions of these towns, and read them to the Senate, he seemed much confused. He finally found the papers and read them.

"Senator Morris was not there all that time—as he is not here now. When he did arrive, Mr. Otis ran to him and whispered something. God forgive me if I heard wrong, but I thought he said, 'Maclay has got that put on the minutes!' When Charles Thomson of the Old Congress—whom the Vice President managed to replace in this Congress with his friend Mr. Otis—was Secretary, such dishonesty was not practiced.

"Between Otis's homebred sneakiness and the Southerners' ingenuity, we are all going to end up on the Potomac! Or just as bad—Pennsylvania will divide, the New Englanders and New Yorkers will win, and Congress will stay where it is tonight!"

The door swung open for Robert Morris's entrance just as George Clymer finished thanking Senator Maclay for insisting that all the petitions become part of the record, and adding that "we on the House side" must stir up a motion naming a Pennsylvania town—any Pennsylvania town—for the federal city.

Robert Morris's jovial voice broke in. "We must, indeed, stir up a motion—not offer it ourselves! Good evening, Gentlemen, good evening!" Six feet tall, fleshier than he had ever been in his 55 years, he was all pink-cheeked and perspiring, smiling, breathing high energy, and ready to get down to business.

Old and ailing Thomas Scott from a western county rose to let it be known that he put himself "entirely in the hands of the group, to stand up in the House tomorrow and make a motion for any-

PENNSYLVANIA DELEGATION LEADERS

Senator William Maclay   Congressman George Clymer   Speaker of the House Frederick Muhlenberg   Congressman Thomas Fitzsimons   Senator Robert Morris

121

thing the group agrees upon tonight concerning the federal city."

"I'd rather go to the Potomac than stay in this high-price, rowdy town. There are too many foreigners here in New York!" exclaimed Clymer.

Senator Morris loudly answered, "But we can bear it for a few years in exchange for New York's support for Falls of the Delaware as permanent seat! That is the way to defeat Potomac, and that is the offer we have and should accept."

A little chorus broke out: "Yes, I think so, too...That's right...Yes, that's right."

"As I have said many times, the Falls of the Delaware site, a central location geographically, offers more than any other place!" Morris added.

"I disagree!" thundered Senator Maclay. "The Susquehanna, being west of the Delaware, is more central by far, and it has the possibility of connecting with the Great Lakes and Ohio River. The Susquehanna, running north-south from New York's western hills to the head of the Chesapeake Bay, is the natural dividing line between the northeastern states and an equal number of states to the south. I shall nominate a location on Susquehanna!"

"Well, Senator Maclay," Senator Morris said sweetly and provocatively, "the Susquehanna is a long river. Would you not like to recommend Maclayville on the Susquehanna?"

Maclay, his grumpy old face deeply lined, got up stiffly from his chair, straightened his rheumatic shoulders and knees, and replied with cold dignity. "No. Deals—vote trades—are no way to advance our state. I am leaving. I shall go to my boarding house and rest for tomorrow's ordeal: I am invited to dinner with the President, and it is my duty to go. Good night, Gentlemen."

SCENE 3
TABLE-TALK: MORRIS-DEAL FLOP

PLACE: President Washington's dining room in his rented mansion on Cherry Street.
TIME: 4 p.m. the next day, Thursday, August 27 (the President's weekly dinner for officials)

The President, sitting opposite Mrs. Washington midway along the banquet table, made no effort to start general conversation. The air was heavy meteorologically as well as socially. The hottest day of the year had drawn out beads of sweat on brows, a high flush to cheeks, with clothing sticking to damp skin.

Hot vegetable soup went slowly down 17 throats, producing more perspiration. Senator Maclay dabbed his forehead with a handkerchief. Soup bowls were at last collected. Still no conversation. Senator Richard Bassett of Delaware, sitting beside his old friend Maclay, ventured to murmur, "Are these flowers real?" Maclay boldly touched one. "Fake." They smiled at each other, and looked to see if anyone was eyeing them. But the others had their eyes on three liveried servants, each bearing a large fish on a platter. A low murmur of surprise arose when one platter was placed in front of the President for serving. Beginning the job deftly, the President remarked that these fish, sea trout, were a favorite of his, and that the crew of a Robert Morris ship had caught them.

Senator Bassett leaned close to Maclay and joked, "Perhaps that was where Morris was this morning instead of on the Senate floor—out fishing for the President's dinner!"

Maclay sniffed. "I noticed he had no time to sit even one minute in today's session. He is only playing at being a Senator."

"Oh, but he came—after we adjourned. He had business with a House member," Bassett whispered.

Guests:
Sen.Maclay
Sen.Bassett
Rep.Smith(S.C.)
Sen.Dalton & wife
Sen.Langdon & wife
Justice Jay & wife
Gov.Clinton & wife
V.P.Adams & wife
Aides Lear, Lewis

Food and events of this dinner from Maclay's Journal, Aug. 27, 1789. Maclay-Bassett conversation reflects events of Aug. 27 recorded in House Journal (Gales/ Seaton). Maclay's simple account appears in his Sept. 2 journal entry.

Every Thursday at 4 o'clock in the Executive Mansion, the President dined with a dozen members of Congress and officials. The cuisine ranked high in quality—Washington spent $165 a week for food, plus wines, spirits, and cider. General conversation often ranked low in quantity, the President being noted for his lack of small talk.

"I stayed at my Senate desk to work an hour, and coming down the stairs, I heard him, then saw him, in the lobby outside the door of the House, still in session. He almost had Benjamin Goodhue by the ruffles on his shirt.

"Their voices were falling on top of each other. Both their faces were angry red. My! the sparks were flying. I saw and heard this remarkable scene while well out of sight behind a marble column."

A voice interrupted. "Excuse me, Sir." A serving man sat plates of fish before them.

"Morris angry at a Massachusetts man—a Northeasterner?" Maclay exclaimed behind his napkin, pretending to dab his mouth.

"Oh, very angry," said Bassett. "But let's eat the fish while it's hot. Suffice it to say that the subject was the 10-mile square."

No one at the table spoke for the next few minutes as fish was forked from plate to mouth. The silence held while servants removed empty plates, then brought great platters of roasted mutton, ham, chicken, and wild pheasant to place before the President and his aides. In the quietness, Maclay whispered to Bassett, "This is the most solemn dinner ever I sat at!"

"Mr. Maclay, sir!" called the President's nephew, carving meats at the near end of the table. "What is your pleasure?"

"Ham, if you please, and a sliver of mutton."

"I'll take the same," Bassett volunteered. In the wait before the servant brought their plates, they gazed at the President, who was also asking his neighbors, "What is your pleasure?" then carving for each guest. Behind him, the steward, "Black Sam" Fraunces, dressed in wig and formal clothes, whispered instructions to the servants.

When the President finally picked up his fork, his guests lifted theirs. After a few bites, Washington asked Adams how the gardens at his rented house, Richmond Hill, overlooking the Hudson,

No record of such a Morris-Goodhue confrontation, but it is likely that a scene like this occurred.

Richmond Hill house stood at present SE corner Varick and Charlton Streets.

123

were taking the heat. A horticultural conversation spread around the table.

Maclay hurried his long-suppressed question to Bassett. "I take it that you learned from the dust and feathers what Massachusetts had done to upset Morris." He leaned toward Bassett as inconspicuously as he could to hear the answer, which came muffled through the chewing of mutton.

"They were making so much noise, the door keeper came out to calm them down. Morris barked at him, 'Go tell Roger Sherman I want to see him!' Then he pushed his finger against Goodhue's chest and said, 'Senator King and you made a deal with me about the Falls! You both broke your word!' Goodhue was shaking his head and talking like a whirligig—I could catch no words—for at the same time, Morris was shouting, 'I don't know what to make of men who agree to a thing at night and deny it in the morning!!'"

"Lower your voice, Bassett," Maclay muttered, lowering his head. "The President and Massachusetts Senator are looking at us."

"I'll finish my mutton," answered Bassett, taking a big bite.

The meat course finished, apple pie was sat before them. Between pie eating and comments around the table about the President's fare—"Great dinner!" "Best of the kind I ever was at!"—Bassett reported more words he overheard in Federal Hall's three-storey high lobby-lightwell.

"I see now," said Maclay, fitting Bassett's story to his memories of the previous day's events. "After I left the City Tavern meeting, Senator Morris got agreement from our state's delegates to make a deal for Massachusetts and New York votes. Since becoming Senator, Morris has had no object other than settling the federal city on his acreage at the Delaware Falls. The more land he buys there, the harder his bargaining for votes to put the seat there."

Maclay stopped, gratefully glanced to his left at the rising voices of his neighbors discussing the latest attacks of Indians on settlers in the Ohio region.

Bassett murmured, "To make it look unarranged, he told Thomas Scott to open the 10-mile subject with a motion listing a set of 'principles' to describe the ideal place to build the capital city. He included not just geographic center, but center of wealth and population—to disqualify Potomac!"

Maclay's Journal p142

"Excuse me again, Gentlemen." The servant reached for their empty pie plates, and sat bowls of raisin pudding in their places.

Maclay, Aug. 27-28

"Two desserts?" murmured Bassett, smiling.

"What a schemer Morris is," mumbled Maclay. "He calls it 'strategy.' Pennsylvania opens the subject with 'principles' and Massachusetts rises to say Falls of the Delaware fits those principles exactly. Pennsylvania and the Northeast win the vote for the Falls, then Pennsylvania rises to nominate New York for temporary capital. Before a cat could blink an eye, the long argument would be settled with the Morris deal. But it sounds as if the Massachusetts marionette didn't play—"

Bassett, who had been digging into the pudding, held his spoon like a finger before his lips, and hissed a faint "sh." Aloud, he said, "You should try this excellent pudding!"

Maclay growled on, "Even if he had, and the Falls had won in the House, the Senate would never have accepted it."

"It may never be asked to—but let's eat our pudding. The servant is waiting behind us—we're the last to finish."

When glasses of wine had taken the place of empty pudding bowls, Maclay looked up and down the table, hoping to see someone else conversing. No one was. Finally, the President remarked again on the day's heat and oppressive summer weather in general, exciting another rumble of talk about hot weather experiences.

History of Congress, House Journal (Gales and Seaton) Aug. 27, 1789

Bassett began whispering again. "It wasn't that Massachusetts reneged. Their man—Goodhue—never had a chance to speak! A Southerner beat him to it—William Smith of South Carolina—"

"Careful—he's sitting at this table!"

"—is a man fast on his feet. Scott had hardly finished listing his 'principles' when Smith was shouting a motion to kill them! Other Southerners hopped up. 'Postpone this 10-mile subject until North Carolina's men get here!' Then—who do you think joined them? CONNECTICUT'S Roger Sherman! NEW HAMPSHIRE'S Sam Livermore! MASSACHUSETTS' Fisher Ames!

"Ames ended a long, hot speech with a hint that he was incensed at others who made deals assuming his support. He shouted, 'The reasons for decisions of this magnitude ought to be made public!'"

"Hear, hear!" Maclay breathed into his handkerchief, brought out to dab sweat from his face. "No wonder Morris was so upset." Beaming, Maclay looked past figurines and fake flowers until his roaming gaze met an inquisitive stare of Washington's blue eyes. Maclay nodded pleasantly.

"I suppose the House killed Scott's principles," he murmured to Bassett.

"No, they voted to debate them next week."

"WHAT!? Augh! They will chew on them and nothing else through Christmas. Morris will throw Pennsylvania's votes this way or that to get the capital on his land."

"But today's collapse of his deal," Bassett whispered, "should show him we are past the time when arranging a deal in Congress is simply pulling a few strings in one decrepit Assembly."

Just then, a murmur of pleasure arose among the President's guests. Maclay and Bassett looked up and saw the arrival of the latest high society novelty—frosty glasses of ice cream served in summer.

During the next few minutes, the diners heard only the clicking of silver against fine crystal, and a remark from Washington that Senator Morris's ice house supplied the ice, sawn from the frozen river in winter and stored in sawdust underground for use in summer. Maclay, laying his spoon by his empty glass, whispered to Bassett, "Do you suppose the President knows what his good friend Morris is doing to grab the 10-mile square?"

Bassett nodded. "He probably knew the details of today's story before I heard them from my state's one delegate in the House, John Vining. Madison, the President's man in the House, is said to report to him every little and big event, especially concerning this most interesting city-to-be."

Silver trays heaped with fruit—melon slices, balls, and cubes, apples and peaches—surrounded by nuts, were placed upon the table. After a few minutes for his guests to peel, slice, and chew, the President moved his chair back, rose, filled his glass with wine, and with great formality drank to the health of every individual by name around the table.

Every diner imitated him, charging glasses and creating a buzz of "Health, Sir!" and "Health, Madam!" and "Thank you, Sir!" "Thank YOU, Madam!" Dead silence closed in again.

"I think the President has not entirely recovered from the near-fatal carbuncle on his bottom," murmured Bassett to Maclay. "To be sure, he's been up and riding his horse about a month, but he looks pale and listless. It is said that when the doctor cut out the terrible abscess, he groaned not once, but only told the surgeon not to be afraid to cut deeper. The President thought he had a cancer, such as killed his mother. We are lucky it was only a boil. We need our greatest man at the helm in these uncertain first years."

Maclay agreed. "Washington is our most admirable man. I have no quarrel with that sentiment. My main question about any executive is whether we, representing the people, should ever be treated as empty bottles that can contain nothing but what

Private Affairs of GW (Lear/Decatur)

the executive pours into them."

Servants cleared the table. Brandy bottles passed. Mrs. Washington at last withdrew with the ladies. The President told a story about a clergyman who lost his hat and wig in Brunks River. Everyone laughed. Mr.Jay told a story about how the Duchess of Devonshire had traded kisses for votes to elect Fox. A few smiled.

The President had kept a fork, and in the awkward silences, tapped it lightly on the table. After one particularly dead moment, he rose from the table, and led the men to drink coffee with the ladies in an upstairs room. Senator Maclay hung behind, found his hat, and departed.

Looking old, thin, and grumpy, Senator Maclay walked out in the late afternoon sun and heat. All the way to his rooming house, he mumbled to himself about the habit of merchants for gain, lawyers for wrangling, and fools for being the tools of knaves.

SCENE 4
DISENCHANTED DELEGATES

Maclay's Journal
Sept. 2

PLACE: Federal Hall, House lobby.
TIME: Wednesday, September 2, the day before the debate on Scott's "Principles."

Senator Maclay propped himself against a cold marble column to take the weight off his rheumatic knee while he waited for fellow Pennsylvanian, Thomas Scott. As he nodded politely to handsomely dressed gentlemen passing in and out of the House chamber, he mused to himself:

Maclay, Aug. 29

"I have not been well in health since I dined with the President, but this is not all. I feel a heavy kind of melancholy hanging on me, as if I were disgusted with the World. With the Senate I certainly am disgusted. I came here expecting every man to act the part of a god, expecting the most delicate honor, the most exalted wisdom, the most refined generosity was to govern every act and to be seen in every deed.

"What must my feelings be on finding rough and rude manners, glaring folly, and the basest selfishness apparent in almost every public transaction! They are not always successful, it is true. But is it not dreadful to find them in such a place?

"Just minutes ago, for example, Morris whispered to me in the Senate, 'The whole business is settled, and you must come to a meeting at Clymer's lodgings at 5 o'clock!'

Sept. 2

"What can this mean except more underhanded deals so he can locate the seat of government where it will profit him most?"

Congressman Scott, lumbering across the lobby, called, "Senator Maclay! You sent for me? What can I do for you?"

"Ah! Mr. Scott! I came by to tell you that as I find myself scarcely able to move one step with my rheumatic knee, I will not be able to attend the meeting of Pennsylvania men today at 5 o'clock at Mr. Clymer's."

"Meeting?" exclaimed Scott, "what meeting? This is all news to me! Who called it? What is the business of this meeting?"

Maclay tried his weight on his left knee and winced in pain. "It is odd that you have not been notified, since it is your motion on the seat of government that will be taken up tomorrow. I assume the business of a meeting today is to plan for the event tomorrow. Senator Morris told me as he was leaving that the New England men will be at the meeting, and that the 'whole business of the permanent residence is settled.' Representative Goodhue of Massachusetts and Senator Rufus King of New York were mentioned—I don't know who else will talk for the Northeast."

"Well. Hmm," said Mr. Scott. "I see why I am not notified—although," he hastily added, "perhaps the messenger is just tardy. Senator Morris has no doubt heard that I am disgusted with the manner in which King and Goodhue handled the deal we had with them last week —leaving us open to Fisher Ames's nasty attack when I introduced our 'principles.' That episode caused a violent schism in our delegation. In the future when Morris says 'Jump!' only half will say 'How high?' If they join any more Capital deals, it will be with the Virginians."

"The VIRGINIANS?!" exclaimed Maclay.

"Why not?" replied Scott with a shrug."They have an offer, they sound more trustworthy than Northeast men, and they will have as many votes—NEXT year after five North Carolinians arrive. Madison has said to us, 'Vote with us for the Potomac, and we will vote Philadelphia the temporary residence,' which does not require giving Congress legal control over the city. If we can convince the rest of our state delegation in the House to join us, we can say 'devil take you' to Senator Morris and his deals for Delaware Falls. Instead, we will do something for Philadelphia."

Maclay grimaced. "Mr. Scott, I am disappointed! Another deal! It is YOUR motion that lays down PRINCIPLES for locating the capital. Do you not want us to VOTE principles and conscience for the good of the Union? Abandon all these deals, plots, and cabals!"

"Let's look at Truth as our Principle," answered Scott patiently. "The Truth is we can and will talk for hours tomorrow about the 'Principles' in my motion, but at the end we will be counting votes. Is it not a Truth that you, I, all the Pennsylvania delegates, want SOMETHING for our state? A Truth that the North wants SOMETHING for its region, and that the South wants SOMETHING for the South?

"Pennsylvania's seven votes MUST strike a tit-for-tat deal with a solid North OR a solid South BE-FORE the rollcall—for we can expect nothing to fall our way on simple merit."

Senator Maclay's head had wagged from side to side through all of Scott's talk. "You are auctioning off our votes to the highest bidder, sir!"

"Should we let Morris auction them instead, for his personal gain?!" Scott said intently but at a discreet volume. "That's what he expects to do this evening! I think our Philadelphia delegates should surprise him with a hard jolt to show him he cannot shoo us around like chickens. Since he has invited King and Goodhue to talk to us about RENEWING the Delaware Falls-New York deal, I shall invite James Madison of VIRGINIA to talk to us about setting up a Potomac-Philadelphia deal!"

Scott was suddenly struck by the humor of it all, and broke out in a merry laugh. "Oh, but the deal-makers confronting each other in the same room would hurt Mr.Morris's sense of propriety, wouldn't they? I'll arrange for Madison to sit in a downstairs room while Morris, King, and Goodhue sit upstairs! We delegates can go back and forth, up and down, seeking the best offer!"

With the briefest of glances at Senator Maclay's pained expression, Congressman Scott excused himself to hurry into the House chamber and extend his invitation to Mr. Madison, leader of the "Potomac Crowd."

Members of the First Federal Congress await the Speaker's gavel in the cavernous chamber L'Enfant added to the back of Federal Hall for the House of Representatives. With its blue carpet and drapes, golden oak wainscoting, white upper walls and ceiling 46 feet high, the room impressed all with its elegance and monumental size. Here the viewer sees it from one of the two balconies hanging above the main entrance.

128

CHAPTER 13

Morris Down, Maclay Up

SCENE 1
DELAWARE FALLS OUT, SUSQUEHANNA IN

PLACE: House of Representatives, Federal Hall.
TIME: Thursday, September 3, day of debate on Scott's "Principles" for determining the best location for the seat of government.

N.Y. City in 1789
(Smith)

Voices of 500 people filled the cavernous House chamber with a chattery rumble. Half the sound came from 200 visitors sitting high above the House floor in two iron galleries hanging one above the other on the wall over the main entrance. Some guests were invited relatives and friends, including ladies in startlingly large hats and hooped skirts. Others were city officials, speculators, prominent attorneys (Alexander Hamilton and Aaron Burr among them) and a few Senators.

Foreign envoys and their aides joined them. The Marquis de Moustier of France, noted for his heavy nose, supercilious smile, love of Bourbon kings and red-heeled shoes, wore the latest French fashion in blue satin, a profusion of ribbons, earrings, long-curl wig, and perfume enough for House members below to enjoy. Short, slight, Spanish Minister, Don Diego de Gardoqui wore pearly silk and the odor of strong cigars—neutralized by his charming informality and large brown eyes sparkling under heavy black brows.

History of the
Centennial Celebration
in 1889 (Clarence
Bowden) Portraits

"Federal Hall
Revisited" (Louis
Torres) Jour.Soc.Arch.
Historians, Dec. 1970

Underneath the galleries, 200 or so of the public crowded into long pews on both sides of the aisle from doorway to a railing separating them from the House Floor. Like the spectators in the galleries, they faced the Speaker on his platform against the far wall. On the Floor in between, 65 House members, a half-dozen clerks and a dozen short-hand reporters for newspapers added their voices to the oceanlike roar of words.

All awaited the start of the most exciting and, to them, the most important, Congressional debate of the season—the locations of the future capitals, one temporary, one permanent, of the new Federal Government.

For all the spectators as well as members of Congress, officials, and clerks, the "where" decisions would affect their jobs, purses, office and living arrangements, and their personal importance for years to come. New York had already taken a step expected to influence the decision. Just a few blocks away, the tearing down of the old Dutch fort was well advanced and the construction of a Presidential mansion about to begin. The cost would burden New York taxpayers, but if the splendid new building and the renovated Federal Hall lured Congress to remain here, prosperous times would be sure to follow.

N.Y.City in 1789
(Smith)

In the private talk on the Floor, various names of towns and rivers had risen through the general buzz of talk. Among the Virginia delegates, James Madison was saying to young Richard Bland Lee that the evening before, he had spoken about a Potomac-Philadelphia arrangement with Pennsylvania delegates meeting in Clymer's rooming house.

"With what result, I cannot be sure. But it was

Maclay's Journal
Sept.2

clear that my presence, though not in the same room with Morris and visitors Goodhue and King, upset those three considerably. In short order, Morris left with the visitors for City Tavern, where Massachusetts and New York delegations were having meetings.

"I heard this morning that they struck a Delaware Falls-New York deal. However, my talks with Pennsylvania delegates convinced me that the group is seriously split. Perhaps half of them are rebelling against Morris and will refuse to vote for his Delaware Falls."

Lee smiled as he said, "And, as we saw last week, King and Goodhue cannot count on full, unquestioning support from their delegations, either. If Fisher Ames, Sherman, and Livermore will protest lengthily again—as lengthily as we—then we have a chance to hold off a final vote this session. If only North Carolina had ratified and we had its men with us now! Well, as soon as Congress passes the last of the 12 items in the Bill of Rights for the Constitution—"

J.Madison (Brant)

"That should be in about two weeks, I think," Madison said. Lee was observing that the Northeast and Morris would try every twist and turn inventable during these last days of the First Session, to get a vote on Delaware Falls and New York—when just then, Speaker Muhlenberg whacked his gavel on the block.

Quickly the House voted to shift to its sparring mode—a Committee of the Whole House with Elias Boudinot as Chairman.

He called up Thomas Scott's "Principles" for determining the location of the permanent seat of government.

All the House actions from History of Congress (Gales and Seaton) Sept 3, House Journal.

Immediately, Benjamin Goodhue of Massachusetts gained the floor. Unknown to Morris, Goodhue and King the night before had attended a late, joint meeting of New Yorkers and Massachusetts men. Now, in an oratorical, deliberate voice, Goodhue

declared, "The motion on 'Principles' being too indefinite, I will add something— specific!"

A low "Ahh!" from the gallery. "Shh!" Shh!" from several directions produced silence. "Here come Morris's Falls and New York's Hall," whispered Madison to Lee.

Goodhue frowning as usual, smoothed the short bangs fringing his forehead and turned to glance up at the galleries. He let his gaze travel higher yet to the alcoved ceiling then down the length of an Ionic column. He briefly scanned high windows framed by blue curtains, a vast field of wainscoting below, and the row of newspaper reporters sitting against it.

N.Y City in 1789 (Smith)

Rubbing his exceptionally long chin thoughtfully, Goodhue looked quickly at the two rows of Congressmen watching him intently. "First," he said, "I remind you that we in the Northeast had not wanted to take up at this time the question of the location of the seat of government."

("Pouf!" Lee muttered with a roll of his eyes.)

"Much important business should be transacted before adjournment on the twentieth. But our opinion being overruled by a vote of the House last week, we have taken the matter into consideration, and are now ready and willing to come to a decision."

Goodhue paused, enjoying the suspense—and the surprise he had for everyone south of New York. "The Eastern members with the members from New York have agreed to fix a place upon national principles, without regard to our own convenience. We have turned our minds TO...the banks OF...the SUSQUEHANNA!"

A rumble of exclamations came from the galleries and from the crowd of spectators under them. On the House floor, Congressmen looked with puzzlement from one to another.

J. Dawson letter to Madison, Sept. 9

Madison turned to Lee. Both smiled. "It's a hard, angry, insulting rebuff to Morris," said Madison. "The

Madison letter to H. Lee, Oct. 4

Robert Morris wanted the permanent capital at the "Falls of the Delaware." As Senator he made deals and motions in Congress to get it. But in 1790, he wrote Gouverneur Morris, "It has constantly been in my view to bring the Ramblers (Congress) back to the banks of the Delaware, but the obstinacy of one or two, and the schemes of others, prevented my getting them so high up as The Falls." Philadelphia, chosen for a 10-year-capital, lies 30 miles downstream from The Falls.

Based on "Cox Land Survey 1789" in the Trenton Public Library Archives, and on records of Recorder of Deeds, Bucks County, Pa. Researcher: Betty Huber, Morrisville, Pa.

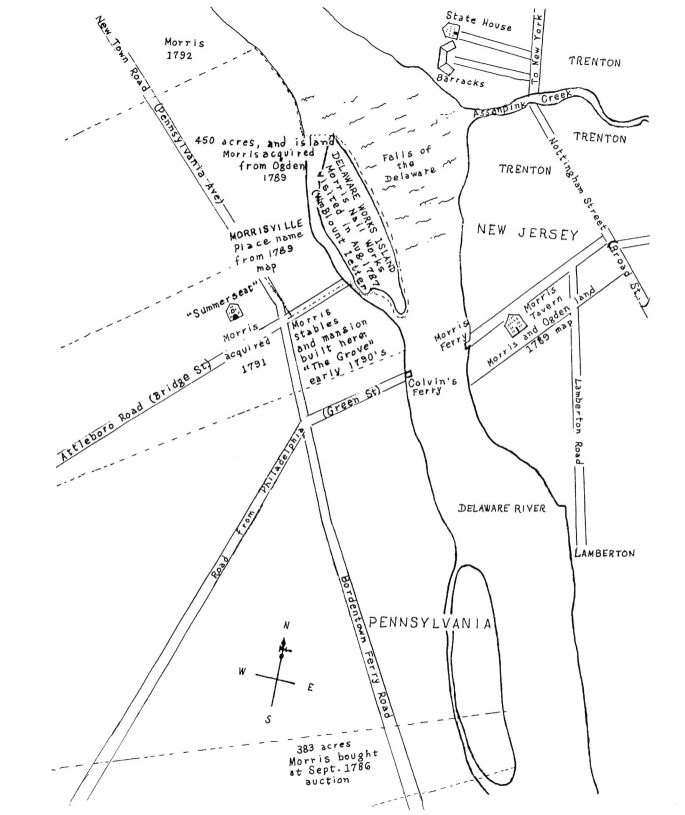

Susquehanna is Maclay's river!" His smile faded. "But," he whispered, "it may be more of a threat to Potomac's chances than the Delaware."

"No, they've made our task easier," Lee whispered back. "Morris will find some way to kill Susquehanna. I suspect the Northeast men know that—expect that."

When the exclamations had died away with a bang of Boudinot's gavel, Goodhue continued. "Motives of convenience would have led us to fix upon the banks of the Delaware. It was supposed, however, that it would give more lasting content to go farther south. Until suitable buildings can be erected on the Susquehanna, we are unitedly of opinion that the Government should remain in the city of—NEW YORK!"

The galleries and public broke into hand-clapping, exclamations of pleasure, and one "Bravo!" before Chairman Boudinot banged his gavel.

Lee had all but shouted to Madison, "Now he's insulted US! 'Give more LASTING content to go farther SOUTH'—when it's not south at all, and gives US not one tittle of content—which he knows!" Madison nodded. He reached into his coat pocket for a paper, and handed it to Lee.

While Goodhue read to the Committee of the Whole his formal resolution for Susquehanna and New York City, lanky Henry Wynkoop of Pennsylvania was seen hurrying out the door. There, Senator Morris had been waiting, not wishing to risk any negative effect his presence in the House might have on his deal for Delaware Falls.

At the moment that Wynkoop's news about the Susquehanna struck Morris with disappointment and anger, young Lee, inside the House chamber, stood up to listen to the last phrases of Goodhue's resolution. He began to dab his brow with a large handkerchief, using extravagantly large movements to do so. "Mr. Chairman!" he called, even as Goodhue was pronouncing "New York."

Boudinot recognized the gentleman from Virginia. "I offer a preamble for the 'Principles' the Committee is discussing."

It was a long preamble, heavy with more "Principles" and guidelines. Each was followed by a full explanation.

Two hours and 17 speeches later, Lee's preamble lost 17 to 34, despite Mr. Madison's pointing out lengthily that it was not a preamble to a preamble as some charged, but contained "luminous truths."

With Scott's "Principles" at last before the House, Madison spent another half-hour considering one word in them. "Wealth," he said, "should not be a guide for choosing the location of a capital city." He lost, but with a better score than Lee's.

Immediately, the vote was called on Scott's "Principles." They—wealth included—were adopted 32 to 18.

Now the attack began on Goodhue's Susquehanna-New York addition to the "Principles." Lee and Madison wanted to have carefully explained to them exactly how and at what places the Susquehanna fitted each "Principle." They encouraged long and tedious detail.

Details gushed forth from Pennsylvanians, not only about the Susquehanna and its connections with Lake Ontario by way of the Tyoga and the Genesee, but also with the Delaware by the Swetara, the Tulpehoken, and the Schuylkill. In addition, Susquehanna could reach the Ohio by the Juniata, the Kisskemanetas, and Allegheny rivers. Perfect 10-mile squares awaited a capitol building at Wright's Ferry, Peach Bottom, and Harrisburg.

During an hour of measuring and remeasuring the land, the wealth, and the population to find their exact centers, then their common center, New York and New England members declared Susquehanna was SOUTH or southwest of that center—and thus a truly disinterested choice.

Not so! countered Madison. "You told us, Sir, you

Out-of-doors: Privately, outside the House sessions.

had preconcerted this measure out-of-doors, disposing of more than half the territory of the United States, and nearly half its inhabitants without their knowledge, without their consent!"

Burly James Jackson of Georgia boomed, "Are Eastern members allowed to dictate and fix our seat of Government?! This looks like aristocracy! When our people learn about this, the words will blow the coals of sedition—and endanger the Union! This Susquehanna is not central! It's 900 miles from Savannah, Georgia—and only 400 miles from the top of New Hampshire!"

Goodhue assured him his mileage was wrong. Sedgwick, another Massachusetts member, assured the Georgian that Madison's population figure was also wrong because he was counting slaves. "If black men who have been deprived of all rights are counted for this purpose," said Sedgwick, "then we might as well include a count of the black cattle in New England!

"As for the Potomac, its climate is not only unhealthy, but destructive to northern constitutions! Vast numbers have met their destruction as soon as they arrived in the Southern states!"

This was a prime moment for a Pennsylvania member to move that Harrisburg be named as the site in the Susquehanna motion, and Daniel Heister did so, with a full description.

It was nearly two o'clock, only an hour before adjournment for dinner. Madison and four other Southerners began taking turns to call for the Committee of the Whole to rise now, debate later—to give delegates time to consider the facts, particularly the Potomac facts. Madison announced he had much to say replying to many points, but he'd like to say it tomorrow when the hour was not so late and when the patience of the gentlemen not so exhausted.

"No," replied Fisher Ames of Massachusetts. "You are only intending to delay. We know all the nec-

essary facts now. I hope the Committee having adopted the 'Principles' will go on and agree to the Susquehanna resolution without delay!"

By half past two o'clock, despite Mr. Madison's flow of words asking for another day to debate, the House voted "Nay." Now the Harrisburg motion could be taken up.

In the galleries, the foreigners, somewhat perplexed by the procedure, voting, and boring (only to them) speeches, rose to depart for taverns and coffeehouses. Half the galleries and the public-space spectators also followed their rising appetites, especially when they saw Maryland's Michael Stone, whose district was the upper lip of Potomac's mouth, take the floor, a sheaf of papers in hand.

His slow and hesitating monotone and his roundabout approach left most of his audience uncertain which river he was extolling. When it became clear that it was the Potomac, a commotion of objections broke out among the Pennsylvanians. "Out of order! Out of order, Mr. Chairman!"

Stone in a burst of surprisingly loud tones declared, "I will stop—and wait until you gentlemen are inclined to give me a hearing! I hardly expect that my observations will be agreeable to you! But you will have to excuse me for speaking now since you have forced me to rise at this time by your precipitancy!"

Boudinot's gavel and disapproving frowns restored order and Stone's slow monotone proceeded.

Ten minutes later, the protests broke out again, the protesters having congregated in front of the Chairman's table. "The motion now before us is to insert 'Harrisburg' into Mr. Goodhue's resolution for naming the Susquehanna! But the speaker is not talking about Harrisburg—he is only comparing Potomac to Susquehanna, and he is therefore out of order!" said Ames for the group of Heister, Hartley, Sherman, and Clymer.

The Chairman said, "Are you sure he hasn't once

mentioned Harrisburg?" for his attention had wandered away from the Stone monotone.

Madison, Lee, and Daniel Carroll had hurried to join the group. Now they insisted that Stone was in order since any Susquehanna town necessarily involved Susquehanna River and was inseparable from it, which river needed to be compared with Potomac River.

The Chairman pulled at his chin thoughtfully. "Mr. Stone," he said, "you are out of order, and we will vote on the motion to insert 'Harrisburg' into the Susquehanna motion." The vote was taken, the answer was "nay", and Stone's monotone was allowed to proceed.

("It's quarter-of-three o'clock," Madison whispered to Lee. "In another half hour or so, all the boarding house dinners will be cold, or even eaten up. Can you take the Floor after Stone runs dry, and hold it another quarter-hour? I'll take it then, and hang on until hunger drives this House to rise and adjourn.")

("I'll do better than that," growled Lee. "I'll move to strike Susquehanna and substitute Potomac.")

Stone ran dry, and young Lee's Potomac motion flowed into the House Journal. Fertile soil and salubrity of climate recited, he set his voice to rise in alarm at the prospect of "a Northern dominance."

As Lee's quarter hour neared its end, his oratorical voice and fervor warmed to the terrors confronting the Union. "With what difficulty the Constitution was adopted by the State of Virginia! If, as predicted, the Northern states will now consult their partial interest without regard to their Southern brethren, the faith of all south of the Potomac will be shaken! The interests of the Southern and Western country should be consulted! These interests will be sacrificed if Congress fixes upon any place but the POTOMAC!" he shouted.

A breath of laughter ran through the audience of New Yorkers in the public space and galleries. Very shortly it changed to a loud murmur of shock when

Madison, who in '88 had wrung ratification out of the Virginia Convention, took the floor and fiercely announced, "If a prophet had risen in that Assembly and brought the declarations and proceedings of this day into view, I firmly believe that Virginia might not be a part of the Union at this moment!"

Out of the rumble of voices that followed, a motion was heard for the Committee of the whole House to rise so that the House could proceed to vote on the Susquehanna-New York proposition.

Madison heard from Sedgwick of Massachsetts a hint that a vote would favor Susquehanna: "Will it be contended," Sedgwick asked, "that the MAJORITY shall not govern? Shall the MINORITY, because they cannot carry their points, accuse the House of want of candor?"

Standing small but commanding, Madison pushed his voice to its limit. "The majority ought to govern!" he cried. "YET—they have no authority to deprive the minority of the right of free debate! We have the right to bring forward all the arguments that we think can, ought to, have an influence on the decision! On less important questions, it is UNUSUAL to decide in the course of a single day. I wish to make some observations—at present there is not time.

"BUT IF THERE WAS, I DO NOT WISH TO ADDRESS A DETERMINED AND SILENT MAJORITY! No, sir, if this be the temper of today, let me appeal to a more favorable temper tomorrow! If gentlemen refuse this appeal, I submit. But I will to the last minute assert my right, and remonstrate against a precipitate decision!"

Fisher Ames made some sarcastic remarks —"they allow no time when they're winning, and want much delay when they're losing. They seem to think the banks of the Potomac a paradise and that river a Euphrates"—and Massachusetts Congressman Wadsworth feared the whole of New England would consider the Union destroyed if Congress dared go to the Potomac.

Then, bending either to Madison's appeal or to the rumblings of their stomachs, the Congressmen shouted "Yea!" for the Committee to rise, "Yea!" for the House to adjourn.

From the galleries and the public seats came no applause, only a mix of loud voices. House members leaving the Chamber stared at Robert Morris in the lobby, talking to his one-time protege, Alexander Hamilton. Philadelphia's richest merchant looked quite subdued, even perplexed, his mouth so compressed that its corners pointed to the cold marble floor.

SCENE 2
MACLAY SICK-ABED, BUT WINNING

PLACE: Maclay's bedroom in his rooming house at Vesey and Greenwich Streets.
TIME: Friday, September 4, in the evening.

Maclay's Journal Friday, Sept.4 (all the scene)

Senator William Maclay, confined to his bed all day with a swollen knee, pulled himself up into sitting position and began to write his journal:

"Mr.Morris just left. He called on me to talk about Susquehanna. I never saw chagrin more visible on the human countenance. I heard yesterday that Morris was exerting his utmost address in engaging votes against my river, trying to obtain votes for his Delaware—proof of how far interest will blind a man.

"Mr. Morris sat with me a long time. 'Well,' he said, 'I suppose you are gratified.' I said cooly, 'I could not be dissatisfied.'

"I really was vexed to see him so deeply affected. He repeatedly declared he would vote for the Susquehanna if it ever reached the Senate, because he had said he would vote for any place in Penn-

sylvania, but that he would do everything in his power to turn votes against it in both Houses. This he called candor.

"It has long been alleged in this place that Mr. Morris governed the Pennsylvania House delegation, and I believe this idea has procured Mr. Morris's uncommon attention. This delusion must now vanish with their determination to vote for Susquehanna.

"He made a long visit with me. I said everything to soften his attitude against the Susquehanna, and seemed to gain upon him. He mentioned with apparent regret some rich lands he had exchanged for lands close by Falls of the Delaware."

SCENE 3
BEST MEDICINE—GOOD NEWS

PLACE: Maclay's bedroom in his rooming house.
TIME: Saturday, September 5, about 6 p.m.

Maclay's Journal (all the scene) Sept.5

Dressed in his nightshirt, Maclay lay propped in bed, his leg with its badly swollen knee, red and raw from cupping and blistering, stretched out. He was in a most miserable way.

Dr.Treat and Dr. Rodgers hovered over him, one to take his pulse, the other to look at his tongue.

"Say 'ahhh.'"

"Knee! The only place I want you to look at is my knee!"

"It's not material, Senator. You are all-over indisposed. You must undergo a course of physic. You must take—you're a good hand at taking medicine, aren't you? (Faintly: "No.") Yes, you must take a course of antimonials to alter your blood."

"And a vomit agent—to clean your stomach."

"Doctors!" exclaimed Maclay, "I beg leave to observe that I am well circumstanced in my body, both as to urine and blood. My knee, Gentlemen, my knee! Look at it, flayed with blisterings though it be! Here is my great pain!"

"Poultice it with Indian mush. We will send you some stuff to put on the poultice—"

"—and the antimonial wine, and the drops."

"And the laudanum to make you vomit. We will order your medicines and send them by a runner. Good evening, Senator."

Clymer visit actually was on the following day.

To a gentleman entering the door as they were leaving, the doctors chorused, "Good evening to you, Congressman Clymer."

Senator Maclay glared at their backs and growled to his visitor, "Antimonial wine! Laudanum! I'm not taking any of that!"

"Oh, but Senator Maclay, you should, you must. In a few days, the House will send the Susquahanna bill to the Senate and we shall need you there to counter Morris. He has some mysterious scheme brewing. Oh, he is up to no good—he will ruin us all yet! He hates Susquehanna!"

"Take my mind off my knee, Clymer—tell me what is going on. When will the house vote on Susquehanna?"

"We adjourned again today without voting—now, don't get upset! We had voted Thursday to let Madison have his say, and he talked more than two hours yesterday. It was the same story we have heard many times and know by heart, only much more stretched out. I've heard him speak better. He must have been up all night working on his speech. His logic—well, one sentence came out like this: 'Anybody who looks at a map,' he said, 'would confirm that if the Potomac is not the geographical center, it is because the Susquehanna is LESS so!'

History of Congress, House Journal, Sept. 4, 1789

"Oh, he's wearing himself out trying to hold us down," said Maclay.

"The only new thing he said was that the place where the seat is located will benefit by $500,000 a year in commerce! Then Daniel Carroll of Georgetown threw in something of interest. He said the canal-building on the Potomac is nearly finished for bypassing the falls in the river. President Washington's Potomac Company is ready to sink the lock seats and insert the frames. In a little time, he said, there'll be nothing to obstruct the descent of produce to tidewater.

"But all such talk never slowed the rise in the Susquehanna tide. Fisher Ames talked as long as Madison and cut down every argument—even the feet and inches lengths of the two rivers and God knows how many creeks. All of this was to make the Susquehanna look good and the Potomac look bad."

"This is good medicine for my knee," Maclay said, managing a feeble smile.

"But Madison is very insistent, you know. He jumped right up with another amendment. 'Insert Potomac in the motion so it says Susquehanna AND Potomac!' he said. 'That will enable us to take more time comparing the two!'"

"I will need a poultice on my head if this keeps up," groaned Maclay.

"Don't worry," soothed Clymer. "That motion lost, too. Today there was only desultory talk. The Potomac looks to be on its way out of the race entirely. On Monday, the end of this tale can be told!"

A chagrined Senator Morris visits ailing Senator Maclay in his rooming house to puzzle over the astonishing events of the day in the House of Representatives. The Northeast men reneged on their promise to nominate Morris's Falls of the Delaware for permanant capital, but instead nominated Maclay's Susquehanna River! "Well," Morris said, "I suppose you are gratified." Maclay answered cooly, "I could not be dissatisfied."

Across shallow, rock-strewn Susquehanna River near its entrance into Chesapeake Bay, a slender, easy-to-maneuver ferry makes its hazardous way. In September 1789, the House of Representatives voted to locate the permanant capital on this primarily Pennsylvania river. Northeast members and some Southern sympathizers carried the vote, frustrating Robert Morris's deal for Falls of the Delaware. Fellow Senator Maclay, Morris's rival and a Susquehanna resident, was delighted.

CHAPTER 14

Tripping Up the Susquehanna

SCENE 1
VIRGINIA SNARE

PLACE: House of Representatives, Federal Hall, New York City
TIME: Monday, September 7, about 11 a.m.

Hist.Congress, House Journal (Gales/Seaton) p 919-20, 1789, and Jan. 15, 1790 (discussion of reporters' presence in the House)

All of the House action from the reporters' records. Hist.Congress, House Journal, (Gales/Seaton) Sept.7, 1789.

Newspaper editor and reporter John Fenno entered the House chamber by the side door that connected with the clerks' offices. He sat down in the first chair at a long table where other reporters had settled against a wainscoted wall near the Speaker's platform.

The interested public had sat for an hour squeezed into the seats just inside the main entrance to the chamber. In the two galleries hanging above them, nearly all seats were occupied by distinguished visitors, officials, and friends and relatives of the House members. They conversed discreetly.

For many of them, this was the fourth day they had come expecting to hear the House vote finally and conclusively on the resolution to name Susquehanna River for the permanent capital, and (more important to the local audience) New York for the temporary capital.

Speaker Muhlenberg and his gavel called for order, the minutes of the last meeting, and other routine matters. Visitors quieted, settled themselves. Congressmen broke off their greetings, small talk, and plans of strategy—all just in time for the Speaker's call for the first order of business.

Richard Bland Lee, his large handkerchief and his handful of papers waving violently, gained the floor. "Mr. Speaker! I wish to amend the resolution locating the seat of government on the river Susquehanna. I wish to replace Susquehanna with north bank of the river Potomac, in the state of Maryland!"

A rumble that mixed groans with sighs arose. "So today we will hear repeats of the Thursday, Friday, and Saturday speeches and votes," grumbled reporter Fenno. "Oh these undaunted, talky Virginians and their Potomac."

Mr. Fenno, a Boston innkeeper's son, ex-importer, ex-school teacher, wrote down words and actions in his own personal shorthand. The account would appear in the *Gazette of the United States,* a two-times a week newspaper started in April with the financial support of Alexander Hamilton and friends.

Beside Fenno at the table, seven other reporters, all expecting big news at last, rapidly scratched their inked quills on paper for New York's *Daily Advertiser, Packet, Journal,* and *Daily Gazette* as well as the *Congressional Register,* and newspapers in Boston and Philadelphia. Suddenly they reached for their score sheets. A rollcall on Lee's motion!

Before Fenno could identify the man who demanded a vote, the clerk was calling names. "Ames!" (no response) "Baldwin!" (Yea!)

Fenno grabbed his scoresheet.

As the rollcall neared its end— "Vining!" (Yea!) "Wadsworth!" (Nay!) "Wynkoop!" (Nay!) Fenno felt a light tap on his shoulder and heard a familiar

The Press and America (E/M Emery) p79

N. Y. City in 1789 (T. E. V. Smith) p208-13

Daily Newspaper in America (A.M.Lee)

Standing on the House floor to listen by a doorway was probably permitted since even in the "secret session" Senate it was allowed. See George Turberville letter to J. Madison, Jan. 20, 1790, Madison Papers

voice speaking low, close to his ear. "What's the vote for, John?"

"Mr. Hamilton, Sir!" Fenno whispered, turning to look at his employer who stood at his elbow in the half-open doorway beside him. "Oh, it's the Virginians again, trying to put Potomac in the place of Susquehanna. The count is (he quickly looked down his list) 21 for Potomac, 29 against, about as usual."

"That means," whispered Hamilton, "that the Pennsylvanians came on time this morning and are sticking with the Northeast men. It appears that the deal we've put together will hold fast. Excellent, excellent. I don't care where they put the permanent capital as long as Congress stays in New York a few more years.

"Ah! Good morning Mr. Childs! Mr. Greenleaf! Mr. McLean, Mr. Loudon!" Hamilton spoke very fast, very low, one hand shielding his lips as he leaned to pass his glance down Press Row. "I see we have a full house on Press Row for this dramatic occasion," he murmured to Fenno. "We now hear John Vining of Delaware opening the Local Pride Hour—'the humble claim of Delaware' he's saying, and soon he will reveal that his home town of Wilmington is possessed of eminent superiority as to salubrity of air and fertility of soil for a federal city! I leave you to scratch these words on paper as many times as there are speakers with home towns!" He leaned forward again to bid the row of reporters, "Good day, sirs." Their quills scratched and dipped even while they smiled and threw appreciative glances at the rather small, handsome, dark-blue-eyed young man with auburn hair.

"Oh, Mr. Hamilton!" John Fenno called to him just before the door closed. "Will you be back?" he whispered. "I must confide in you a matter—but the speech at hand—excuse me—"

Hamilton nodded, chin uptilted, a pleasant smile on his fair, almost rosy face. "Later," he mouthed, and was gone.

Wilmington had its vote and failed to dislodge Susquehanna—an event that brought Mr. Boudinot of New Jersey to his feet to deliver a tirade against that river. "I am surprised," he said, "that so many gentlemen have been led astray! Susquehanna has no advantages—secluded from the world, no main roads, a river abounding in rocks, falls, and shoals, insuperable obstructions to a connection with western waters, sterile soil, unhealthy from flooding, then vast quantities of stagnant water, whence proceed noxious exhalations, the cause of a long catalogue of disease—no wonder there's hardly a soul living out there!"

He wanted to strike "Susquehanna" and insert "Potomac." Once more, in a quick vote, the Northeast and Pennsylvania stuck together and defeated Boudinot and the Southerners.

Boudinot, back on his feet, scowled and threw one last javelin: "Strike Susquehanna! Insert Falls of the Delaware—either side of the river!" A groan mixed with laughter led off the rollcall.

"Nay! Nay! Nay!" 46 times! Only Gerry of Massachusetts, loyal to the "cow-pasture" site more convenient to Boston, despite the shadow of powerful, rich Morris hanging over it, voted "Yea" with the three New Jersey men.

Ten minutes later, the reporters' quills were checking off rollcall after rollcall. The Virginia dam of speeches built up on Thursday, Friday, and Saturday to hold back voting on Susquehanna might be on the brink of crumbling with a final vote bursting through.

The newsmen whispered back and forth: "Who was the man wanting 'east bank' changed to 'both banks?'" "Sounded like Michael Stone of Maryland." "Why would he be so interested in the WEST bank of the Susquehanna?" "Maybe his wife's hometown is there." "Well, he won it by one vote."

"But he's up again! He wants more—he wants to insert 'or Maryland' after 'Susquehanna in Pennsyl-

Hist. Congress, House Journal, Sept. 7, 1789 (Gales/Seaton)

vania.'" "Maybe he owns land where the river crosses 10 miles of Maryland to enter Chesapeake Bay." "Ah. He lost."

"Ha! the Virginians are beginning to move again! Did you hear that? Lee and Page talking back and forth on the Floor as if they were at the dinner table—'Don't you think it would be better if we include ONLY the permanent residence in this resolution, Sir?' 'Yes, Sir, that's a good idea, Sir—I so move—'"

"Look at that—he lost by only three votes! A scare for the New Yorkers!"

"Another jolt for them—John Vining of Delaware wants to throw out New York and put in Wilmington for the temporary seat! But—21 to 30—easy win for New York."

"What's this?—a Virginia man, Josiah Parker, moving to replace New York with PHILADELPHIA?? That puts both permanent and temporary capitals in Pennsylvania! What are those Virginians up to?"

"OHHH—these tricky Southerners! They're setting a trap! I hope Hamilton returns in time for the fun—my bet is the Pennsylvania men won't turn greedy, reneg on New York, and jump into this trap. But listen to the sweet song Mr. Lee of Virginia is singing!"

"How well we have fared in this fair city of New York!" sang Lee. "It possesses every convenience and accommodation! I am strongly impressed in favor of its inhabitants—their urbanity and industry do honor to America! So strongly do I feel this, nothing but a sense of duty can induce me to vote for STRIKING New York as the temporary seat of government and inserting PHILADELPHIA in its place!"

(Fenno to the *Daily Advertiser:*) "He's smiling while he sets the trip stick in his trap."

"I flatter myself that by naming Philadelphia," Mr. Lee's song continued, "proper regard is paid to the great principles of centrality. CENTRALITY Phila-

delphia possesses in a great degree. In addition, its conveniences and accommodations are equal if not superior to what New York presents. Philadelphia's public buildings are, I believe, at our command. The inhabitants are industrious, temperate, and frugal. In short, every principle operating in favor of Susquehanna as a PERMANENT residence applies with equal or more force in favor of Philadelphia as a TEMPORARY seat of government!"

(*Philadelphia Advertiser* to *The Gazette:*) "My God, that's the first kind word I've heard a Southerner say about Philadelphia since the soldiers cornered the Congress in '83! Strange things are going on here!"

(*New York Journal* to *Boston Globe,* three minutes later:) "What's your tally? I make out that all the southern states, plus Delaware and New Jersey went for Philadelphia—22 votes—but Northeast and Pennsylvania didn't part company in face of temptation—29 votes for New York."

(*Globe* to *Gazette:*) "Oh, but FIVE of those 29 were SOUTHERN! FIVE Southerners couldn't swallow Philadelphia! Two from South Carolina, two from Maryland, one from Virginia! If they had voted with their Southern brothers, Philadelphia would have WON 27 to 24!"

(Philadelphia to Boston:) "What an uproar! Everybody talking! I'll bet Mr. Madison is wringing his hands—who was the Virginian who voted for New York? Mr. Bland? He's probably a plantation owner with a lot of slaves, and hates Philadelphia on account of the Quakers pestering him every day to emancipate."

"But the big news is," broke in Fenno of the *Gazette,* "the Pennsylvania men didn't kick their New York deal, jump off, and vote for Philadelphia! It must have looked devilish tempting—both temporary and permanent seats in Pennsylvania!"

"Yes, but—" replied the *New York Journal,* "had they betrayed and shattered their Northeast strong-

Hist. Congress, House Journal Sept. 7

hold of votes, in the future they could turn only to the South—and you know what place on what river THEY'RE after for the permanant seat!"

Fenno suddenly exclaimed, "Oh, Mr.Hamilton! You're back! Did you hear what happened?"

"Yes! I talked to Senator Morris in the lobby outside the House door. Wynkoop had just told him that Goodhue of Massachusetts rushed to warn the Pennsylvania men that Lee's motion was a trap. If they took the bait and jumped to Philadelphia, that would end trust and alliance with the Northeast—which would then seek an alliance with the South. Potomac and New York would win, for sure—Pennsylvania would get nothing! Only one Philadelphian—Heister—ignored the warning!"

Speaker Muhlenberg's heavy gavel and voice sounded again and again. "The House MUST come to order! Those in the public space and galleries—SILENCE, PLEASE, or I shall have to clear the areas!" He waited a few seconds. "Will the clerk read the resolution as amended."

"Resolved," the clerk read rapidly, "that the permanent seat of the Government of the United States ought to be on some convenient place on the banks of the river Susquehanna, in the state of Pennsylvania; and that, until the necessary buildings be erected for the purpose, the seat of government ought to continue in the city of New York."

"VOTE! VOTE!"

"All in favor, say 'YEA'! (A chorus) Those opposed, 'NAY!' (An equal chorus) The clerk will call the roll!"

With the last name, the public and the galleries, all of whom had avidly kept score, broke into applause and cheers, drowning out the clerk's announcement of 28 for Susquehanna and New York, 22 against.

"When Bland of Virginia didn't answer to his name in the rollcall," Hamilton whispered to Fenno, "I knew Madison and Lee had severely reprimanded

All the debate details from History of Congress, House Jour. Sept. 7 (Gales/Seaton)

him. He probably left in a huff."

Fenno responded only with, "We've won, Mr. Hamilton, we've won! It's Susquehanna and New York!"

Hamilton shook a forefinger at him, saying, "We're winning, but we haven't won, my friend. It's a horse race of 10 laps, and we're only in lap six—or less. The Speaker just ordered this resolution drawn up as a bill!

"As you know, a bill waits until it's on the House schedule to be picked over, gnawed on, argued through THRICE! If the final vote is 'yea,' and the bill at last goes to the Senate, the wildest imagination could not predict what will happen to it there. But that's about two weeks away. Now—what was it you needed to tell me? Speak up, John. Everybody's talking and only I can hear what you say."

"Sir, I can't keep the Gazette and myself going with the money I take in from subscriptions. I have 632 now—paying ones—which don't include those I send out, as you instructed, to the newspapers in various states for republishing. I haven't enough money to buy paper for our Saturday edition. I haven't paid my September rent, and I will have to pay a midwife next week when my wife expects to be confined."

"Come by my office, John, after today's session. Sending this newspaper—the voice of George Washington's government—to the presses of the country is essential. I'll call on benevolence and patriotism to help me keep the *Gazette*, and you, going."

"Thank you, Mr. Hamilton. There's some other news, or rumor, to mention, Sir. I heard from various people this morning that the President is about to appoint you Secretary of the Treasury."

Hamilton gave a short laugh. "I've heard that, too. But hold on to it as a rumor until the President has spoken."

"I'm honored to obey, Mr. Secretary."

Journalism in the U.S. (F.Hudson)

Hist. of Printing in America (I. Thomas)

N.Y.City in 1789 (Smith)

Fenno took up his quill as another rollcall vote began. The *New York Journal* whispered that Maryland was trying to tack on an amendment to a resolution allowing commissioners to borrow $100,000 for the federal city."The amendment says Pennsylvania must clear Susquehanna's channel BEFORE work can begin on building a capital."

"Ah ha!" murmured Hamilton when Fenno passed the news to him. "The Southerners would tie an iron weight around the bill's neck!" Minutes later, 24 Southerners and sympathizers said "Yea!" but 25 Northeastern and Pennsylvania men said "Nay!"

Hamilton whispered that it would have been a tie if Bland of Virginia had been on hand to vote. "He disappeared after voting against the Philadelphia trap—remember? But even with a tie, the Speaker from Pennsylvania would have voted like a Pennsylvanian—'Nay!'"

SCENE 2
FATAL "YEA" FOR SUSQUEHANNA

PLACE: New Fraunces Tavern, 49 Cortlandt St. near Broadway, thence on foot across Manhattan and up the East side to the President's mansion on Cherry Street.
TIME: Tuesday, September 22, 2 p.m. to 3:30.

"Josiah! You've finally arrived!" Congressman Elias Boudinot greeted his friend stepping out of the Boston stagecoach.

History of Travel in America (S.Dunbar)

"Only two hours late," replied Bailey, a jaunty, gray-haired merchant just short of 50 like Boudinot. "We've been bouncing and jostling since three this morning—and indeed from three until 10 at night for five days. I am sore all over!"

While they waited for the trunks and boxes to be handed down from the coach top, Bailey rubbed his neck, stretched, exercised his shoulders, and joined passenger-talk of potholes, stumbling horses, dust, heat, rain beating in, poor inns, bad food, and (as they walked away) fellow travelers they hoped they never met again.

Bailey, a Boston merchant engaged in exporting, was eager to know from Boudinot if New York would keep the seat of government and the commerce that went with it, and for how long. "What has happened, Elias? It seems I've spent a year bumping about in that coach, cut off from all the world."

They followed a porter carrying Bailey's wooden trunk by shoulder to a large room on the second floor of the inn. "So far," said Boudinot, "New York will be the temporary seat—meaning perhaps four, perhaps 10 years depending on construction speed, which depends on money flow. Tomorrow, the Senate begins gnawing on Susquehanna and New York in the House bill passed only today.

"But the big news is, the President has appointed Hamilton Secretary of the Treasury! The House has charged him to draw up in 90 days an economic plan that will bring the government—and country—credit and cash."

Odd Destiny: Alexander Hamilton (Marie Hecht)

"Excellent! Excellent! and Congress must work fast," Josiah said. "Massachusetts is near another crisis as bad as Shays' Rebellion three years ago."

"Let's get you settled," Boudinot said, "then I'll give you some details of the two-week tussle in the House about where Congress will sit. The porter has put your trunk by the middle bed in the common snoreroom—one, two—eight beds. This will have to do for one night, Josiah, for I could find no other. But tomorrow, a bed in my rooming house will be available.

"With Congress still in session, even the most expensive rooming houses are full. Six dollars a week for bed and board! Meals at set hours, everybody at one table! As soon as Congress adjourns in

N.Y.City in 1789 (T.E.V.Smith)

GW's America (Tebbel)

a few days—I hope—you can have your pick of rooms at half-price.

"Now fast as you can, clean up, dress up, and we'll hurry to the President's Tuesday afternoon reception. I thought you'd like that. (Yes, Yes!!) I want to bid President Washington goodbye before I go home, and I'd like to hear the talk about the House action today.

"We have a mile to walk to Cherry Street—far enough for me to relate what I was doing this past week when you were enduring 200 or so miles in a stagecoach."

"Start now, Eli, while I change clothes. How close is the final, final vote?" Josiah said. "You said New York and Susquehanna are still firm? How did that happen? The Virginians haven't given up, have they?"

Hist.Cong., House Journ. (Gales/Seaton) *Sept.22*

"The final, final vote?" Boudinot laughed. "I wonder if it will ever happen. But today, the House voted 'Yea' its third and final time for New York and Susquehanna—PROVIDED Susquehanna is first cleared for navigation!"

"Cleared for navigation?" asked Josiah, puzzled. "How—why—did they require that?" He stopped his sponge bath from a small tin pan of cold water to hear the answer.

"Move faster, old friend, or we'll be too late to see the President. Suffice it to say that I had quite a bit to do with the navigation clause—and I'll tell you how, but later.

"To finish today's story, the Speaker sent a clerk running upstairs to take the bill to the Senate. Four days from now—on Saturday—Congress is supposed to adjourn. If the Senate changes a single word in a House bill, it must be sent back to the House for another vote. I predict that Robert Morris will change quite a few words, and the Southern Senators will try to change more. Time will run out and that will be the end of Susquehanna. Come, Josiah, button your coat while we walk the stairs.

We must be on our way—the President's door is closed at 3:15 exactly!"

Josiah Bailey was worried. He said nothing until they had passed the noisy tavern of the inn, greeted Mrs. Fraunces who was managing the business while her husband served the President, and turned left on Cortlandt Street, then crossed Broadway.

"Elias, if this bill dies," Josiah blurted, "New York loses the temporary seat, doesn't it?"

"Josiah," Boudinot laughed, "Susquehanna will die, but New York will still have the seat for at least one more year!"

Bailey, frowning, said he hoped the bill would win on a quick vote in Senate, so that New York would be secure for more than a year.

Shaking his head, Boudinot answered, "It is certain that this bill will die. Morris will kill it. Let me now tell you the story of Susquehanna's navigation. I have seen the Susquehanna, and I can tell you, as I have told the House, it is shallow and rocky and cannot be made a navigable river.

"Last Thursday, the seventeenth that was, when the bill embodying a House resolution for Susquehanna and New York arrived on the House Floor, I chaired the Committee of the Whole to discuss it. Right away, young George Gale of Maryland's Eastern Shore, who knows that river better than I, once more moved to require clearing Susquehanna's channel from the 10-mile square to Chesapeake Bay—and for BIG SHIPS! He had tried two weeks ago to sink Susquehanna with this weight, and failed by two votes.

"Now he was trying again, with Southerners again making long, logical speeches in support.

"How the Pennsylvanians fussed! 'Can't you be satisfied with canoes or just large boats?' they said." Boudinot and Bailey stopped to have a good laugh.

"Then they accused George Gale of asking for the clearing in order to divert the capital's trade from Philadelphia to Baltimore. 'No,' said Gale. 'I

Private Affairs of GW (Lear/Decatur)

N.Y.City in 1789 (Smith)

Hist.Cong. House Journ., *Sept.17* (Gales/ Seaton)

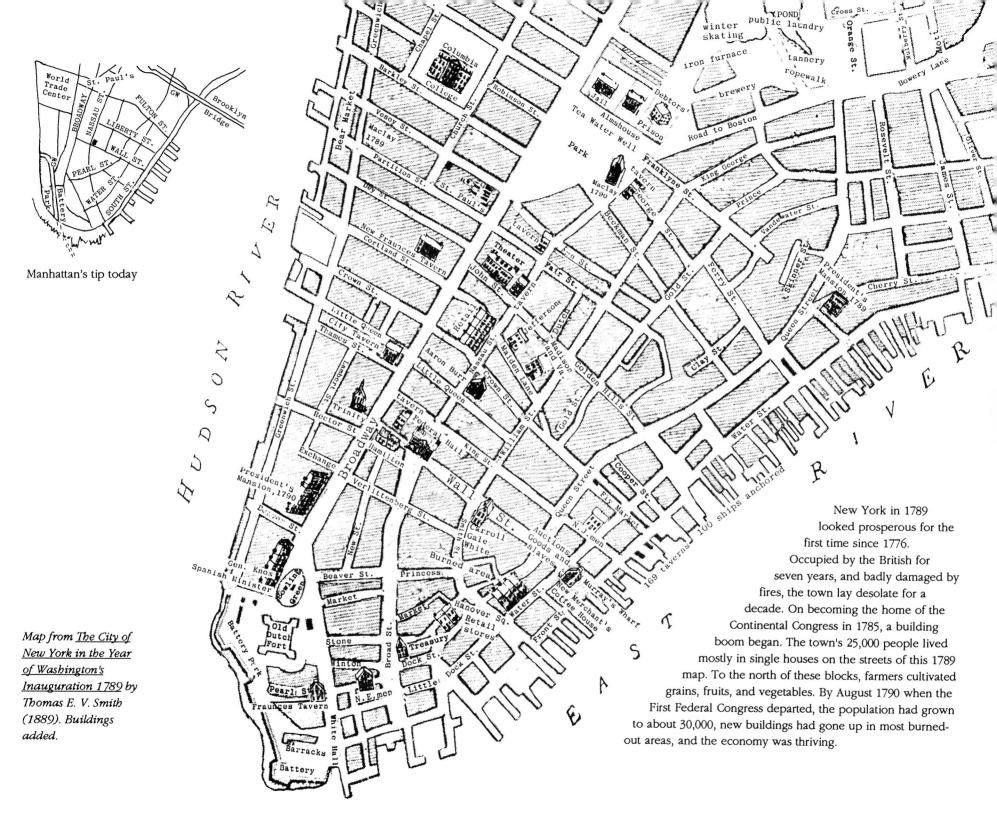

Manhattan's tip today

Map from The City of New York in the Year of Washington's Inauguration 1789 by Thomas E. V. Smith (1889). Buildings added.

New York in 1789 looked prosperous for the first time since 1776. Occupied by the British for seven years, and badly damaged by fires, the town lay desolate for a decade. On becoming the home of the Continental Congress in 1785, a building boom began. The town's 25,000 people lived mostly in single houses on the streets of this 1789 map. To the north of these blocks, farmers cultivated grains, fruits, and vegetables. By August 1790 when the First Federal Congress departed, the population had grown to about 30,000, new buildings had gone up in most burned-out areas, and the economy was thriving.

asked for it because I doubt the Susquehanna can EVER be cleared! Congress should know BEFORE it seats itself there!'

"Well, the vote was a tie. I, in the Chair, had to break it. I voted 'yea' to REQUIRE clearing that unclearable river, thus giving Morris the best of reasons to attack the bill in the Senate. The House vote affirmed our Committee vote. Now Morris will get the Senate to kill it.

"But New York will live in the next bill, too! Morris will do political acrobatics to replace Susquehanna with Falls of the Delaware. If he and the Northeast make a deal, New York stays in their bill. The South will counter with Potomac. To win, they also need Northeast votes—so New York would necessarily be in THEIR bill, too."

"I hope you're right," said Josiah earnestly. "I've been thinking of asking a New York lady to marry me, in which case I'd move here."

"Ah! One more excellent reason why both Pennsylvania and Potomac men should agree to New York for the temporary seat! Good luck, Josiah, in both love and business."

N.Y.City in 1789
(T.E.V.Smith)

"This town could amount to something," Bailey said, "if only the temporary capital stayed here several years. It's not urban like Boston even though Boston has only half as many people. Look at those hogs running loose in the middle of the street, dogs chasing them. Such barking! Lord! they almost knocked down the man carrying milk cans on his shoulder yoke!"

After watching that drama's favorable end, Boudinot said, "I'm told that more hogs live in this town's streets than people in its houses. Hogs are New York's garbage department. Without them we could not bear the stench."

They crossed Nassau Street where Cortlandt became Maiden Lane, and passed a droopy horse hitched to a wagon loaded with barrels. "Fresh, clean drinking water from Tea Water Pump! Cask or gallon!" shouted a youth in wooden shoes, a shapeless shirt, and knee pants.

"Chimblies swept!" shouted two men with sooty faces and twig brooms. "Fresh clams, five for a penny!" "Roasted corn!" cried sidewalk cooks. Bailey, very hungry, cut his eyes at them, but thought of his fine clothes and the President's reception.

"New York is still like a big village," the Boston visitor said. "So many houses sit apart in the middle of a yard—and when I was here last, I walked three or four blocks north of this street and came to farmland. It will take many years of prosperity to change it into a neat town like Boston. The British occupation ruined New York. Having the new federal government here for six months has begun to revive it. Ah! Elias, I smell the Fly Market! Perhaps we'll find apples—I am faint with hunger."

GW's America (JW
Tebbel)

Maiden Lane angled into Crown Street and absorbed it. Two blocks more and the Fly Market stalls in the middle of the street separated two throngs of people, carts, horses, boxes, crates of chickens, rabbits, ducks, and geese. Smells of horse manure mixed with aromas from apples, bunches of dried herbs, wild grapes, and flowers, hanging smoked hams and strings of hot sausages.

Both men bought an apple to eat on the way to the President's house—no food offered at receptions. "Our driver stopped for 15 minutes at six o'clock this morning," Bailey said, "and kept going until we arrived here at two."

With Bailey biting off great mouthfuls, they turned north on Queen Street leading to Cherry. "In April, I walked with Washington on this street," Boudinot said, "a most thrilling hour. We had just arrived on the new, beautifully decorated barge that brought him, and a group of us in Congress, from Elizabeth Town, my home town in Jersey. This was the final hour of his week-long journey from Virginia after his election. All around us sailed hundreds of boats,

GW arrival derived
from Boudinot letter to
his wife, Apr.24, 1789
and N.Y.City in 1789
(T.E.V.Smith) accounts
from newspapers.

sloops, and big five-masters decked out in all their naval ornaments. Two with choruses of ladies and gentlemen drew close and odes written for the President were sung.

"I could see he was greatly affected, although one might wonder how he could be after a week of adulation on the way from Mount Vernon. At Murray's Wharf near the foot of Wall Street where we landed, and along Queen leading to his mansion, tens of thousands of people stood as thick as ears of corn before the harvest. Hats waved like a field of grain in the wind. He had chosen to walk, but troops exerting themselves with staves had difficulty making passage for us through the pressing crowd. Many people had tears running down their cheeks as they gazed at this man. They seemed incapable of being satisfied, of having enough of looking at him. Some later said his arrival thrilled them more than the inaugural procession or balcony scene later, because they had been able to get close to him."

Boudinot and Bailey had slowed down, then stopped, absorbed in the scene the words evoked. "I wish to God I could have been here," Bailey exclaimed.

"Good heavens!" Boudinot exclaimed. "It must be three o'clock! We must make haste! We are still some blocks from Cherry Street. While we walk, I'll complete the tale of our tussling over the location of the capital.

Hist.Cong., House Journ. (Gales/Seaton) Sept.18

"The day after the navigation vote, Mr. Madison gave us a surprise. You might think nothing new could be devised to block the path of this bill. You don't know how busy Mr. Madison's mind stays. During an hour or so, he held the Floor and constructed for us, with logical brick and legal mortar, a Constitutional wall against naming a temporary seat, particularly one located in New York!

"Well, you know, Josiah, Madison's draft of a Constitution provided the framework for the Con-

vention debates. Everybody acknowledges that he is an astute and thorough scholar who is certain he perceives 'truth' and is able to trace it through long mazes without losing sight of it. He lays his thoughts out clearly, sometimes eloquently. He wrote Washington's inaugural speech, it's said, and we all know he wrote Congress's response to that speech, and Washington's response to that! As a speaker, he is agreeable to listen to—sweet-voiced, even-tempered. He speaks softly—too softly in our cathedral-size House—and slowly, with convincing logic for many, though I often disagree with him.

J.Madison (Brant) J.Madison (Ketcham)

"I think he persuaded quite a few members that naming New York temporary was unconstitutional! He said that, since the President was forbidden to have any say about when or to what place Congress adjourned, a law NAMING a place was unconstitutional—because the President had to SIGN the law for it to become effective! New York, in any case was unacceptable since the 'Principles' Congress adopted called for 'centrality' even for the temporary, and New York was not central!

Hist.Cong. House Journ. Sept. 18 (Gales/ Seaton)

"A lot of talk went on about Constitutionality and held off the vote for FOUR days!—which was the prime purpose. We knew that, if in the process, New York were knocked out, Northeast men would abandon the Susquehanna. They don't love that river. Young Lee, Daniel Carroll, and noisy Jackson of Georgia spoke again and again, lengthily, to impress us with how convinced they were that Madison was right. Fisher Ames and John Lawrence—Massachusetts and New York—told us several times how UNconvinced they were. Finally, the vote. The Southerners lost 23 to 29!"

Sept.18, 19,

20, 21

Sept.22

They were turning from Queen Street into Cherry Street, and could see the carriages and horses lining the sidewalks near the President's house. Bailey, wiping his hands with his handkerchief, asked, "Which side did you vote with, Elias?"

"The Southerners—the losers—just as I voted

today. Why so surprised Josiah? I was voting against Susquehanna—an abominable place for a capital city. In the Senate, Morris will strangle it with Falls of the Delaware, both banks—my state and his state. And New York will keep the capital a few years. So be of good cheer, Josiah, be of good cheer! Especially since I see Robert Morris himself alighting from his grand carriage at the President's door."

Bailey, excited by the scene and intrigued by the glimpse Boudinot had given him into the behind-the-vote twists and turns, exclaimed, "I'm curious to see how cordially Morris and the President greet each other after all this Potomac-Falls of Delaware rivalry."

Private Affairs of GW
(Lear/Decatur)

In a moment, Congressman Boudinot was greeting Senator Morris, introducing his Boston friend Josiah Bailey, and walking with them into the President's front door. A doorman led them into the reception room, empty of furniture, full of Gentlemen, and alive with voices.

The President, dressed in a black velvet suit, white shirt with ruffles at the front and wrists, satin waistcoat, black silk hose, silver knee and shoe buckles, stood on the far side of the room facing the door. One hand rested on the white leather scabbard of his dress sword; the other helped secure a tricorn under his arm. He was making a stiff bow to a visitor, speaking a few words to him before looking to the next in line.

In his turn, Boudinot bowed and greeted Washington, eliciting a benevolent smile and response. Then the President smiled broadly, his lips closed tightly against his false teeth, at the beaming, round face of Robert Morris, his much esteemed family friend, his rich and powerful political supporter, and the reliable, faithful provider of supplies, munitions, and money for the Revolutionary Army.

Each asked avidly after the health of the wife and children of the other, travel plans when Congress adjourned, and expectations of dining together on Thursday. As Morris moved on, the President turned a left-over smile on stranger Bailey.

At 3:15 o'clock, sharp, the outside door had been closed. When the last visitor in line had left the President, he strode slowly around the room, speaking personally to each man—mostly members of Congress today—for a minute or two.

Bailey, standing with Boudinot, Morris, Senators King of New York, and Bassett of Delaware, watched the President out of the corner of an eye, while listening to the subdued but intense voice of Morris. He was relating what he had learned from Pennsylvania House members about the "clear the Susquehanna" amendment. As he talked, his expression looked more angry and disgusted. The volume of his voice rose steadily. The last, loudest sentence rode over 40 other voices.

Derived from Maclay's
Journ. Sept. 22,23

"By God, I never will vote for the bill unless that proviso is thrown out!!"

In the sudden silence, President Washington turned slightly, head raised, but did not look across the room at his friend. He slowly turned back, leaning a little forward to continue his conversation.

Senator Morris, cheeks flaming in his plump face, smiled, and said, very softly, "One way or another, I will locate that seat of government where I want it—you'll see!"

A gentleman who looks remarkably like Robert Morris glares at a garrulous politician in this cartoon of the time. The occasion and place might well be the President's mansion during a Tuesday afternoon weekly reception.

On the same day that Senator Maclay realized Senator Morris had smouldering plans to send up in smoke Susquehanna's chance to win the capital, a hot air balloon during a grand exhibition did go up in smoke and flames. Congress adjourned early and members rushed to the racetrack to watch the newest advance in travel. Maclay saw the balloon's fiery end as a sign of Susquehanna's coming fate in the Senate.

150

CHAPTER 15

Two Rivers Go Up In Smoke

SCENE 1
FLAMING BALLOON—PORTENT OF DISASTER?

PLACE: Gallery outside the Senate Chamber, and on to the Race
Track out Nassau Street to Bowery Lane.
TIME: Wednesday afternoon, September 23.

All the scene reflects
Maclay's Jour. Sept.23;
newspaper descriptions
of the balloon event the
same day, reprinted in
Washington After the
Revolution
(W.S.Baker); and
descriptions in The
Eagle Aloft (Tom
Crouch)

With a cry for adjournment to see Deeker's hot air balloon released to fly, the Senate was leaving early. A half-mile out Nassau Street behind Federal Hall, and a mile along Bowery Lane to an empty lot on Eagle Street, the racetrack was drawing a crowd of 10,000 spectators for the exciting event.

James Deeker, unlike French balloonists, did not dare to ride on the balloon's platform. A few weeks ago the sack of hot air had sailed 15 miles in 20 minutes! Frightening! Sensational! At last men were uncovering the secrets of transporting themselves above the earth!

Just outside the Senate chamber, Senators Robert Morris, tall and heavy, and William Maclay, taller and thin, moved slowly across the picture gallery at the head of the stairs. They stopped and started between outbursts of hot words. Other Senators stopped and started with them, watching intently.

MORRIS: "Don't YOU tell ME that I am risking the state's chance to get the seat of government! YOU are the stubborn risker! Your golden goose will be dead in 24 hours if you persist in keeping the proviso for Susquehanna channel clearing! I told you an hour ago—and our House members told you—that ALL Pennsylvania delegates have agreed to vote for Susquehanna IF the Senate strikes the proviso and sends the bill back to the House! BUT—if the Senate keeps the proviso, we will go

for Falls of the Delaware and Germantown!"

MACLAY: "You're EXAGGERATING! I heard one of our Pennsylvania men tell you 'no!'"

MORRIS: "NO MATTER! New York's men also agreed, and New England is friendly. I asked you to join us, and I gave the Senate a good reason for striking the proviso—but what do you do?! YOU rush out to find a copy of some old law, wave it around in the Senate, make me out a liar—embarrass me—wreck my motion to strike the proviso!"

MACLAY: "SIR, you were—INDEED—LYING to the Senate! Your 'good reason' put our state in such a bad light—like a blackmailer—not allowing river-clearing unless Maryland allowed a Chesapeake-Delaware canal—that the Southerners had sport for an hour abusing Pennsylvania! That was intolerable! I sought to correct the picture of our state that your lie had drawn for them!"

MORRIS: "I had my information from a reliable source. That it was incorrect I was not aware—"

A strong voice with a heavy Southern accent blared at Morris's elbow.

SENATOR BUTLER, South Carolina: "AWARE!? You appear UNaware that every Senator in the chamber knew WHY you want the proviso struck! We all saw you yesterday sitting with this Senator, calling that Senator outside, following another Senator around, to do your soliciting! You don't want the Susquehanna navigable to Baltimore—cutting Philadelphia's trade! A greedy design!"

MORRIS: "What kind of design is YOURS? We know it's to talk away the time, then hit us with a motion to postpone—meaning KILL our bill—hold us off until next year when the South gets two more Senate votes—"

BUTLER (talking on top of Morris's voice): "You would barefacedly drive Congress away from Susquehanna rather than see a few barrels of flour float down a river not leading to Philadelphia!"

Virginia's Richard Henry Lee and Maryland's Charles Carroll spoke to Butler to turn him away. Maclay turned also and stepped onto the iron balcony that encircled the huge light well-lobby in the center of the building. He would descend by the left stairs, away from Morris taking the right stairs.

Senators King and Schuyler of New York, two of only four who had voted with Morris to drop the proviso, laughed. King called out, "There's enough hot air in here to raise a balloon a mile high! We should lend it to Mr.Deeker at the race track! Anyone want a ride? My carriage is on Nassau Street!"

Charles Carroll of Carrollton (EM Smith)

Senator Carroll—rich Charles Carroll of Carrollton, cousin of Congressman Daniel Carroll—caught up with Senator Maclay limping down the stairs. "Come to the show—it should be a spectacle, a diversion. My carriage is waiting on Wall Street. Is your health not improving, Mr. Maclay?"

Biog.Dict. of the Am. Congress 1774-1949

"Not fast enough, Mr. Carroll." They were the same age, 52, one majestically tall and pained by rheumatism, the other almost a foot shorter, and frail in lungs and digestion. "Good health plays no favorites, they say, but it is evident poor health does." They nodded at each other in sympathy.

The horses were trotting smartly along Nassau Street before either man spoke again.

"I suppose," Maclay finally said, "it was useless for me to show up Morris's lie."

"Probably." Carroll's thin, finely-featured face

smiled. "But satisfying," he added.

Maclay grunted. "Tomorrow, Morris will move straight-out to replace Susquehanna and New York with Falls of Delaware and Germantown."

"No, Mr. Maclay. The New Yorkers said 'no.' The best they will give him is Germantown and NEW YORK. They must have New York. He must have New Yorkers."

"And you Potomac supporters—?" asked Maclay.

"Will continue as usual. Some will pray. Some will talk a lot. Some will devise a trip-up."

"Ummf. If only Morris had left the House bill alone!" grieved Maclay. "I think the Senate would have accepted it. Tomorrow it will fall to the ground, I expect. You Potomac men—probably you specifically—will worry a postponement out of us. Next year, five North Carolina House members and two Senators will arrive and strengthen you. Add two or three Pennsylvania men noted for jumping in contrary directions, and Congress goes to the Potomac. A vote NOW would secure Susquehanna."

"Ummf. Not desirable." Senator Carroll briefly flashed a boyish smile and sidelong glance at his rheumatic companion.

Along Nassau to the Bowery racetrack, horsemen galloped past the slow-moving carriage, stirring up dust. Through glass windows, the two Senators saw streams of men, women, and children walking, riding carts or horses, heading toward the entertainment in the sky.

Carroll's driver paid the $2 entrance fee at the gate of the wooden fence surrounding the race track, and drove inside to park near a gate in a space reserved for Congress. The colorful balloon towered in the middle of the arena and pulled at its tethering ropes in the breeze. The two Senators watched the activities of Deeker and his crew readying the balloon for flight, while hundreds of paying spectators streamed past to take seats in the racetrack bleachers. The rumble of 10,000 voices

All the following balloon descriptions: The Eagle Aloft (T.D.Crouch) p64-67, 100-2

rose outside the tall wooden fence.

The varnished linen bag, tear-drop shape, was attached by cloth strips to an outer, open frame holding the sack upright. From its iron bar equator, chains equally spaced hung down to secure a platform resting on the ground seven feet below the bottom opening of the sack. A wood–burning stove with a stovepipe reaching inside a short, stiff curtain around the sack opening, was filling the sack with hot air. Tethering ropes would hold the balloon until the moment Mr. Deeker felt the full sack tugging hard, eager to fly.

Once aloft, the balloon would fly where winds pushed it, and sail as long as the hickory wood in the stove kept feeding it hot air. To the paying crowd inside the fence, and the bigger, standing crowd outside waiting for the balloon to rise like magic into the air, it was a wondrous event.

James Deeker, wearing a bright green suit and a tricorn hat was directing his helpers in packing the iron stove with hickory sticks. Sparks and smoke flew into the sack from the end of the stovepipe.

"That looks dangerous," remarked Carroll. Maclay grunted. After a minute, he asked, "Do you think the sack is 100 feet in diameter as he advertised ?"

"It's more like half that." A longer silence. "What good is it, flying high in the air?" Carroll said. "I hear that some Frenchmen have taken a ride in one and come down all right, but they could go only where the wind blew them—no control as we have with a horse. In Baltimore, a 13-year-old boy climbed in one that a fellow Carnes was exhibiting, and flew some miles until it bumped down to earth. Didn't seem to hurt him. But can it ever be more than entertainment?"

After a minute, Maclay remarked that, with quick and easy transport above the bad roads of the country and even above mountains, the seat of government could reasonably be placed in western Pennsylvania. "But probably few in Congress would ride it, even if they could guide it where they wanted to go. Too scary.

"That's one big trouble with the steamboat John Fitch keeps working on at Philadelphia," Maclay went on. "I've seen—and heard it—but I would be loath to get on it for fear of an explosion."

Carroll suddenly exclaimed, "Look at the way the balloon is swaying! The wind is up."

They silently pondered the scene. Deeker and his men stood some feet from the platform under the balloon, watching the sparks and smoke fly, getting ready to cut the tethering ropes loose.

All at once, a gust of wind jostled the balloon, drafting the stove so it blazed tongues of fire out the end of the stovepipe.

An edge of the hanging curtain flamed! Quickly the varnish on the fabric interior burst into a sheet of fire. In seconds it had burned through, and huge flames were licking at the bottom of the balloon. Rapidly it spread upward, eating yards of fabric at a burst, and giving off a thick, black smoke.

At the first flaming, Deeker and his crew had walked rapidly away, but did not run. The bleacher crowd rose with a great cry. Deeker stopped, waved his arms in the air slowly, motioning a calm message. Behind him a hundred feet, all of the balloon flamed, crackling furiously. The breeze luckily blew heat and smoke away from the bleachers. Deeker bowed, turned, and flung out an arm as if presenting the star of the show, a collapsing, burning sack.

"AHHH!" the crowd responded, and stood still.

In a moment, the show had ended, the danger of crowd panic had gone.

Senators Carroll and Maclay, who had watched with fixed attention and silent alarm, now sank back on the coach seat staring at the crowd streaming through the gate.

After a while, Maclay spoke. "It reminds me that tomorrow another great balloon will go up in smoke—-the Susquehanna. MY Susquehanna."

SCENE 2
MORRIS-MONEY FOR GERMANTOWN

PLACE: Senate Chamber, Federal Hall.
TIME: The next day, Thursday, September 24

All the scene derived from Maclay's Journ. Sept.24, 1789, and History of Congress, Senate Journal, Sept.24 (Gales/Seaton)

Limping but stately, William Maclay of Pennsylvania had come at 10:30 to begin his day's work in the Senate. At 11:30, too few members had arrived to begin business, and Maclay had once more cast a baleful eye on the chair and desk next to him. Empty. Robert Morris is always late, thought Maclay.

"But Bonny Johnny is never late," he said to himself, looking toward the canopied platform in front of the semi-circle of Senators' desks. Maclay's mouth puckered in distaste. Wigged, pink-cheeked, and plump, Mr. Adams in his fine and stylish clothes sat primly in the sofa-chair of the President of the Senate— "ever and anon dimpling his visage with the most unmeaning simper," grumbled Maclay.

More Senators began to take their places. Maclay sat with his newspaper, reading and watching over the top of it who came and who went. No one strolled over to talk to him. "It is certainly a defect in my political character," he mused, "that I cannot help embarking my passions. It has its inconveniences. But I shall not change one tittle."

He read another paragraph and looked up. There in his line of vision was the bulky figure of Robert Morris leaning over the Delaware Senators. They rose and walked off with him to the door of a committee room. Shortly, New Hampshire's Senator Langdon came out of the room. Maclay read a news column, and looked up to see Morris leading Massachusetts Senator Dalton toward the same door.

Maclay drew out his watch. Eleven forty-five. More than an hour's wait and no gavel yet. He rose, limped down the row to Maryland's seats and muttered to Charles Carroll of Carrollton, "What is going on? I see Morris running backwards and for-wards like a boy, leading out one Senator after another. Who's back there in the committee room, and for what?"

Carroll looked up with his mild, humorous smile. "The New Yorkers are meeting in that room, and have been there since 10 o'clock. It looks as if they and Morris, and anyone who can be bent their way, are putting together a deal. The man under the canopy does not see fit to call them out."

Maclay stood silently studying Mr. Adams. Shortly, Carroll murmured, "The door is opening. It appears that they're all about to come out."

Within a quarter-hour, Morris, in his chair next to Maclay's, was moving that the words "on the banks of the Susquehanna" be struck, and that only a blank be left, into which any Senator could put the name of any place he wanted.

Maclay immediately called out, "Mr.President! Mr.President!" all the while scrambling painfully to his feet and straightening. "That is NOT fair! I appeal to the Chair! Throwing out the name 'Susquehanna' in favor of a blank gives its friends no chance to vote for it, but scatters their votes to many places. The usual mode is to strike words in order to insert other words, and thus men can easily see their way clear—AND the intention of the mover!"

Adams laughed, "Heh," a mannerism very irritating to Maclay, and fumbled with his answer. "I think—I believe—I'm sure it's fair. All in favor, please stand."

Maclay looked around, counted, smiled, and said to himself, "Ha! Only seven out of 18 voted for it. But what's this? Morris is up—and saying—"

"Mr. President, I do believe that the question was not understood, and should be reconsidered. Let me explain. The fact is—" (Morris's voice rose in pitch and volume), "Pennsylvania HAS NEVER WANTED SUSQUEHANNA FOR THE SEAT OF GOVERNMENT! (A rumble of exclamations.)

"It will now give substance to that fact by offering $100,000 to place it where we DO want it, and where Congress can have jurisdiction—GERMANTOWN, suburb of PHILADELPHIA! (Loud babble of voices. The gavel banged.)

"I want to move that the blank be filled with GERMANTOWN!"

Maclay painfully scrambled to his feet again, all the time calling, "Mr. President! I appeal to the Chair! The Senator is out of order! His recent motion having drawn a minority vote, he is not eligible to make a new motion at this time!"

Adams looked from one to the other, indecision dimpling his cheeks. "Unfortunately it seems (his "heh" escaped him again) none of our rules reaches the point. The honorable gentleman from Philadelphia alleges he has new matter to present in argument. He is thus within his rights."

Morris nodded his thanks to Adams, and waited for Maclay to sit down. Looking about the handsomely columned walls, at the sun and thirteen stars painted on the ceiling, he proceeded boldly.

"Gentlemen, let us be particular about the rules. I hope some of you will move to reconsider my previous motion to strike out Susquehanna and leave a blank. In this blank, I intend to place the name of Germantown, AND Pennsylvania's offer of $100,000. No better place exists than Philadelphia for the seat of our government. But jurisdiction of the city, so suitable in buildings, accommodations, culture, and services, ought not to be taken from its 35,000 citizens and turned over to Congress in a 10-mile square of federal land.

"Yet," he went on, "all the advantages of Philadelphia—its elegance, wealth, location on a river connecting with the Atlantic, on the main road across the Alleghenies to the Ohio and Mississippi—can be available to the government by building the Capitol and the President's House on vacant land ADJOINING Philadelphia. The area around Germantown, about eight miles inland and to the north

of the State House, is most suitable.

"It will cost a sizeable amount to construct the needed buildings," Morris acknowledged. "To aid the new federal treasury, (which as yet has so little that some in Congress think it extravagant to pay members $6 a day instead of $5,) the state of Pennsylvania has offered $100,000. This it offers in appreciation for settling the seat of government in a suburb of Philadelphia."

Maclay was already struggling to his feet before Morris stopped. "Gentlemen, I believe I enjoy the confidence of Pennsylvania in as unlimited a manner as my honorable colleague. I KNOW NOTHING about any state appropriation for such a purpose! I call on my colleague to produce the authority on which he makes this offer!"

All the Senators leaned forward staring in fascination at the two Pennsylvania Senators, standing within arms length of each other, tempers afire.

Looking Maclay straight in the eye, Morris said, "While the State has not formally appropriated this money, I am certain it will if Congress accepts Germantown as the seat."

Morris then turned his gaze to the other Senators, and added, "But if for some reason the state will not, then I MYSELF WILL FIND THE MONEY!"

Astonished stares from 17 senators bore down on Robert Morris, rich and daring merchant prince.

Whispered sibilants between Connecticut's William Johnson and Massachusett's Tristram Dalton became audible in the silence.

Quickly Dalton rose, gained the Floor, looked straight at Morris, his head cocked, his smile faintly mocking, and said, "We would like to propose that the law include phrasing to say that the law will die if the money is not immediately forthcoming."

Morris leaned back, his hands clasped in front of him and replied cooly, "Words to that effect can easily be included."

"Shall we work out the motion on paper here

and now?" Dalton offered.

"I am ready," replied Morris graciously. Morris, Dalton, and at Dalton's beckon, Johnson, moved to a committee room.

Senator Bassett of Delaware rose and described the several ways he had not understood Mr. Morris's motion about replacing Susquehanna with a blank, and thought the motion should be reconsidered. "Now that it has been sufficiently, uh, explained, and since it is an inoffensive, even a fair measure, I would like to give it my support."

Maclay stared and said to himself, "You cannot trust even an intelligent man to make sense all the time. That man has told me repeatedly, of his own accord, that the Susquehanna is the only proper place for the seat."

Maclay rose to rail, and rail again, but all in vain. Susquehanna fell to a blank, 7 to 11.

Into the blank, William Grayson and Richard Henry Lee of Virginia whisked Potomac easily since Morris and advisers had not returned with their handiwork.

Maclay rose to duel the Southerners one at a time. An hour of clashing extolments of Potomac and Susquehanna, a vote, and Potomac was dragged away dead. ("This wretch Lee," Maclay said to himself, "is emaciated in person, slovenly in dress, and awkward in address. He seems the prototype of covetousness. His appearance shows no passion, property, or affection but the love of money.")

In the next minute, Maclay rose in great startlement. South Carolina's Pierce Butler had moved to put Susquehanna back into the space from which it had been thrown—without detaching Federal money to pay for land and buildings, or "Maryland and Federal money to clear the river for ships!"

Suppressed laughter suggested to Maclay that Butler might be poking fun at him. "The others snicker," he thought, "knowing I am a state commissioner long charged with clearing Susque-

Maclay p161

*Maclay's Journal
(introduction)*

hanna—and no money to do the job. Federal money would be a godsend! Joke or not, I will save my vote for Susquehanna." He hurriedly seconded Butler's motion.

Suddenly, there was Morris rushing from the committee room waving a paper and shouting, "NO, NO, Mr. President! My motion for Germantown is ahead of any other motion!"

"NO, NO!" shouted Butler. "MY motion is first! Yours is in your hand! Your earlier speech wasn't a proper motion—and had no second!"

"That is not a good reason," Morris shouted back, "and I have no need for a good reason—I have enough votes on hand to vote you down!"

New Yorker Rufus King gained the floor and moved that, for the sake of order, the question be settled by a vote. "I move to postpone Susquehanna to last!" Postponement won.

"Now," said Morris, "now for my—our—motion to fill the blank replacing Susquehanna in the House bill. I move to fill the blank with these words naming the location of the 10-mile square for the federal seat 'in the counties of Philadelphia, Chester, and Bucks in the state of Pennsylvania, including within it the town of Germantown, and some part of the Northern Liberties of the city of Philadelphia.'"

"VOTE! VOTE!"

In a few minutes, Germantown sat in a tie vote, 9 and 9, Maclay and Connecticut's Johnson having voted "Nay" with the Southerners.

All eyes fastened on Vice President John Adams, whose duty now was to break the tie.

He kept them waiting while he made a speech. He said nice things about the Potomac, declared Susquehanna had problems, observed that Philadelphia AND New York both had facilities and offered to build more.

"I would be happy," he concluded, "to see Congress stay in Philadelphia and New York, alternating every four years. But since Pennsylvania has

*Hist. of Congress
Senate Journ., (Gales/
Seaton) Sept.24, 1789*

For a few hours, the fenced fields and pleasant rills of Germantown, stylish country suburb of Philadelphia, had the vote of the House and Senate as the site of the national capital. A series of fine houses by the side of the road, Germantown lay only a few hours' carriage ride from the pleasures and business of the big city. By accepting Germantown in place of Falls of the Delaware, and by promising $100,000 to start construction, Morris gained votes, kept the capital on his river, and off the Potomac. James Madison, however, snatched away his victory at the last second.

offered money, I vote for—Germantown!"

Maclay groaned to himself, "Morris's money has bought the vote. He's barefacedly bought it." Later, the thought struck him that Morris's adding Bucks County to the admissible bounds of the 10-mile square would allow him to tilt it to reach within 15 miles of Morrisville at the Falls of the Delaware.

SCENE 3
CAN NEW YORK TRUST PHILADELPHIA ?

PLACE: New Merchants Coffee House, southeast corner of Wall and Water Streets.
TIME: Saturday, September 26, about 6 p.m., just after the Senate's final approval of Germantown, and two days before the House debate.

Colonial Coffeehouses (R.E.Graham) Am.Phil.Soc.

Sipping coffee poured from a hissing urn, or stronger drink trickled from jugs at the bar, a number of men sat reading newspapers that New Merchants Coffeehouse made available, free, for its customers. In front of a Public Notices board, a little crowd of men leaned forward to read handwritten notices of articles for sale, real estate to be auctioned, the arrival and departure time of vessels. They talked about city events of the day, about politics, the President's rides or walks in the town, and the doings of Congress.

Actual scene of striking this bargain between NY and Pa. is not recorded, but the terms and the events in Senate and House are recorded in Maclay's Journal, the House Journal for the week of Sept.25, 1789, and Life and Correspondence of Rufus King.

Into this noisy news center, Congressman Elias Boudinot and his visitor, Boston merchant Josiah Bailey, had just arrived to look at newspapers—those of Boston for Bailey and those of Philadelphia for Boudinot.

"How is your coffee?" Bailey asked, smiling at the barmaid. "I like it hot as hell, black as the devil's heart, and sweet as sin."

"It's biled for an hour," the maid replied quickly, "and sugar's dear, so I'll charge you double for a ha'f mug."

Congressman Boudinot looked about the room, as dim as day's-end and tobacco smoke could make it, and waved briefly at New York Senator King facing him on the far side. King was talking to a large man who, from the back, looked like Morris.

Boudinot noted the drinkers and smokers in stalls and standing in groups, nodded to John Fenno, the editor, bowed politely to Pennsylvania Congressmen Clymer and Fitzsimons sitting in a stall, curtains open, wine glasses on the table.

"Come, Josiah, George Clymer is a Philadelphia merchant, and since it looks now that his city will become our Number One center of government, you may find it useful to make his acquaintance. His good friend Thomas Fitzsimons, born in County Tubber, Ireland, as he tells us over and again in Irish sing-song, has counting house and banking connections, and is quite accommodating."

Biog.Dir. of Am.Congress 1774-1949

As they sat down with Clymer and Fitzsimons, Senator King and Senator Morris—for it was he—moved towards them. Clymer saw them coming, and with eyebrow and head movements told Fitzsimons. Both half-rose to greet the Senators. "Join us in a Madeira, Gentlemen?"

Morris greeted Boudinot as "old friend." Over the years, Boudinot's motions had put Falls of the Delaware before the Congress on occasion; recently, he had provided an escape route from Susquehanna. Boudinot introduced his "trusted friend," Josiah Bailey of Boston, to Senator King; Morris remembered meeting him at the President's reception.

Smiling and effusive, Morris went straight away to business. "Senator King has asked me," he began, "whether he can trust us Philadelphians to leave the temporary capital in New York for three years—or whether New Yorkers in the House should amend our bill to say 'no less than four years.'"

Derived from Maclay's Journal p.162 Sept.25

Arms folded across his chest, King said, "When the words are in the bill, we will not need to ask

Maclay Sept.26

Life and Correspondence of Rufus King, p374, the signed pledge.

'what does it mean?' when various Pennsylvania men spread the word that you will build a Congress House and President House in a short time—working night and day—ready for occupying in a year. Yes, Mr. Morris, that's the news all over town.

"Have you forgotten the promise you signed only a few days ago, Mr. Morris? Pennsylvania gets the permanent seat, New York gets FOUR years as temporary. Have you forgotten, Mr. Morris, that New York's House members must all vote 'yea' if Germantown is to stick?"

Clymer burst out with much intensity, "Mr. King, we have not forgotten that we will use our INFLUENCE as we promised! NOR that New York depends on our seven votes to gain the temporary seat! You will get them! You are worrying needlessly about holding the seat only one year. Fitzsimons and I have discussed this matter with the other Pennsylvania delegates, and there is not the slightest reluctance or disagreement about three years in New York. I urged them to guarantee FOUR years, but some insisted that the buildings could be ready in less time, in which case they ought not to be left standing empty—"

Morris interrupted. "I assure you, promise you, Senator King, that my word, our word, is solid, trustworthy. I can also assure you that if New York members in the House move to amend the bill, they are dooming it!

"You know Madison and the Southerners—they will grab any such opening with teeth and nails and rattle it all day Monday and Tuesday, our new adjournment day, until time runs out. You see in the Senate how they have hung on during the second and third readings of my bill this past week.

"Even if they fail to kill your amendment in the House, like all amendments it must come back to us in the Senate for a vote.

"In the last minutes before we adjourn to go home on Tuesday—today's extension is the last one possible—we can be certain that Senator Carroll would move for the tenth time this session to postpone a Senate decision on the seat. For the vote on postponement, Maclay may not stay in his sick bed as he did today for the third reading and final vote. Johnson may switch back to the Southerners. Some of our men may be on their way home.

"At the last second, the great prize, now within the grasp of Philadelphia and New York, could slip away in the Senate for lack of one vote to stop postponement.

"Next year, when the South gains North Carolina, what chance will we have to win?"

Senator King's face still held a shadowy, dubious little frown. "I would like to recall to you the scene in the Senate yesterday," he began. "You came in with a final version of the Germantown amendment for the 10-mile square. It passed in the affirmative. There was a long pause. Finally Mr. Adams called on you—'We are waiting for the addition you promised us,' he said. And you said, 'Addition? What addition?' (Morris began shaking his head, laughing, and waving a hand like a fan.) From all parts of the Senate," Senator King continued, "members shouted at you—'Hundred thousand dollars, Sir!' 'Guarantee! Guarantee!' 'No money, no seat!' 'New vote! Kill Germantown!'"

Maclay's Journal Sept.25, 1789 p162

Hist. of Congress, Senate Journal, Sept. 25, 1789

Morris broke in. "Yes, yes! I was greatly embarrassed! My thoughts had been carried away by the excitement of the voting for Germantown! But you saw that I immediately brought forth from my pocket the paragraph stating that no building would start until the state—or citizens—paid the money."

King wagged a finger at Morris. "A year hence, is it not equally possible that some excitement will affect your memory of today's promise for New York to keep the seat no less than three years?"

"I will not forget," Morris said solemnly. "As these four men are my witnesses, I will personally guarantee New York three years."

New Merchant's Coffee House (right) on Wall Street three blocks from Federal Hall, and within sight of ships' masts on the East River, had become a favorite with members of Congress for private meetings and a source of news. Like Tontine's Coffee House on the corner diagonally across the Wall and Water Street intersection, it provided newspapers from far and wide for its customers to read at no charge, a public notice board, private stalls, and drinks of every kind—including coffee. Wall Street in these blocks won the nickname of Auction Lane from the frequent bidding sales on merchandise, barrels and bales of commodities, and slaves.

160

Senator King and Senator Morris were looking each other straight in the eye. They held their gaze for a long moment. At last, King nodded his head. "I must trust you."

Morris clasped King's shoulder and gave it an approving shake. "Madeiras!" Morris called to a bar-maid just then finishing the lighting of 50 candles, and pushing the chandelier back to the ceiling.

A half-hour later, Josiah Bailey, walking with Boudinot in the shadows that flickering whale oil lanterns cast on Wall Street, laughed and said, "That was a lot more interesting than reading newspapers! Elias, do you believe those three Pennsylvania men can personally guarantee New York three years as temporary seat? They may be voted out of office—or Philadelphia builders may actually work night and day and finish the buildings in ONE year! Look what the Frenchman—what's his name?—did to Federal Hall in six months!"

"True," said Boudinot. "But if New Yorkers see short-changing about to happen to them, I suppose they can—well—appeal to the President."

"What could HE do about it?" queried Bailey. "The wording in that bill soon to be law says 'WITHIN four years.' The President could not change that. Ours is a government of law!"

"True," the Congressman said. "The President could do nothing, except appeal to honor. He's no King—thank God!"

SCENE 4
TRIFLING, DEADLY AMENDMENT

PLACE: Federal Hall's portico.
TIME: Monday, September 28, about noon, the day before adjournment.

"Mr. Maclay! Mr. Maclay!" The limping, gray-haired Senator stopped in the archway and looked around toward the call. He saw Senator Izard of South Carolina coming out the great entrance door and hurrying toward him.

"I must ask of you a great favor, Mr. Maclay!" said Izard breathlessly. "STAY, Sir! or at least come back in an hour or two. We need your vote to kill Germantown when it comes back from the House to the Senate with a tiny amendment. I know you feel quite unwell, else you would not be leaving. But the next few hours are critical! At this very moment, the House is taking up the Germantown bill. I've just heard that Sherman of Connecticut, who a week ago spoke so forcefully for Susquehanna, has taken the lead in speaking forcefully for Germantown!

"New England, New York, and Pennsylvania are all set to vote for it, just as they did in the Senate last week, no matter what arguments are thrown against it—high price of land at Germantown, for example. Morris's $100,000 won't go far."

Izard lowered his voice. "Our Southern House members already know they will lose again on today's third-reading vote. However, they plan to snatch victory from Morris. They will start the action in the House, but the Senate must complete it. Senator Maclay, sir, twice during the past week you have voted with the South against Germantown. We need you now to vote with us one more time."

Maclay had begun limping away. Senator Izard moved alongside him, almost whispering. "The plan is this. Just before the final House vote, which even

All the scene:
Maclay's Journal
Sept.28

Madison concedes will approve Germantown and New York, a member will offer a trifling amendment to the bill—an amendment eminently necessary, he'll point out—no one can refuse to allow it—one the Senate would surely approve by a quick voice vote.

"BUT! In the Senate, a lightning call for POSTPONEMENT (Izard said the word softly, and behind his hand), followed by a vote that carries it—there'll be some surprise votes there—and Germantown is postponed until next session—perhaps forever! What do you say, sir?"

Maclay's face contorted into a grimace of pain. "I say I wish nothing so much as to see an end of the business. But I am too ill to attend. My knee pains unmercifully unless I am lying stretched out. But even if this were not so, and I stayed, I could not vote to postpone after a majority in both Houses has approved Germantown."

Maclay turned away, limping painfully toward his rooming house. Izard stared after him, frowning. Suddenly, he ran to Maclay and said, "Don't tell Morris!" Maclay shook his head in irritation.

At 3 o'clock, Maclay in his bed was awakened by his next-door neighbor, lanky Congressman Wynkoop, knocking loudly before bursting into the room with a whoop.

"Germantown got it!! Happy Germantown, our own Germantown, has got the Congress! The House's final vote is 31 to 24! It's ours! OURS! Hurray, hurray, hurray! Pennsylvania has won! We won, Maclay, we won! I'm taking the next stage to Philadelphia to tell the glorious news!"

Wynkoop rushed out the door, called down the stairs for a porter, ran into his room singing a tune with a one-word verse, "Germantown!" and dragged a wooden trunk to the door.

Two hours later, as Maclay lay writing about Wynkoop in his journal, there came a knock at the door. A bespectacled little man, Maclay's old friend Parson Lynn, his face set in an expression of astonishment, opened the door and stared at Maclay. "My dear Mr. Maclay!" he said in a greatly agitated voice. "What news I have just heard on passing by Federal Hall! It looked as if the entire Senate and House had gathered at the entrance and talk was flying! Germantown is lost! Did you hear me? GERMANTOWN IS LOST!!"

Maclay laid his pen down and nodded. "Postponed, you mean. I can guess which Senators took back today the votes they gave Germantown on Saturday. Any specifics, Parson Lynn?"

"They said Madison did it! A trifling amendment—something about assuring people now living in the 10-mile square in Germantown that they will remain under the laws of Pennsylvania until Congress moves there. I heard Mr.Clymer say that the propriety of the provision was so apparent, he didn't conceive of anything but a quick acceptance by the Senate. The House itself voted by voice to amend, he said, only two 'nays' at most.

"The clerk RAN with it to the Senate, the hour was so late—after four o'clock. When the clerk was still reading the last words, Carroll called for recognition, and moved for postponement! Mr. Izard seconded. And then—NEW YORKER Rufus King called for a standing vote—no rollcall! Postponement carried by ONE vote, they said! It was the damned New Yorkers who did it! What happened to switch them away from Germantown?!"

The parson's chin quivered. Maclay's chin dropped to his chest. His head wagged slowly from side to side. "The postponement keeps the capital in New York another year. Somebody persuaded King that Morris would reneg, cut New York down to a year. So King decided he had nothing to lose by waiting to see what offers next year's session will bring. Ah, me. Mr. Madison. Mr. Carroll. TWO Mr. Potomacs. One day, they will drag Morris and all of us to Washington's river."

SCENE 5
CONFRONTATION

PLACE: Wall Street waterfront.
TIME: About 7:30 in the morning on the last day of the First Session of the First Congress, Tuesday, September 29, 1789.

James Madison, hurrying along the wharves looking for a sloop loading freight for Philadelphia, suddenly slowed his pace.

Ahead a few yards, he had just seen the shape of a familiar figure—"The Man" as Robert Morris was still called by men he had worked with during the Revolution. A large man, a fat man, his plump round face, neck, and bulging middle had expanded in harmonious proportion. Gray hair hung to his shoulders.

His horse and landau waited nearby while he spoke intently to a pair of men whom Madison recognized as Morris employes. Each held a sizeable carpetbag. With a quick hand shake for each, Morris turned and advanced toward his landau; his employes walked to the gangplank of the sloop "Charleston Star" and boarded. "Until December!" they called. Morris called back, "Good hunting!"

Then he saw Mr. Madison almost at his elbow.

His intensely blue, aggressive eyes stared into the fearless hazels of Madison. For a moment, neither spoke. Then with an odd twist of a smile, Morris held out his hand, as he exclaimed, "Mr. Madison!"

"Senator," said Madison, taking his hand briefly.

"Well! I suppose you are pacing the wharves to make certain of your accommodations to the port nearest home—Baltimore, I presume."

"To Philadelphia." Madison waited, cautious, expectant.

"Philadelphia—of course! Who would go to Baltimore when he can go to Philadelphia? I will expect to see you there, but"—he wagged a finger briefly—"I shall not wait to say to you that I am NOT mad at you. I am disgusted, infuriated by New York. Once more its two Senators broke their promise. We were so close to settling this tedious, distracting, acrimonious debate—we were within an inch. You did exactly what I had persuaded the New Yorkers not to do—stuck on an amendment in the House.

"Nooo—I do not blame you! I would have done the same in your place. It should have amounted to nothing when it came back to the Senate—New York was committed to vote with our deal. Instead, I was dealt a stunning blow and in a flash the prize we had held in our hands had vanished.

"So—Mr. Madison, it is time to bring alive the Southern project of an arrangement with Philadelphia. You made an offer a short time ago when you came to Clymer's—and many of the Pennsylvania delegates were interested. Let us awaken your project—have it ready and firm when we reconvene in January."

Madison's face did not soften. His voice had a sharp edge. "I think it likely that it cannot awaken. It will sleep from distrust. For us, Pennsylvania men cannot be depended upon any more than New York's."

Morris stiffened. "Then I shall give the New Yorkers a chance to redeem themselves in another vote in January. In the first week I will call up the postponed Germantown-New York bill. With one quick vote, we can approve your amendment, Mr. Madison, and Potomac is out of the picture."

"Perhaps it will not be so simple to bring it to the floor," Morris heard Madison say. "The New Yorkers—and others—may block it. If they don't, WE will see that it is blocked in the House!" Madison added stiffly. "A bill should pass on its own merits, not merely slip through on the twist of a procedural rule. Why not take up a new bill when we are under no adjournment pressure?"

The Madison-Morris confrontation, reported in a letter from Madison to GW, took place in Philadelphia not long after Congress adjourned. Had it taken place in New York on adjournment day as used here, their conversation would undoubtedly have been little different.

Madison letter to GW, Nov.20, 1789

Morris, frowning, studied Madison's stiff, defiant expression. Then he smiled, shaking his head. "Mr. Madison, you fight hard and well. The two of us working on the same side could lick the devil. Well—let me say this: In January, I will use the threat of quick action to test the New Yorkers, alarming them that to fail me again means I will jump to the alternative waiting in the South—Potomac and Philadelphia. If the New Yorkers turn their backs, I shall be freed from all my commitments to them. I shall renounce all confidence in that quarter and speak seriously to the Southern states."

"Very seriously indeed," Madison flung back, "if you expect anyone to listen to you."

Morris letter to his wife, Sept.15, 1789.

In a tone both injured and cajoling, Morris declared that Madison seemed to imply that he did not trust the Senator from Pennsylvania. "I believe no one will pretend that my conduct justifies the least distrust! I make a bargain, I keep my side of it. It is my deal-making to favor Falls of the Delaware and Germantown—all detrimental to Potomac—that upsets you. It even upsets the President! He had a talk with me about it. He was polite and cautious in what he said, but I think he is not a little angry at me for pushing so hard for my capital choices."

Madison declared grimly that it did not contribute to a reputation of trustworthiness for Morris to have spent the past afternoon and evening searching Congress for players in a game Morris called "Play the Yorkers a trick."

Maclay's Journ. Sept. 29-30

"I have heard," Madison added, "that you have plans to call up the Germantown bill MINUS New York, during the final 10 minutes of today's meeting, the last of the session—"

"Wouldn't you, Mr. Madison, exert yourself for Potomac with ANY ingenious—"

"Ingenious is one thing—tricky is quite another, Senator."

"Yes, Mr. Madison, of course—only if it wins can it be called 'ingenious'. But I have no such plans for today. It is too late. We will have the matter to torment us next year. Too bad, Mr. Madison! Congress will have its hands full dealing with the financial plan that Congress ordered Mr. Hamilton to bring in. I expect it will look much like the one that you and Hamilton and I worked out in '82 for the Old Congress. It was refused then, and it will stir much argument now, but I think its time has come. It should require only 90 days to pass, then we can once more pummel the capital matter."

Madison allowed himself a wry smile. "Ninety days?" he said. "It took us that long to talk the House doorkeeper into ordering Franklin stoves for the fireplaces. Good day, Senator."

"Good day, Mr. Madison."

Mr. Madison

Outside the covered walkway of Federal Hall, Congressmen linger on Wall Street talking politics. Monday through Saturday sessions usually adjourned at 3 for dinner. Then hungry Representatives and Senators walked to nearby taverns, or waited for rented coaches to take them to their boarding houses.

Part Three
Second Session of the First Federal Congress
January-August 1790

In the first Executive Mansion, a rented house at the corner of Queen and Cherry Streets in New York, Washington's family of four, three aides, and probably 10 servants, lived crowded in two upper floors. The first floor barely had space for official entertainments and an office. Washington's 16 horses, six of them white, had to stay in commercial stables. After 10 months, the president gratefully moved to a bigger house on Broadway.

CHAPTER 16

New Year De Novo, Mansion, and Money

SCENE 1
RECEPTION AT THE PRESIDENT'S

PLACE: Residence on Cherry Street, New York City.
TIME: New Year's Day, 1790, about 2 p.m.

Private Affairs of GW (Lear/Decatur) Annals of N.Y. (Watson) p204, 300

Gentlemen in velvet, brocade, lace, and powdered hair waited in line for their turn to speak New Year's greetings to President Washington. He stood beside the fireplace where a fire burned low in the furnitureless dining-reception room. Through several large windows, bright sunlight of an unusually clear and mild day illuminated the scene—a good sign for the coming year, the guests told each other. They half-whispered, keeping the noise level low in order that Washington, increasingly hard of hearing, could catch the words of guests stopping one by one in front of him.

Washington After the Revolution (W.S.Baker)

Three Virginia Congressmen, Brown, White, and Coles, stood in line and moved a few steps at a time towards the President. Now close enough to hear Tobias Lear, the President's secretary, announcing loud and clear the name of each man greeting the President, the three Virginians peered judiciously around the line to observe the ceremony.

Recollections of Washington (GW Custis)

"The President looks to have regained all his strength and good health," murmured John Brown, young Congressman from the Kentucky district of Virginia. "I heard that the wound from cutting out his abscess had not entirely skinned over by late September when Congress recessed. I hear now that he is completely recovered."

GW Writings, Letter Sept.1789

"The absence of Congress for three months is bound to have done him a world of good," said

Alexander White. The Virginians smiled.

"His stamina is in good fettle," remarked Isaac Coles."Imagine standing in one spot from noon 'til after three o'clock, steadily greeting all these men. There must be more than 200, judging from the noise, heat, crowding, and length of this line."

"Yes, I see city and state officials, important New Yorkers, the President's men, the Spanish minister, Congressmen and Senators," White said.

"Look several places ahead of us—that's Otto, diplomat in charge of the French Legation since Count Moustier left. He's just a M'sieur. Otto sounds German, but he's dressed very Frenchy—red shoe heels like the Count's," reported Coles.

Private Affairs/GW (Lear/Decatur) N.Y.in 1789 (Smith).

White whispered behind his hand, "Perhaps Count Moustier left them when he went home last fall!"

"If so," said Brown, "he didn't leave his high manner to wear with them. I'd like to see how the Count, the Bourbon King worshipper, is faring in Revolutionary Paris right now."

"I'd much rather see certain Virginians right here right now," said White."What a relief if Mr. Madison and Senator Lee walked into sight. We hardly know what to do without them here."

At that moment, a wigged gentleman who had worked his way from the front door around the edge of the crowd, then along the receiving line glancing at each face, clasped one of his fellow

Virginians on the shoulder.

"Coles! White! Brown! I thought I'd never find you in this crowd! Glad to see you all!"

"Sam Griffin!" all three Virginians exclaimed, and added questions one after another—"How's Richmond? What news of Madison? The Lees? Grayson, Moore, Page, Parker, Bland? How long have you been on the road?"

"Sh! Quieter!"

The four Virginians nodded apologetically to their neighbors, moved a few steps ahead, and began a whispered exchange.

Griffin had news from Madison. "There's not an hour to lose," he said. "I'm glad I got here in time to come in. Ten seconds later, the door was closed." Griffin assumed an air of light-hearted nonchalance while his voice became suddenly serious and subdued. "When I passed through Georgetown four days ago, I found Mr. Madison there, sick abed. On his way here, he was struck down with severe dysentery. (Groans of dismay) Dr.David Stuart, the President's relative, was attending Mr. Madison, and he told me Madison should not travel for another 10 days! Even then, it should be only a few miles a day. We cannot expect to see him for two, perhaps three weeks.

"Hearing this, Mr. Madison gave me some instructions for the delegation," Griffin went on. "He called attention to the Morris bill of last session naming Germantown the capital, and to the Morris's threat that he will call it up at the Senate's first meeting.

"Since my arrival just this noon, I have learned that Morris could quickly win since neither of Virginia's Senators, nor Carroll of Maryland, is even on his way here! Enough Northern men are on hand that they could fix the seat at Germantown tomorrow—unless someone in the Senate and we in the House immediately demand the de novo rule, which says postponed bills of one session are dead at the next and must be started anew. Our legislature has

Madison letter to his father, Jan.21, Papers of Madison, Vol.13 (Rutland)

it, but Pennsylvania and some other states do not.

"Morris may even claim that this session and last session are the FIRST CONGRESS and therefore ONE session, so postponed bills are alive, open to continue where we left off in September. Is Morris here? (No one had seen him.) Surely he will arrive for the opening of Congress tomorrow and has already woo'd and won back the New Yorkers.

"If he calls up Germantown and we say nothing, Adams alone might decide old or new session, de novo or no de novo. Adams likes Philadelphia—and he may want a quick vote on Madison's trifling amendment, hoping Germantown wins."

White tugged at his wig and exclaimed, "Oh, that must not be allowed to happen! We must find a Senator to stay at his seat, alert, ready to challenge! And the fight must be long! And we must win de novo when both Houses vote on it! If we don't win, we must mourn Potomac's loss forever."

The men took two steps forward in line. After a moment of looking about to bow to nearby gentlemen, Griffin continued his message from Madison. "He was in much physical and mental torment in Georgetown. He hated not coming on with me. 'Tell the delegation to watch for the slightest move by anybody in either House about ANY postponed matter,' he said. 'Immediately demand de novo. Once the question is raised, no action on any postponed matter can proceed until a decision is voted on the rule. Before that event, I expect to be with you,' Madison said."

Coles, quite agitated, exclaimed, "But perhaps too late! If de novo comes to a vote any time soon, we cannot win—!"

"Sh. We must be more guarded," Griffin warned. "You are looking too agitated. Let me say this and no more until later: Madison says we must alert our friends in both Houses, gather our arguments, plan our strategy, and be ready to talk, talk, talk. Stave off a vote. Give Southern members time to get here.

Hist. Cong. House Journ. Jan. 8-25, 1790 (Gales/Seaton)

"Gentlemen, it's on our shoulders to gain another chance for Potomac. Now let us brighten our demeanor, casually dab our handkerchiefs to our brow—it's uncomfortably warm in here—and move up closer to the big moment of this reception."

They had moved almost in front of the President. Only the French diplomat and two others preceded them. Tobias Lear announced loudly, "The French char-jay daf-fairs, M'sure Looey Otto!" Monsieur Otto bowed elaborately, wrist lace fluttering, wig curls glistening.

Washington solemnly made his slight, dignified bow, towering over the stocky Frenchman. "Excellency!" said the envoy. "From the King of France Louis Sixteen, and his Queen Marie Antionette, I bring you cordial wishes for success, prosperity, and peace!" He bowed elaborately once more.

"I receive the greetings of the King of France and his Queen with pleasure and gratitude," replied the President. "I beg you to convey to them my most sincere wishes for their happiness in the new year. I also offer to you, M'sieur Otto, my cordial wishes for success and contentment during the coming year—your tenth in America, I believe."

"My eleventh, Mr. President!" Monsieur Otto answered in his high tenor voice. "May I add the felicitations of the former minister, the Comte Francois de Moustier—and a message for Your Excellency. He wishes you to know that he delivered your letters, and has presented to the King a favorable representation of the government of this country, and in particular of its head."

GW (D.Freeman)

GW Diary Oct.14

GW Diary Oct.9

Washington bowed and said, "That the Minister has given a complimentary report of us to the King, whose extraordinary assistance enabled us to win independence, gives me much satisfaction. May I assume that the situation in Paris is stabilizing? And that Count de Moustier himself or a new minister will soon arrive to head the delegation in your Broadway residence?"

The diplomat, a man in his mid–thirties, hesitated. He then said carefully, "His Majesty is uncertain whether the situation has stabilized. It is certain that the Comte de Moustier will not return. For the time being, a reduced staff will continue. However, with our financing uncertain, we will not long remain on Broadway in such a splendid residence as the Macomb mansion."

NY in 1789 (Smith) p89

The President's face suddenly changed from formal politeness to animated interest. His blue-gray eyes lighted up, his expression became quizzical, his voice lively. "Are you contemplating a move in the near future?"

"I believe so, Excellency. I perceive that you are quite interested in the house—for use as the Presidential palace? It would serve well, being very large, elegant, and having a grand view of the Hudson River from the back balcony."

Washington replied that, indeed, he was interested in the Broadway house. "As you can easily see here, this house, these rooms—" the President lifted a gloved hand from his sword to gesture toward the crowd, then the low-ceiled room— "are too small for proper entertaining, and for comfortable housing of all my family and duties. The Macomb house on Broadway would be much more suitable. I pray you will inform me immediately when it becomes available."

"I shall be honored to do so, Excellency."

The envoy bowed and stepped away, the two men after him had their Presidential moment, and the Virginians, moving one by one in front of Washington, were announced—"Congressman John Brown of Virginia! Congressman Isaac Coles, Virginia! Congressman Samuel Griffin, Virginia, Congressman Alexander White, Virginia!" The President beamed, addressed them as "my fellow Virginians," greeted them warmly, calling each man by name.

"I had hoped to see Mr. Madison here today," he said to them. "What is the news of him?" Griffin

J. Madison (Brant)

Philip Schuyler

*A.Hamilton
(B.Mitchell)*

replied by handing Washington an envelope—"from Mr.Madison, Excellency. He is in Georgetown recovering from dysentery. Dr. Stuart, weather, and roads permitting, he hopes to arrive in New York in two or three weeks."

"That he is indisposed is regrettable," the President said. "His presence here is much needed." Avidly, the four men agreed, and Griffin added, "He gave me instructions for the delegation, and we will do all he asks, Mr. President." With bows, they moved away.

They passed close by handsome young Senator Rufus King and his fellow New York Senator, aristocratic Philip Schuyler, richly dressed in silk, lace, four sparkling diamond buckles, and a stylish wig. The Virginians and New Yorkers bowed briefly and said New Year's greetings before the Virginians made their way through the crowd to the front door.

The New Yorkers stood absorbed a moment, watching and listening as the parade of Congressmen, diplomats, the Vice President, New York Governor, and numerous respectable citizens each received a loud and clear introduction. "Washington a year from now will recognize every face he saw today, and recall their names," mused the aging Schuyler. "I wonder how he does that."

"Our President is, indeed, doing extremely well," King said. "The best thing he has done for us is to appoint your son-in-law Secretary of the Treasury."

"Ah yes, my son-in-law has added glory to the Schuyler family," Schuyler said, beaming with pleasure. "As I said to a VERY rich man who was bragging on and on about his money and power, 'My family is better off than yours—we have Alexander Hamilton!'"

King laughed appreciatively. "From all I hear, a lot of people will soon be enjoying more than glory from the work of your brilliant son-in-law."

Schuyler gave King a sharp look and frowned. He glanced around at nearby company. Shaking

his head briefly, he murmured, "Where did you hear that?" and then said jovially, "I see South Carolina Senators Butler and Izard in the line. Surprising that they from so far away could arrive here before Senators from New Jersey or Pennsylvania."

King nodded. Voice low, Schuyler added, "Of course, we know two reasons why Morris hasn't yet left Philadelphia—and WE are reason number one. We have told him hot and loud we will not allow the Germantown bill to slide through on a quick vote. Until it has three years for New York written into it, all the Northeast will vote against it.

"But he's afraid such an amendment will open the whole seat question, thereby delaying Hamilton's financial plan. I hear that Morris is already deep in speculating, buying items he thinks the plan will suddenly make valuable. And that is reason number two: He is too busy making money to come here."

King's nodding became vigorous. "Yes, yes! For some time he's been buying war debt certificates and selling them to Holland bankers. He, Gouverneur Morris, Bill Duer, who is Hamilton's assistant, William Constable, who is Morris's partner, and Andrew Craigie are in it together. Months ago they asked me to join them. I wouldn't.

"They buy debt-paper from farmers, soldiers, merchants, who think they are worthless.The certificates are then sold to Dutch bankers for at least 200 percent profit. The bankers double their money when they sell to Dutch shopkeepers and farmers. Morris told these foreigners that ALL American debt paper will be redeemed by the federal treasury at full value. Is this what your son-in-law will propose?" Schuyler grimaced and shrugged.

King declared it a meritorious plan—"But how," he asked, "did Morris know about it so early?"

Schuyler clasped King on the shoulder and quietly remarked, "You are becoming unwisely audible, Rufus."

Rufus King

*GW and the New
Nation (J.T.Flexner)*

*A.Hamilton
(B.Mitchell) p154-5,
162-3*

King nodded but charged on in a lower tone. "If Morris didn't know, but took a chance he wouldn't be caught in a lie, then he is stealing from us. If his promises to the Dutch do turn out to be a lie, he's stealing from them—which will ruin our credit forever.

"What dangerous speculating and profiteering! And debt paper isn't the only American commodity he's selling in Europe! LAND! He has three big deals going now—including the million acres he bought last August in our own state. Practically the whole western end! I hear he's selling it in Europe for $1 an acre—10 times what he paid.

"I hear, too, that he has bought more land at Delaware Falls—which probably means he will approach us for a new deal, the Falls and New York—again! I've had enough of him. We should busy ourselves making a deal for Potomac and New York!"

"Excellent!' Schuyler declared in an intense half-whisper. "Let us begin this hour. On our way home, we must stop by Maiden Lane to see the Virginians. Madison will be rather pleased to hear from us, I predict. Perhaps he will agree to FIVE years for New York!"

King, who had smiled and nodded until he heard Madison's name, began shaking his head. "Madison was not with the Virginia men today. We must wait, for his delegation can decide nothing without him. If we talk to them it will only amount to news racing to Philadelphia that we were seen talking to them. Morris might come running. Who wants that? Nobody!"

R.Morris (Oberholtzer)

SCENE 2
POSTPONED=DEAD, DEBTS=400% PROFIT

PLACE: Vast reception hall inside the Wall Street entrance of Federal Hall.
TIME: Three weeks later, Wednesday, January 20, 1790, a cold, windy day.

Even the New Englanders, Roger Sherman of Connecticut and George Thatcher of Massachusetts, shivered in the drafty, spacious hall. In addition to the cold, cold stone floor, the huge space was blasted with frigid air when men went in or out the Wall Street door. Cold air also swept in through the open arches separating the reception hall from the House of Representatives' great lobby, a large space open all the way up to a colorful skylight 50 feet above in the roof.

"Brrr," Congressman James Jackson of Georgia complained, shaking himself and drawing his cloak tighter about his middle. "The French architect must have thought the Senate Chamber needed to rest on top of an ice box—for temper control," he said.

"Let me help warm you," said Thomas Hartley of Pennsylvania in a brisk, cool manner. "While we wait for our coaches, I will wrap you in words of advice about the committee we five have just been assigned to serve upon."

He cleared his throat lengthily. "We owe it to future Congresses, as well as the present one, NOT to recommend a rule that solves one of your special problems today, but makes for much wasted time in the years to come—"

"WHOSE special problem?" broke in jowly Alexander White of Virginia. "It was noticeable, my good Philadelphia friend, that you were two weeks late coming to this session, and in your very first hour, the problem you were primed to call up and oppose was DE NOVO in regard to unfinished and POSTPONED business of last session. Perhaps you

"Federal Hall Revisited" (L.Torres) Journ.Soc. Arch.Hist. Dec.1970

Hist.Cong., House Journ., Jan. 15-25, 1790, Vol.2, p1041-75 (Gales/Seaton)

Hist. Cong., Senate Journ. Jan. 15-25, p938-9

Maclay's Journal p.175-181

will inform us which piece of business caused you to drop your speculating in Philadelphia, hurry—"

"I resent your insinuations——!"

"—to New York! Bankruptcy law? the census? patents and copyrights? or was it the 'importation of certain persons'? Could it possibly have been the Germantown bill? Without a de novo rule, it needs only one small action of the Senate to give Pennsylvania the federal capital!"

Hartley answered coldly, "You are gifted, sir, at turning facts wrong side up—it is you—and two other Virginians—who began the agitation to declare postponed matters dead, for the purpose of resurrecting Potomac—"

"How would you know? You weren't here! It was Mr. Boudinot who tried to tiptoe the question before us and get a commitment before we noticed the import. 'Shorten the title of our Journal,' he said, 'it's too long and cumbersome—drop "Second Session, etc." and say "First Congress" only'—as if we were having one unbroken session." White's voice shook in anger.

"But," replied the Pennsylvanian, "English Parliamentary rules provide that in—"

"I can't stand to hear you tell us that again, Hartley!" boomed Jackson of Georgia, now quite warm except underfoot. "We in America, and especially we in the South, have a lot of good reasons why we shouldn't hang onto ALL the rules of the British Parliament!"

Square-faced Roger Sherman of Connecticut cut in to remind the four other men that he and they were the House committee that would join a similar Senate committee to thresh out the matter, and bring a recommendation to both Houses. "While I favor de novo, perhaps members of the Senate committee will not, but we abide by the majority vote. Now, I hear noises outside that mean we can ride home."

Sherman leading the way, they passed to the long

arcade fronting the whole width of the building, and having the same 12-foot depth as the inaugural balcony above it. Architect L'Enfant had torn out half of the first floor's front rooms on both arms of the old building to help create this sheltered walkway.

The House Committee on Unfinished Business, arriving there, found three men deep in conversation. In his strongest, raspiest voice, Senator Maclay was making a pronouncement.

"—undeniably certain," he was telling Oliver Ellsworth of Connecticut and John Henry of Maryland, "that a particular fact has given rise to this business of de novo. It came to the surface in regard to the Senate's unfinished crime and punishment bill, but affects ALL unfinished business—and we all know the true target is the Germantown bill. Here then, to control a single incident, some are attempting to establish a general rule. To get rid of Germantown as the seat, some would involve us in perpetual inconvenience!"

"Hear, hear!" cried Hartley heartily. "I see you gentlemen of the Senate's De Novo Committee remained after adjournment to organize, as we did. I've just been trying to tell my fellow committeemen here the folly of de novo—"

Five voices at once protested the word "folly." They quieted as Senator Ellsworth said, "Senator Morris—" and even the arriving coach gained none of their rapt attention.

"Senator Morris," Ellsworth was saying, "appears to think that de novo is the rule in Congress! Otherwise, would he not have come the first week—or surely by now, the third week—and called up the Germantown bill while so many of the Southern Senators are absent?"

Senator Henry of Maryland spoke up. "I can tell you I find the arguments I have heard FOR de novo have changed my mind to favor it, and when our committees vote—"

Hist.Cong.,House Journ. Jan.11, 1790 Gales/Seaton)

Hist.Cong., House Journ. Jan.8

Hist.Cong. House Journ. Jan.15/25

"Federal Hall Revisited" (L.Torres) *J.Soc.Arch. Hist.,*Dec. 1970

Maclay's Journal Jan.22, 1790

Hist.Cong., Senate Journ. (Gales/Seaton) Jan.20, 1790

Maclay's Journal Jan.21

Maclay's Journal
Jan.15 1790

"Connecticut has subverted Maryland!" Maclay interrupted. "And Hamilton's financial plan, just announced, which will redeem all our Revolutionary war debts, back interest, and paper money at full value, has subverted Mr. Morris—who seems to have known weeks ago what was in the plan of the Secretary of the Treasury. Senator Morris is much too busy running his speculating business to attend to national business. I regret that. But it's just as well, since New York loses out, too—a year or two more in New York and King would have devised some tricky way to hold Congress and cheat Philadelphia!"

"Tricky!" exclaimed Congressman Thatcher of Massachusetts. "You call Rufus King 'tricky' when you have just let slip the words 'ONE or two years in New York'? The deal was FOUR!"

Maclay had begun to walk slowly to the waiting coach. He shook his head, gave Thatcher a glance and sigh. "I am not able to stand here and answer you. It is too cold."

"It is too HOT!" shouted Jackson of Georgia, and everyone laughed as the stiff old Senator and his fellow Pennsylvanian, Hartley, climbed into the hired vehicle.

Hist.Cong., House Journ.,Jan.11, 15, 20, 21, 22, 25

"Well," said White of Virginia. "I've been counting the votes under this portico for de novo, and it looks as if the South is backed by Massachusetts and Connecticut. New York, too—according to King's remarks in the Senate last week. Even without Carroll, or a Senator from Virginia, and only half of North and South Carolina's delegates on hand, the vote for de novo looks very promising—which surely indicates the sentiment here is against Germantown."

Jan.25

The door behind them had opened and James Madison, with Senator Benjamin Hawkins of North Carolina, in joining them, heard White's comment as they entered.

It was Madison's first day of attendance, and he had remained silent while the House argued and voted, agreeing to a joint committee on de novo, and selecting its members.

Jan.20

Now he complimented the Southerners for their good work on de novo, and thanked the Northeasterners for their support.

"You have just missed the fun out here waiting for the coaches," smiled Alex White. "Senator Maclay entertained us with comments about Senator Morris and his speculating in war debt paper."

"Oh, much wild speculating must be going on!" exclaimed Senator Hawkins. "Just the other day, on my ride here from Carolina, two coaches with drivers, outriders, and postilions carrying guns passed us heading south. The curtains were drawn—no passengers visible.

Maclay's Journal
Jan.18

"'Treasure coaches,' our driver later told me, 'boxes of hard coin going to the Carolinas to buy something, maybe land', he said. He'd met one or two every week since November, he said—long before WE knew Hamilton's plan!"

Power of the Purse (E.J. Ferguson)

So stirred by these words that he did not notice his cloak flapping in the cold wind, Georgia Congressman Jackson declared vehemently, "So! These rich merchants in Philadelphia and New York knew months ago the Big Secret of Federal assumption of state debts, and funding of old certificates at full value months ago!

"WE heard about it only last week—and then through only ONE COPY of Hamilton's plan available to the House! Folks down home don't know about it yet! They're going to sell their debt certificates, their indents for unpaid interest, their old 'not worth a Continental' paper money—any and all for a few cents!" he exploded.

Hist.Cong.,House Journ Jan.14, 15, 16, Feb.22 (Boudinot)

From all directions questions came flying: How many in Congress were in on the Big Secret? Who told them? When would promised copies of Hamilton's plan be printed and delivered? How many million dollars did Hamilton say Federal and state wartime debts amount to? Senator Ellsworth had a few answers.

"I was told by Senator Elmer of New Jersey—a man many confide in—that HALF the Congress knew last month, and put money in the speculating. I also heard just today that Morris has a contract for $40,000 worth of debt-paper! We can assume, can't we, that the speculating half of the House and Senate will argue for and vote for the Hamilton plan."

"Ohhhh! Aughhh!" "And the OTHER half will vote against it!"

Madison commented that the pity of it was that the soldiers who fought the battles, and the patriots who furnished flour for the Army, had long ago spent their payment certificates greatly discounted for local debts. Speculators buying the certificates from uninformed merchants would in a few months profit 400 to 900 percent—millions of dollars.

"Who slipped the Big Secret to speculators?" Madison said. "If you look at the plan MORRIS proposed in '82 when he was Superintendent of Finance, you will see that Hamilton's present plan is almost identical. MORRIS taught Hamilton about business, money, and taxes. They are long-time friends. MORRIS recommended Hamilton to the President for Secretary of the Treasury.

"Gentlemen, draw your own conclusions."

In the silence that followed, a coach drew up. "Shall we go together?" Madison inquired. "The driver can drop each of us at our door."

All the men climbed in except the two from Connecticut who had only a half-block to walk to their dinner. Before the coach door banged shut, Senator Ellsworth called, "What did Hamilton say is the federal and state debt total?" Madison replied, "About $65,000,000, including back interest!"

Senator Ellsworth and Congressman Sherman looked after the departing coach, then at each other. Ellsworth spoke first. "I know a Philadelphia bar-

ber who papered his shop with Continental money. I think I should pay him a visit and take a sponge and scraper."

Sherman replied, "I know an old man in New Jersey who will shovel through his necessary pit when he learns every readable piece of used debt paper is now worth close to FACE value!"

SCENE 3
JEFFERSON'S ARRIVAL IN NEW YORK

PLACE: The President's Broadway residence between Wall Street and Battery Park, in the block between Beaver (Morris) and Exchange Streets.
TIME: Sunday afternoon, March 21, 1790

Spring sunshine warmed a brisk, chill breeze exercising the trees on Broadway, deserted on Sunday. Thomas Jefferson, tall, gangly, red haired and freckled, stood at the low front steps looking up at the four-story facade of the rowhouse into which Washington had moved from Cherry Street a month before. Only four years old, the pink-red mansion, formerly the French Legation, had 30 rooms, a deep backyard, stables, and other outbuildings.

For a moment, Jefferson studied the architectural details of the mansion, then straightened his cravat and coat. He felt unkempt after a 10-day ride in his coach bringing him 350 miles from Monticello, Virginia, to New York. He had stepped from the Hudson River ferry only minutes before, and walked the few blocks to the President's house. As he had approached Bowling Green Park on Broadway, he noticed the old Dutch fort in Battery Park was now a rubble-strewn construction site for the Presidential mansion the city was building.

Farther up the slope of Broadway, he had seen the weather-beaten ship labeled "Hamilton" sitting

Maclay's Journal
Jan. 15

A..Hamilton
(B.Mitchell)
p154-5, 162-3

J.Madison (Ketcham)
p136

Hist. Cong., House
Journ., 1790 (Gales/
Seaton) Hamilton
Report

Descrip/Analy. of
Remarkable Collection
of Unpub. Ms. R.Morris
(H.Homer)

Sources:

GW, Vol.6 (Freeman)

T.Jefferson (T.Fleming)

GW (Flexner) 243

GW Diary, Mar. 21

G.Washington Private
Affairs (Lear/Decatur)

NY 1789 (Smith) p17

President's Broadway
house

Private Affairs of GW
(Lear/Decatur)
p39, 331, 42, 130

GW's America (Tibble)
p289

GW , Vol. 6 (Freeman)
p252

in Bowling Green Park. A little beyond, he had arrived at Number 39-41, the President's front door, a few houses from Beaver Street.

Even though it was Sunday and he had no appointment on the President's one free day of the week, the new Secretary of State knew Washington would welcome his visit.

Excited, feeling a little in awe of the situation and of the central character, Jefferson rapped with the brass knocker on the massive door. Almost instantly the door opened and a young black man in red and white livery was saying, "Good morning, Sir."

"Thomas Jefferson, Secretary of State, to report his arrival to the President."

"The President is expecting you, Sir," he heard as he walked into a large hallway. In front of him, a winding flight of stairs lighted by a window in the roof led to the top floor. On each side of the entrance hall, Jefferson saw a spacious, high-ceilinged room, one a dining room with an extremely long table, the other a reception room sparsely but elegantly furnished. In each, two great mirrors in ornately carved and gold-leafed frames hung over the fireplace mantels.

From each ceiling hung an elaborate chandelier of whale oil lamps.

An older servant led the Secretary of State to the second floor. As they took the last steps on the stairs, Washington appeared in the doorway of a nearby room. Jefferson moved toward him, right hand extended. "Mr.President!"

The two men clasped hands and stood silently gazing eye to eye for a moment, their faces beaming. "It has been a long time since we met," said Washington. Jefferson nodded. "I see," the President added, "that both of us have acquired much more white hair in the passing of that time. Seven years, is it not?"

Silenced by a rush of emotion at his old friend's

words, his changed yet imposing appearance, Jefferson followed him into his office. He found his voice and recalled the scene seven years before in Annapolis, Maryland. "Your handing to Mifflin the paper by which Congress had given you great power as Commander-in-Chief of the Army deeply agitated my emotions. I had last seen you seven years before that day when, as newly-elected General, you set forth to fight a war. Majestic on your horse, you were departing Philadelphia to join the army at Boston.

"It was June 23, 1776," said Jefferson. "All the Congress, the Philadelphia Light Horse in white breeches and shiny hightop boots, and hundreds of men, women, and children came out on the road to see you off—a festive, sunny morning. You weren't three hours gone when Congress was handed the terrible news of the battle 10 days before on Breed's Hill and Bunker Hill in Boston. Even though we knew full-fledged battles would start, news of the first one shocked us. The one fact that buoyed our spirits was that you were on your way to take command."

Seated, Jefferson lolling sideways on one hip with legs crossed, Washington leaning against the back of his chair, soldier-straight, the men talked of Jefferson's new job. It would include more than foreign affairs. He would be in charge of weights and measures, lighthouses, patents, internal improvements—and other business that Congress had no better place to put.

Jefferson would have two chief clerks, two assistant clerks, and a part-time translator. Secretary of the Treasury Hamilton had an assistant secretary and bigger staff, but he had been pressed by Congress to work out a financial plan for the country in only three months, then to see it through Congress, and set it to work.

"I have not yet met Mr. Hamilton," Jefferson said, "but Madison has told me he will introduce me

GW Vol.6 (D.Freeman)

TJ (T.Fleming) p39

TJ (Fleming) p168

TJ (Fleming) p165

p246

Hamilton (Hecht)

T J. (Fleming) p245

shortly. Madison! There is truly a great man and mind! And a great friend—he found for me a house in Maiden Lane near the Virginians' rooming house."

The President nodded strongly. "I agree whole-heartedly with you about Madison. He has been—is—of inestimable value and assistance to me. Per-haps you have already heard how he and the Vir-ginians found a way to provide the Potomac an-other chance in the contest for the seat of govern-ment. Madison from his sickbed alerted his men to the danger of a call for an early, quick vote in the Senate to pass the bill of last session locating the capital at Germantown. They followed his direc-tions, and in his absence won treatment of post-poned bills as dead bills."

The two men smiled at each other. "I suppose," ventured Jefferson, "that a new bill will be forth-coming naming Potomac for permanent—with the temporary in New York? Or Philadelphia? What is Morris's plan? Madison wrote me that on the day of the Senate debate and vote on de novo, which was soon after Morris's arrival three weeks into Janu-ary, Morris was strangely silent."

Maclay's Journ., Jan. 25

Maclay's Journ., Jan. 25

Abruptly Washington rose from his chair and stood holding his right jaw in his hand, his head bowed. Alarmed, Jefferson got to his feet. "Some-thing is wrong!?" he said. The President shook his head, mumbled, "Excuse me," and walked into the adjoining room.

"Toothache," Jefferson said to himself. "I thought he had the last ones pulled at least a year ago. His hair is practically all white and he's wearing spec-tacles. He looks sallow. His face is deeply lined and sagging. His dentist-made teeth don't seem to fit well. But 58 is quite old, and a man's health is naturally less firm. If he can be preserved a few years more till habits of authority and obedience can be established generally in the country, we will have nothing to fear."

T J. (Fleming) TJ letter to Lafayette

The door opened and Washington, his teeth gone,

his mouth and cheeks sunken, returned.

"I have had great trouble with the one remain-ing tooth in my lower jaw," he said, his pronuncia-tion less distinct, "and I fear I must lose it. Dr. Greenwood—an excellent man, best dentist I have ever had—let it stay to anchor the lower plate." The President shook his head sadly. "My teeth have pained me almost all my adult life.

Private Affairs GW (Lear/Decatur) p124

"But let us go on with our business for a few more minutes. We were speaking of Mr. Madison. He is still smarting from his defeat in the House a month ago when he proposed that the original owners of debt notes be paid half the funded value, and present owners—speculators—receive the other half." Washington shook his head slightly.

"I know how much he hates the unfeeling, avari-cious speculators in the North who now possess these debt notes. I am convinced that Madison waged his fight from the purest motives and most heartfelt convictions. But the subject IS delicate, and perhaps had better never been stirred by our friend."

GW Writings Vol.31, p152

GW (Flexner)

Jefferson, hearing Washington's hint of his own support of funding and assumption, shifted to his other hip, and slouched back down into the chair. "If the House members continue to fight," Jeffer-son said, "voting half of them for, the other half against federal assumption of state debts, as well as the taxes to fund the interest on ALL these war-time debts, I see the greatest of all calamities—the total extinction of our credit in Europe!

GW (Flexner) p247-8

T J Papers (Boyd, Ed.)

"Just before I left Europe, Dutch bankers from whom we must have loans to pay interest on our nearly $12,000,000 of foreign debts, became very nervous about the American debt notes they hold. To get the money we needed from them on that day, I had to assure the bankers that the new American government would pay full value to them for ALL their American debt paper, both federal and state."

T J Papers (Boyd, Ed.) Hamilton Report figure

The President sat silent for a few minutes, eyes half closed and sunken mouth pursed. Jefferson waited uneasily for his comment. When Washington answered, he described an unofficial vote of the House on assumption.

Maclay's Journal,
Mar. 9

"Two weeks ago," he said, "after debating a month, the Committee of the Whole House stood 31 FOR assumption, 26 against, despite all ten Virginians, led by Madison, voting 'Nay.' But no House vote confirming it followed. A week later, still no vote. Instead, the House laid assumption aside and took up petitions of the Quakers and Dr. Franklin's Abolition Society against slavery. Those arguments are still going on, grow more acrimonious every hour, and no prospect for a way to stop them.

Hist. Cong., House
Journ., Mar. 13

"By the time they wind down, North Carolina's five House members will have arrived. They, too, OPPOSE assumption. Virginia delegates will welcome their votes FOR a Potomac capital and AGAINST Assumption. When Assumption next comes before the House, it may well be rejected."

Washington rose. "Come, let us turn our thoughts to more agreeable matters. I will show you our unobstructed view of the river and the Jersey palisades from the second-floor balcony at the back of the house. It will clear our heads to have a breath of fresh spring air."

Private Affairs GW
(Lear/Decatur) p148

As they walked the length of the hallway, Washington remarked upon the relief of living in a house big enough for his family of four, his three secretaries, and six in-house servants. "In the Cherry Street house, Tobias Lear, Colonel Humphreys, and Major Jackson shared ONE room—and a not very big one at that," he said. "Occasionally, I had junior aides—nephews and other lads—or a young relative going to school. To make a place to put them, I had to displace servants in the attic. In this house, the whole second floor is office and private family quarters, the third comfortably houses aides and visitors, and the roomy attic holds the principal household staff."

Below the balcony lay an oval plot of spring flowers ringed by boxwoods—a turnaround for carriages, convenient for the family's frequent drives along "the 14 miles around" Manhattan Island. The backyard sloped down to Greenwich Street, a dirt road bordering the high bank of the fast-moving Hudson, quite wide at this point.

At the far side of the backyard, near the street, a sizeable building was under construction. "Additional stables," said the President. "Twelve single stalls, a hay loft, and racks. Two of the old stable stalls now have cows in them. We need much cream and milk for entertaining. Other buildings house food, carriages, tools, the wash house, and quarters for a half-dozen Mount Vernon slaves.

Private Affairs GW
(Lear/Decatur)
p331, 42, 130

"We slept here for the first time the day after my fifty-eighth birthday," Washington remarked as the two men descended the stairs to the entrance hall. "I was busy three weeks supervising the wallpapering, painting, and carpentering. Then I had to select pieces from the furniture Moustier left behind, move in, arrange everything, decide endless details.

GW Diary
Feb. 23, 1790

"But now the house of the American President fits better his public duties. One benefit I see to delay in having a permanent seat is my pleasure living in this house for the time I must serve."

Private Affairs GW
p130

"Mr. President," Jefferson responded, "Americans are praying that the years you serve will be long, so as to firmly establish this government for all time. The people see you as their safest friend, exalted. They look up to you more than they do the Almighty, for they think you are nearer to them."

Smiling and bowing to each other, they parted.

GW (Flexner) 1790
Baltimore newspaper

Anxiety hangs over the Second Executive Mansion, (center) at 39-41 Broadway in mid-May 1790. Only three months after Washington moved to its spacious four floors—five at back—he lay desperately ill with pneumonia-pleurisy-influenza. In front of the house, chains across the street keep out noisy traffic. All expected Washington would die. Miraculously, he lived. In August, he moved again—to Philadelphia, with Congress.

CHAPTER 17

Grief

SCENE 1
VOTE-SWAP FEVER—SEAT FOR DEBT, DEBT FOR SEAT

PLACE: Senator Maclay's rooming house near junction of Nassau and Chatham Streets.
TIME: Easter Sunday, April 4, 1790, at 4 p.m.

Scene derived from
Maclay's Journal,
Apr. 4, 1790

In the center of a table set for six, women servants had just placed hot bowls of potatoes, turnips, sliced mutton, and rich gravy. Already a few of the men rooming in the house, mostly Pennsylvania Congressmen, stood behind their usual chairs at the dining table.

Within the next five minutes, all but three places had been claimed. Then came Senator Maclay walking slowly but majestically to his chair. He nodded and greeted the other men, looked around the table and asked in his forthright manner, "Where are the Muhlenbergs?"

One of the men mumbled something about "Jackson and Clymer."

"What? Who?" demanded Maclay. "You mean Major Jackson, the President's aide? He's here talking to the Speaker and General Muhlenberg? I see. They're all in the parlor and Clymer has come over to talk, too? Must be highly important business to merit missing dinner."

Midway through the meal, the front door shut with a bang. In a moment, 40-year-old Speaker Muhlenberg and his slightly older brother, the General, strolled into the dining room talking in low tones with emphatic hand gestures. They separated to take their accustomed seats, briefly greeted the other diners, and set to filling their plates.

No one asked a question. They said not a word,

kept their eyes on their plates, and ate quickly.

Maclay went on talking to Congressman Scott beside him, describing his visit to Baron Poellnitz's fancy farm two miles out Broadway from Wall Street. At the same time, Maclay was wondering to himself why the Speaker was making a mystery out of the visit of the President's secretary.

NY in 1789 (Smith)
p51

"Major Jackson's talking up Assumption of state debts, for sure," Maclay thought. "But I'm not going to ask the Speaker—no, I'm certainly not going to ask him."

Maclay finished dessert, a piece of warm apple pie, climbed the stairs to his room, and closed the door. Before he could pick up a quill to start a letter, there was a knock at the door, and the great bulk of Speaker of the House Frederick Augustus Conrad Muhlenberg entered. Carefully he closed the door behind him. He had come to unfold the mystery—and elicit support.

"My dear Senator Maclay," he began in his deep, sonorous voice. "Perhaps the others at the dinner table told you that my guest today was our own Congressman Clymer. He came with a most interesting proposal concerning the seat of government. We must begin making plans, you know. The House members impatiently look to the day when assuming and funding old debts gives way to the more interesting question of locating the federal city.

"Clymer proposed, and we all agreed, that Philadelphia's chance of getting the temporary seat of government is better if we bring up a simple motion for Congress to ADJOURN to Philadelphia. It sounds temporary—but once Congress is there, we'll make it hard for it ever to leave!" (Maclay seemed to nod.)

"Now, to win the vote for adjourning there, Clymer proposes we do a swap—with South Carolina and Massachusetts. Those two have the largest war debts of any of the states. They are anxious for the federal assumption of such state debts to be passed by Congress. On our side, we want the seat of government at Philadelphia. So, we vote for Assumption, they vote for ADJOURNING to Philadelphia!"

Speaker Muhlenberg's large, plump, and quite handsome face beamed with the beauty of the proposal. Senator Maclay's face knotted into a frown of dismay and disgust.

"Mr. Muhlenberg!" he exclaimed. "I am amazed that you would ever consider voting for Assumption! How many times have you publicly declared that if the vote was a tie and you had to break it, you would vote AGAINST Assumption! Now you want to make an out and out barter of Pennsylvania's votes! Was it the President's Major Jackson who persuaded you?"

Maclay's Journ., p220

Muhlenberg, crestfallen, protested. "No—not exactly—it's just that I now understand the plan better, and the effect of Assumption to consolidate and unite the states under a central government."

"Mr. Muhlenberg, you know as well as I do that the Hamilton plan is just one more part of a scheme to reduce the state governments to nothing! I don't like the Hamilton plan! I don't trust Hamilton! I'm going to get up and walk to Clymer's rooming house and ask him point-blank about this villainy of vote swapping!"

Muhlenberg quickly bade "Good evening, sir,"

to the gray-haired man with the formidable expression on his face, and retreated.

A few minutes later, George Clymer in his rooming house parlor a few blocks away, rose quickly from his chair beside Major Jackson when Maclay appeared in the doorway. "Senator!" exclaimed Clymer in a tone pushed close to joyful.

Maclay announced fiercely, "I came to tell you to your face that the proposal transmitted to me by Speaker Muhlenberg is disgusting and abominable! I will have no part in it!" Clymer's somewhat narrow eyes narrowed more, and his manner turned cold.

"Then you will excuse Major Jackson and me to continue our confidential talks," Clymer said stiffly. Maclay ignored his remark and cried, "How many of the delegation know all about these talks— Muhlenberg remarked that 'WE' are ALL agreed! Or is it only the Philadelphia men whose votes stand not for conviction but for monetary gains—which are there to be made in both the Hamilton plan and the federal city!"

Major Jackson rose to proclaim the rewards to both sides when states helped each other gain whatever benefited them most.

"It is a golden opportunity for Pennsylvania that South Carolina and Massachusetts, the two states suffering the most destruction in the war, have the biggest debts and the greatest need for help from the rest of the country! If you give them the votes to get rid of their debt burden, you will get their votes for adjourning to Philadelphia!"

Maclay nearly snarled his answer. "Your interfering for the court party is not proper! Assuming state debts in the proposed Hamilton plan is wrong! Bartering votes is villainy! Pennsylvania need make no such sacrifice to obtain Congress!"

Maclay's Journ. p225-6

Chin high with indignation, he departed. All the way home he vowed that henceforth he would avoid the company and "stinking manner" of Con-

Maclay's Journ., p205, 319

gressman George Clymer, merchant of Philadelphia. "As for 'Hamilton's gladiators'—Major Jackson, Humphreys, Nelson, and others straight out of the President's house—all of whom have been confidentially conversing with Congressmen and Senators lately," he fumed, "they are despicable tools of Hamilton, with the consent of our adulated Washington! Or so it appears!"

SCENE 2
SOUNDS OF SPECULATORS WEEPING

PLACE: House of Representatives, Federal Hall.
TIME: A week later, Monday, April 12.

Maclay's Journ. Apr.12, 1790

At last, after days of dissecting and arguing through Hamilton's plan for the federal government to assume at full value the remaining wartime debts of all the states, House members were about to take a vote on it. While only a Committee of the Whole vote, it was the first in five weeks and would show whether Assumption had a chance to pass or not.

Gentlemen sat or stood crowded in the galleries, and the public in various attire pressed to squeeze into seats and standing room below. Tension and secret anxiety had subdued the usual free-flowing conversation.

The Senators, who had nothing to do today but look at each other or sit by the fires and stoves chatting or plotting, had adjourned in time to find good seats in the House. Senator Maclay took a seat on the aisle in the front row of the public section to make sure he could see and hear all that happened during this vote that could foretell the fate of Assumption.

Hist. Cong., House Journ., Apr.12

Hardly more than an hour was spent on last-minute pleadings—Roger Sherman of Connecticut asking for aid for states (like Massachusetts and South Carolina) that had borne grievous burdens during the war; Pennsylvanians Clymer and Fitzsimons acclaiming Assumption but hoping for "adjustments"; short, blunt remarks from Southerners loath to be taxed for the benefit of states that had paid off few of their debts.

Maclay's Journ. Apr.12

Various Congressmen looked up at the gallery from time to time to observe Hamilton's "gladiators," Morris's business partner, a number of friends, business men, and Senators. Some leaned forward, listening intently to even the most tedious drone. Others sat morosely, chin propped in hand, awaiting the vote.

At last, the call came. Row by row, men in the galleries rose for a better view of who was voting "yea" or "nay."

At floor level, Maclay stretched to see the House members, and cupped his ear, listening for the voices of Pennsylvanians. He heard Clymer, Fitzsimons, and Hartley call, "Yea!"

Maclay's Journ., Apr.12

A few seconds of breathless silence while scorekeepers checked their arithmetic. Then the House secretary announced, "Twenty-nine 'yea', thirty-one 'nay', the question is—negatived!"

A cry and moan rose from the high galleries and the low public space. Men scrambled and pushed to hurry away.

"The price of state debt certificates is about to plunge, dragging down speculators, those in and those out of Congress," sniffed Maclay, and rose to leave.

But the scene on the House floor held him. "Clymer's color, always pale, now verges to a deadly white," Maclay's eyes told him. "And look! His lips are quivering and his jaw is shaking convulsively! His head, neck, and breast are heaving—like a turkey or goose strangling. The face of his friend Fitzsimons is scarlet, eyes brimful of tears. How deep are they in the speculating pit?"

Maclay looked along the two semi-circular rows

of desks on the House floor to locate the Congressman who had begun to speak. It was Sedgwick of Massachusetts bemoaning his state's condition without federal assumption of its debts—warning of violence whenever Federal taxes "invade those funds now pre-occupied by the state!" Sedgwick took his hat and left the Hall, later returning, Maclay noted, with visible marks of weeping on his face.

"And Fisher Ames of Massachusetts—what a total change of face and features! He sits torpid, as if his faculties are all benumbed. Connecticut's Wadsworth hides his grief under the rim of a round hat. New Jersey's Boudinot is frowning so, wrinkles rise in ridges, the angles of his mouth are depressed into a curve like a horseshoe.

"But they and the speculators will quickly dry their eyes," Maclay reflected as he departed. "This was only a test vote, only today's indicator of the opinion of the House acting as a committee. Plenty of time to change minds or swap votes. The bill must now come to the House floor and survive three votes or die. Motions to recommit, to amend, to reconsider, to postpone, can fill months—during which time the pressure to swap Assumption votes for seat-of-government votes will increase.

"The cost of votes for approving Assumption in both Houses will go higher and higher but in the end, whatever Madison and Carroll's price, Morris, Hamilton, and the speculating half of Congress will pay. They MUST pay. They absolutely MUST have Assumption to support their speculating, or they will all tumble from riches to rags—and debtors' prison."

SCENE 3
SOUNDS OF WEEPING AT THE PRESIDENT'S

PLACE: Broadway mansion of the President.
TIME: A month later, Saturday, May 15, noon.

Heavy chains stretched from one side of Broadway to the other in front of President Washington's residence. They have barred all carriages, wagons, horses, and street vendors from rumbling over cobblestones or shouting or clattering or clopping. Several small groups of gentlemen stood waiting in the street, talking quietly. Another group on the sidewalk near the front door of the mansion waited silently, with frequent glances toward the house. Anxiety hung in the air.

GW, Vol.6 (Freeman)

Private Affairs of GW (Lear/Decatur)

A tall, lanky man wearing a brimmed felt hat and plain clothes that looked a bit too small for him, approached the house. He bowed to the men near the door and lifted his hat.

"What are the doctors saying now?" he asked softly. "His condition is desperate, Mr. Jefferson. His death is not improbable," answered Senator Maclay. "Dr. McKnight told me a few minutes ago that he would not trifle with his own reputation nor the public expectation: The truth is, the President's most dangerous moment is imminent. The doctor says he has every reason to expect that the event will be unfortunate—"

Maclay's Journ., May 15

Maclay's voice broke. His eyes filled with tears, and he hurriedly turned away.

Jefferson went through the gate of the iron fence and rapped his knuckles lightly on the door. It opened a crack, then wider for him to enter. Alexander Hamilton's deep-set, dark-blue eyes greeted him gravely. He spoke to Jefferson in a whisper.

"Adams, General Knox, and Randolph are all in the reception room. Dr. McKnight was just here from the sickroom. The news is worse. The President appears to be dying. His breathing is hurried and shallow, and his circulation is weak." Hamilton covered his forehead and eyes with his hand, bowed his head, and turned away.

Jefferson pressed his lips together hard. His head, pounding with the migraine he had endured two weeks, drooped to his breast. A moment later, Hamilton touched Jefferson's arm and whispered, "His Rotundity, the v.p—what do we do about him?"

GW (Flexner) p246

Jefferson lifted his throbbing head, shrugged almost imperceptibly and said, "Nothing—yet."

They walked into the reception room and joined the Vice President and the two other department heads. In low tones, they recalled how and when they heard that the President had a cold a few days before, hoped he had not caught the flu that had struck down many people in the town.

"Madison was here an hour or so ago," Hamilton added, "and told us that the President has peripneumonia, united probably with influenza, a frightening combination. Madison is staying upstairs to help Mrs. Washington. She is exhausted from attending her husband all week, day and night, and is overwrought with anxiety besides."

GW Freeman) p259-60

Adams in his wig of white curls, had said nothing. He stood first with his left hand on his hip, then his right hand on his sword, his expression grim. His discontented blue eyes stared first at one, then another of the men, his lips working though firmly pressed together.

Edmund Randolph, handsome and fashionably attired attorney general, and also Washington's personal attorney, began speaking in a near-whisper to 300-pound General Knox, secretary of war and intimate friend of the Washingtons.

Jefferson and Hamilton standing together, apart from the others, spoke of Madison, his closeness to Washington, and how hard he would be affected by the President's death. "And so would I," murmured Hamilton, flicking a glance in the direction of Adams.

Almost as if he had heard them, Adams all at once announced he was going home. "My wife is ill. I must attend her. Ask Mr. Madison to send a messenger to my house if my presence is required."

Jefferson turned and bowed to the Vice President, saying in a manner that added significant meaning, "You will be the first to be summoned if there is any change, Mr. Vice President. Please give our respects to Mrs. Adams and our wishes for her good health."

Adams gave him a smile on one side of his mouth and bowed slightly as he hurried past, and out the door.

The four appointees of Washington—huge Knox, small and elegant Hamilton, tall and casual Jefferson, aristocratic Randolph—looked at each other, all with the same question in mind. Hamilton voiced it. "How long will Adams keep me as a department secretary?"

Then he added when the others acknowledged the question with various small movements and sounds, "The man has hated me with a passion since last year about this time. He uncovered that it was I who reminded the electors that Washington had said he would serve only if he had a unanimous vote. If Adams should also receive a unanimous vote for the vice presidency, it would create much awkwardnesss. The electors agreed. To avoid this situation, several threw votes to favorite sons. Adams got 39 votes, only a plurality—which he considered an insult, and for which he now blames me. On the other hand, he strongly supports my finance plan—"

Jefferson picked up where Hamilton's shrug left off. "Ben Franklin, whom I had just visited when he died last month, once said of John Adams, 'He is always honest, sometimes great, and often mad.'"

Hamilton blurted out, "I would subscribe to the justness of this picture, adding this: Honest and great as a man excessively vain and jealous and

John Adams

A.Hamilton (Hecht)

T.Jefferson and the Rights of Man (D.Malone)

ignobly attached to place can be."

Without responding, Jefferson continued, "Whatever position he takes—FOR not changing a single word in my Declaration draft, AGAINST the Potomac for the seat of government, FOR titles, forms, and ceremonies, which I deplore—he will fight madly to win."

Hamilton interrupted again. "Should Washington die today—God forbid—it would not surprise me if Adams' first move as President would be for a title change to His Mightiness.'"

"Still," Jefferson said, "if Washington dies, we will have in Adams an upright character, a devoted patriot who gave up family life, law practice, and fine income for many years to serve our country. He has my respect. But when Washington is no more—"

General Knox had been fumbling for his handkerchief to wipe his eyes. Now he blew his nose loudly while chopping the air with one hand. "Please!" he cried. "Do not speak again of General Washington dying! It is unbearable! He must not die or we shall have no use for titles, or seat of government, or finance plan—for the country will fall apart!"

Jefferson (T.Fleming)

J.Adams Vol.2 (P.Smith)

GW, Vol.6. (Freeman) p231

TJ, (Malone) 260

Jefferson, (Fleming) 61

SCENE 4
SOUNDS OF WEEPING AT ADAMS' HOUSE

PLACE: In John Adams' carriage, then at his home, Richmond Hill on Greenwich Road by the Hudson, a mile north of the President's mansion.
TIME: Immediately after Adams left the President's house.

Getting into his carriage on Broadway, John Adams let his feelings rage that none of the Secretaries, possibly excepting Jefferson, had said a word to acknowledge his critical position at this hour. But then they were Washington's men, and Washington was still alive.

As Adams rode away, his succession to the Presidency filled his thoughts. "There is only the failing breath of one mortal between me and the number one position. Until this day, I never expected there was the smallest prospect. Washington is very little older than I, and much stronger—until now.

"I know very well that I am not possessed of the confidence and affection of my fellow citizens to the degree that he is, but—I have done services for North America of which no man is ignorant and which cannot be forgotten. No one can deny that I am now the first prince of the country, and the heir apparent to the sovereign authority."

His carriage turned left by Trinity Church and proceeded down the slope to Greenwich Road and a right turn. In a few minutes, he was past the town. A mile farther along the Hudson River, his carriage ascended a long hill on a lane leading to Richmond Hill house.

All the way, Adams barely glanced outside at newly leafed trees—spring had been cold and late this year—at the expanse of water, or the bright blue sky, or the hills of Jersey. At the end of the tree-lined lane, a two-story brick house, its two-tiered front porch supported by a great column on

J.Adams (P.Smith) p.772-785, 847-851 (Adams's quotes, from his writings)

GW(Ford) and GW(Freeman) (Adams quotes)

Letter, Adams to Knox, Mar. 30, 1797

Dearest Friend: Life of Abigail Adams (L.Withey)

A.Adams's description

each side, matched the mood of the romantic rural scene. Birds fluttered and sang in the big old trees, and flowers bloomed on small trees and shrubs in the open yard. Graceful if somewhat run-down, the house overlooked the river on one side, and the distant town of New York on the other. The sight of the place always gave John Adams a pleasant if brief pause in his self-assessing, or his rambling, emotional rebuttal to criticism, or his brooding over the lack of appreciation for his lifetime of service to his country.

J.Adams(Smith)

Adams sighed with relief to see no sign of visitors. Even when Abigail was ill, which was often, they had callers who were returning visits and expecting tea, or coming to the regular Monday afternoon levee, or coming to talk politics with the Vice President.

Private Affairs of GW (Lear/Decatur)

But of course today was different. For Washington, everything had stopped—Congress, social engagements, even the church bells. Anxiety about the sick hero in the house on Broadway had put all into a waiting mode.

Besides that, Mrs. Adams—Abigail—was still languid from the raging fever of a few weeks past, and her rheumatism troubled her, though it had subsided during these warmer days.

Her husband found her reclining on a chaise-lounge, book in hand, staring out the window. "How is he?" she asked at once. Adams waved her to stay where she was, and sat on the edge of her couch.

"He is dying."

Their eyes met and held. "Oh, my poor John!" she cried and leaned to embrace him. "What a disaster! Only the prestige of Washington is holding this country together! If he dies and leaves you, my dearest friend, to preside over the disintegration of the Union, the difficulties might well carry you to an early grave with misery—even disgrace!" Tears ran down her cheeks. "We must beg Providence to spare him until the country's finances are

A.Adams (C.W.Akers) p119 (quotes)

GW (Freeman) p231

arranged and our government under the Constitution sufficiently cemented to promise duration."

John Adams helped his wife dry her tears.

"Yes," he said quietly, "it is fortunate that Americans have a strong leader, a Washington to adore, a man of virtue so exquisite and wisdom so consummate. We must not think of the Presidency as a prize awarded by historical judgment to the individual who has made the greatest sacrifices, or endured the greatest hardships. For the well-being of the nation, Washington is clearly the man.

J.Adams Vol.2 (P.Smith) (quotes)

"However—" he rose to his feet and gazed at the sky through the window—"there is the fact that tomorrow I may be President. I AM the Vice President. In this I am nothing—but I may be everything. Certain principles follow us through life and none more certainly than the love of first place.

"If I am to have it, we must accept that and think about what we must do tomorrow after the swearing-in ceremony. I wonder where is the best place to have that." Holding his hands together to control their usual tremor, now accentuated by nervous excitement, he called forth a list of duties, actions, decisions, and policy changes that would face him as President.

GW Himself (Fitzpatrick) p170 (Adams quotes)

J.Adams (Smith)

"Certainly some changes in the department heads. A strong statement supporting Hamilton's financial plan should help it through Congress quickly—after which—" Abigail nodded vigorously, "Yes, he must go sooner or later. He is as ambitious as Julius Caesar. Oh, I have read his heart in his wicked eyes many a time! The very devil is in them! They are lasciviousness itself!"

A.Hamilton (Hecht) p322 (A.Adams quote)

"I would prefer," the Vice President continued, "a more fitting title for America's Chief Executive. The courts of Europe can have little respect for this simple title we have settled upon. It will also make considerable difference where the First Lady and I live in an executive mansion. I will throw my weight behind New York and Philadelphia for the tempo-

Maclay's Journ , Spring 1789 (Titles debate)

J.Adams (Smith)
p770-825

rary and permanent seats of government—which will mean, my dear, that you would not be obliged for some years to leave this delicious spot, this most pleasing house, where as President I would choose to remain."

A.Adams (C.Akers)
p.121

Abigail listened attentively and responded sympathetically as he discoursed on how glad he would be to give up the position of Vice President. He had imagined he would be rather like a prime minister. Instead, it had been the most boring, laborious, powerless, insignificant, demeaning job ever contrived. "Yet, my tie-breaking votes have decided most of the main questions thus far, so I do have some power!"

GW (Flexner) p213

They talked for hours. Adams spoke long about the Assumption debate and Madison's stubborn opposition. "Mr. Madison," he fumed, "is a studious scholar, but his reputation as a man of abilities is a creature of French puffs. (He lifted his eyebrows high to emphasize "French".) Some of the worst measures, some of the most stupid motions stand on record to his infamy." Abigail rebuked him for saying too much too loosely.

J.Adams (Smith) p789

A.Adams (Akers) p118

James Madison (Ralph Ketcham) p310 (Quotes J. Adams letter)

At three o'clock, they joined young son Charles, daughter Nabby, her husband Colonel William Smith and four-year-old Willie at the dinner table. All afternoon, whatever they did, the questions of whether and when bore upon their minds.

Soon after 5 o'clock, short, rotund John pulled his wig over his bald pate and invited his shorter, plumper, younger wife to take a walk. The waiting had made him nervous and fidgety. Arm in arm they wandered aimlessly from one flowering shrub to another.

Abigail was breaking a bouquet of yellow bells when Adams suddenly said, "There he is! News at last!" A horseman was galloping toward them on the wooded lane.

Almost before his mount stopped, the rider, one of the military guards at the executive mansion, jumped down and hurried toward the Vice President and his wife.

The messenger was smiling. Saluting, he said, "Mr. Adams, Sir! He lives! The President lives! Our great President George Washington has come through the crisis and will live!"

GW Vol.6, (Freeman) p261n (Jefferson's account of GW illness)

The messenger repeated what Mr. Jefferson had told him—that at four o'clock, the President began to sweat a lot and to cough up heavy expectoration. He began to talk distinctly, with good sense. It was now certain that he had passed through a favorable crisis! He was even sitting up in bed!

From the town, the sound of a joyous jumble of church bells began to sing. Abigail clapped her hands together, saying, "He lives! Thank God he lives! What unhappy thoughts of our future I can now put aside! What burdens we would have had if our worthy President had died!" She threw her arms around her husband's shoulders and kissed his cheek. Immobile, he looked at her, his mouth open, his eyes half closed. Quickly he recovered.

A.Adams (Akers) (quotes)

"Please return to Mr. Jefferson and tell him that Mr. and Mrs. Adams are relieved and happy at the turn of events."

Adams linked his arm in Abigail's, and walked with her toward the house.

When they reached the door, he finally spoke. "So you will not reign tomorrow as First Lady after all, my dear."

Abigail faced him, took his hands in hers and said, "My ambition extends no further than reigning in the heart of my husband. That is my throne and there I aspire to be absolute."

A.Adams (Akers) (quotes) p214

John Adams, Vice President, and his wife Abigail, wait at Richmond Hill house expecting to hear that President Washington has died and Adams is President. But the messenger whose steed galloped the mile from Broadway and Wall in New York to Greenwich Village shouted with joy, "He lives! The President lives!"

President Washington returns from a 3-day fishing trip, his first outing since his near-death three weeks before. Jefferson, suffering from migraine headache, accompanied him. Both feel stronger and Jefferson's pains have abated. The borrowed yacht has brought them within close view of New York's skyline of June 1790, and almost within hearing of the snits and snarls of Congressmen trying to capture the seat of government for their favorite town.

190

CHAPTER 18

Upstairs, Downstairs in Federal Hall

SCENE 1
OFF TO PHILADELPHIA ?

PLACE: Senate, Federal Hall, upstairs.
TIME: Late May, 1790, about 10 days after the near-death of President Washington.

Scene and quotes derived from [Maclay's Journal](#), mid-May, 1790, and [History of Congress, Senate Journal](#), mid-May.(Gales/Seaton)

[NY City in 1789](#) (Smith)

While the proposition to swap votes for anything with anybody still made Senator Maclay's face screw into a frown of disgust, the idea of "adjourning" to Philadelphia had sprouted and flowered in his heart.

Every day he found more and more reasons to dislike being in New York. He made mental lists of little but repeated events when he was overcharged, ignored, spoken to rudely, not spoken to at all, served badly cooked food, or spoiled food in a tavern. He hated dogs barking all night, slops tossed out windows on passersby, runaway hogs on muddy sidewalks, strong sea breezes, night soil collected in buckets that blacks had to carry on their shoulders and empty into the rivers—unless a stumble spilled it on the street.

Philadelphia, he said to himself, was far better organized and maintained, cleaner, better smelling, less costly, more interesting. Besides all that, his travel time would be halved, and he had many friends in Philadelphia, none in New York.

The longer he mulled over his dissatisfactions, the more merit he saw in the idea of Clymer, Major Jackson, and Speaker Muhlenberg to adjourn, IMMEDIATELY, to Philadelphia.

Maclay spoke to Senator Morris about the idea. Morris hung back, doubting that anybody would vote to adjourn in the middle of a session, and unwilling himself to put such a move before the Senate. "If somebody outside Pennsylvania will make the motion, I'll vote for it," he said. Nobody was willing, though Maclay spent a few days looking. "Well, then," said Morris, "I will move to adjourn to Philadelphia for the meeting of the Second Congress NEXT MARCH.

"By implication, Philadelphia then becomes the TEMPORARY capital, and by practicality the PERMANENT CAPITAL—if Congress continues to disagree on the permanent location."

On May 24, Morris made the motion, and Langdon of New Hampshire, his long-time, intimate friend, seconded. A dead pause.

Adams without further ado said, "Are you ready for the question?"

"NO!" cried the New Yorkers. Morris agreed to a one-day wait, then watched King, Schuyler, and Dr. Johnson huddle with South Carolina's Pierce Butler and Ralph Izard, Georgia's William Few and James Gunn, and newly-arrived former Governor Johnston of North Carolina.

When, on May 26, Morris called for debate and a vote on his Philadelphia motion, he did it with a laugh—not a smile, or even a broad little smile, but a hearty laugh. It was apparent he had been doing some huddling, too. "I now call up my motion— HAW HAW—that Congress shall meet and hold— HAW HAW—their next session in the city of Phila-

[Maclay's Journ.,](#) p271

[Hist.Cong., Senate Journ.](#) Mon. May 24

[Hist.Cong., Senate Journ.](#) Wed. May 26

Maclay's Journ.
May 26

delphia! HAW HAW HAW!" With every laugh, he had glanced around, mostly at Mr. King of New York, who laughed back. So did a few others.

Maclay looked on in amazement. What secret doings were afoot?

King then rose to say it would not be fair to New York City to leave it so soon. Butler and Few said they worried that Congress would never leave Philadelphia if it moved there.

Maclay set them straight. "PERMANENT residence? Oh, that could never be! Pennsylvania would not give up to Congress the state's only port, a city holding almost a third of the state's wealth and population! But the deliberations of Congress on locating the permanent seat of government could be carried on there to the greatest advantage!"

Butler called, "Postpone!" and the Senators from the states south of Virginia joined the northerners to postpone the motion for a week.

Morris still smiled. He walked over to King of New York. They laughed together.

Maclay, watching, said to himself, "Morris was not serious about adjourning to Philadelphia. He obviously has made a deal with King. It can only mean Falls of the Delaware for Morris, New York for King." He watched King and Morris leave together, laughing and talking.

Maclay's Journ.
May 27

But the next afternoon, Morris arrived at his desk so angry he could not complete a sentence without swearing— "dammit! Hell's bells!" His pink cheeks flamed, his sharp blue eyes flashed, his tongue spluttered. "That two-faced New Yorker— King—lied—led me on—and all the time he was bargaining for New York and Potomac with the South Carolinians. He made a deal with them! Butler will front for them, announce it tomorrow, launch it Monday—to name ONLY the permanent seat— Potomac! So New York sneakily keeps Congress until the permanent is built! Augh!!

"I shall not be made to look like a fool—I shall

this day withdraw my motion to adjourn to Philadelphia! They would vote it down and laugh! It has no chance to win!"

Maclay thought it might have a chance, but Morris impetuously withdrew his motion anyway.

As they were leaving after adjournment at three o'clock, Congressman Fitzsimons ran up to tell them that he had introduced Morris's "adjourn to Philadelphia" resolution in the House and it would be taken up on Monday, the same day the Senate would take up Butler's Potomac (New York) bill!

During the weekend, words flowed freer than wine in taverns, coffeehouses, and boarding houses about sly implications in both actions and the interesting situation if BOTH succeeded. Or if the House acted first and passed the resolution for Philadelphia, should the Senate stop debate on (New York) Potomac?

Hist. Congress, Senate,
May 27, 1789 (Gales/
Seaton)

With America's two biggest cities antler-to-antler in mortal combat, Maclay, Morris, Fitzsimons, and Clymer moved among the delegates to speak plainly: "Pennsylvanians will NOT STAY in New York, but will vote for any other place whatever!"

For the next 10 days, both Houses came alive, busily engaged in the exciting sport of jousting for the capitals.

Maclay's Journ.
May 27

SCENE 2
DOWNSTAIRS JOUSTING

PLACE: House Chamber, Federal Hall, downstairs.
TIME: Monday, May 31, 1790, 10 a.m.

Quotes and scene drawn from History of Congress, House Journal, May 31, 1790. (Gales/Seaton)

Congressman Fitzsimons of Pennsylvania had just called up his "adjourn to Philadelphia" resolution. Immediately cries of "No!" "No!" resounded.

Sherman (Connecticut) and Livermore (New Hampshire) cried out almost in chorus: "But this is not the time to bring up a resolution on this inflammatory subject!" "It always distracts everybody from more important business!" "We ought to take up the third and final reading of the Funding bill today—and vote!"

Vining (Delaware): "No, no—this seat resolution is different. The question is in its most simple form. No permanency question, no temporary question— it's in an abstract form. It's pure! You can vote simply your feelings—no combinations or deals have been made by anybody!"

Laurence (New York) and Thatcher (Massachusetts): "We should take up funding first! The public does not care two paper dollars whether we sit in New York, Philadelphia, or on the Potomac!"

White (Virginia): "Take up the seat resolution—it can soon be determined. In the last session, a big majority voted for Germantown as permanent—so there can't be much difficulty in fixing on Philadelphia for temporary! Put the question NOW!"

Parker (Virginia): "Think of all the inconveniences of this town we're in! It's not central, Southerners are too far from home, New Yorkers are not friendly, everything is double-priced, the town is smaller and less comfortable than Philadelphia!"

Gerry(Massachusetts): (Speaking at length, he finally said it all in one sentence.) "It is of more consequence t-t-to the people what Congress DO than where they SIT."

Smith(South Carolina): "The members of Congress were chosen to meet at New York. I think it quite unnecessary that the members should be dragged away to another place. Let's vote whether we take up this subject, and get it over with!"

"Take it up!" won, 32 to 27.

Protests from losers broke off when Elias Boudinot threw in a Morriscracker that set off an explosion of shouts.

"I move (he said) that we AMEND to fix the PERMANENT seat at some convenient place on the banks of the DELAWARE RIVER!"

"No! No!" "Yes! Yes!"

"Out of order!" declared Speaker Muhlenberg.

Boudinot appealed the ruling. Yeas and nays tied. The Speaker's "nay" dismissed the amendment.

"Let's discuss fully as Committee of the Whole the resolution to adjourn to Philadelphia!"

"NO!" voted the members.

"Let's amend—strike Philadelphia, insert Baltimore!"

"No, let's amend—insert Wilmington!"

"Sir, you said that to embarrass me! You know Wilmington hasn't a chance!" said John Vining, Delaware's one member.

"Why sir," soothed Fisher Ames of Massachusetts, "the gentleman from Connecticut did not intend to embarrass. We have uniformly discovered a predilection for Wilmington!"

Someone laughed a short, loud "HA!"

An argument began respecting only Philadelphia and Baltimore. After a number of speeches for and against each, Fitzsimons rose to say, "Gentlemen, when I brought up my resolution to adjourn to Philadelphia, I only wanted to remove us from New

York—to ANYWHERE but particularly to my choice, Philadelphia. To open it to YOUR choice, I move we drop Philadelphia and leave a blank space to be filled in by the choice of the House."

The House agreed. Immediately the blank was filled with New York. "No!" voted 35 of 60.

"Baltimore!" "Philadelphia!" (both shouted at the same instant).

"Which shall we vote on first?" said the Speaker.

"I was first!"

"No, you weren't—I was first!"

Baltimore went first. "NO!" voted 38 Southerners and Pennsylvanians, overwhelming 22 Maryland and Northern votes.

Then came Philadelphia. "YES!" voted 38 Southerners and Pennsylvanians.

Elated, the Pennsylvanians shook hands with all the Southerners, especially Virginians. The vote made it clear that when ALL the Pennsylvanians and Southerners voted together in the House, they could win. Today's win meant Senator Butler's bill requiring three readings and debates had lost the time race. "Adjourn to Philadelphia" resolution with the weight of the House behind it, and requiring only one debate and vote, would precede Butler's bill on the Senate calendar.

Or would it?

SCENE 3
UPSTAIRS SNITS AND SNARLS

PLACE: Senate Chamber, Federal Hall, upstairs.
TIME: The next day, Tuesday, June 1.

Minutes after the House had passed the Pennsylvanians' "adjourn to Philadelphia" resolution on Monday, the news had raced upstairs to the Senators creating waves of wordy speculation.

It jostled second thoughts from Mr. King and Mr. Butler in regard to leaving out of their bill mention of a temporary seat. Now that the House had named Philadelphia as temporary, the Senate might in one vote for the House resolution cut New York, by implication or otherwise, out of the running.

In a few hours, the House resolution would arrive in the Senate. What quick change in Butler's bill might spur the Senate to favor debating it first, open up chances for deals, scatter the sentiment for Philadelphia, and thereby kill the House resolution? the New York supporters asked themselves.

Just before Monday's adjournment, Butler rose with an answer. He had changed his mind, he told his fellow Senators, and wished to offer a replacement bill with TWO BLANKS, one into which his colleagues could place any town's name for the permanent seat, the second for the place name of a temporary seat.

By Tuesday morning, Butler (and King) had had third thoughts. Suppose (as rumor said) some obstreperous Senator proposed debating the House resolution and the Butler bill together—a set-up for a Philadelphia-Potomac elopement!

Better to withdraw the Butler bill and concentrate fire on the unfairness of abandoning New York and the expense it had incurred to provide Federal Hall and other facilities for Congress.

"Mr. President," Butler said when Adams opened Tuesday's session with the two-blanks bill, "I wish

Scene and quotes drawn from Maclay's Journal, and History of Congress, Senate Journal, May 31, June 1, 1790. (Gales/ Seaton)

Maclay's Journ.
Monday, May 31

that my bill NOT be taken up at all since the House yesterday passed a resolution on the subject. We may appear to be courting a difference with the House if we take up the same subject but with a different objective."

From various parts of the chamber, voices called, "Agreed! Agreed!"

Adams laid the bill aside. A message from President Washington announcing that Rhode Island had ratified the Constitution was read and some small bits of business were done.

All at once, Adams picked up Butler's bill and began to read it.

Read of Delaware interrupted.   "SIR! I remind you! There is the matter of the House resolution passed yesterday, and on its way over to us. I do not think it proper for the Senate to proceed on a different bill concerning the same subject."

Butler rose to agree. "As I said before, I move that my bill concerning the seat of government be committed."

"You said withdraw 10 minutes ago. What's the point of committing it?" demanded Charles Carroll. "Why not withdraw it?"

Then rose Maclay to fufill the worst fears of Butler and King. "I agree there is no point in committing it. None of us can affect ignorance of the resolution that passed yesterday in the House—for the next session to meet in Philadelphia.

"At any moment the Senate door will open and the resolution brought in. We should not take up any bill on the subject BEFORE we deal with the House action. I move that the bill of the South Carolina Senator lie on the table until the House resolution arrives, and we treat them TOGETHER."

Butler replied hotly, his voiced tuned to the whine of insults.

"The gentleman from Pennsylvania can always be expected to put a stumbling block in the way of anything that brings nothing to Pennsylvania! He is always strict about the right and proper thing IF he expects Pennsylvania is to benefit!"

Just then, the door of the Senate opened, and the clerk of the House entered with a paper in his hand. As Butler saw him give it to Adams, his face and manner flamed with color and frowns, his voice with invectives. "Greedy conspirators! Holier than thou sneaks and hypocrites—!"

Adams rapping his silver pencil case on his desk cut Butler off, laid Butler's bill aside, and ordered the House resolution for debate the next day.

New excitement started off the next morning— the House, first thing, had heard the final reading and taken the final vote on the funding part of the finance bill. It had passed on a voice vote, and was on its way to the Senate.

With this to discuss among themselves, the Senators waited more than two hours for the arrival of Robert Morris; the previous day, after adjournment, he had hurried in, sweaty and dusty from his ride from Philadelphia, and excused himself to spend the next morning tending his own money machine farther down Wall Street.

At half past noon, when Morris took his seat, Adams opened the session with Butler's bill. On a tie vote to postpone and take up the House resolution instead, Adams voted "nay." His "yea" on the next tie vote sent Butler's bill to committee. His next "yea" sent the House resolution to the same committee.

Adams then appointed Senator Butler to head the committee!

Pierce Butler

SCENE 4
FRIENDS OF PHILADELPHIA

PLACE: Private dining room at Brannan's Gardens, an oyster house.
TIME: Monday, June 7, some hours after Senator Butler presented to the Senate his committee report on locating the capital.

"A toast to our enemies!" proclaimed Senator Morris, opening the post-dinner meeting of the Pennsylvania Senators and their guests—nine Senators from Maryland, Virginia, Delaware, New Jersey, and New Hampshire. "To all of them a cobweb pair of breeches, a porcupine saddle, a hard trotting horse, and a long journey!"

They laughed and laughed, and Morris laughed the hardest and loudest. When all had recovered, he addressed them.

"Gentlemen," he said, mopping his brow and pushing back his long, loose, gray hair, "Mr. Butler and his committee have circumvented us by suppressing the House's Philadelphia resolution and offering the Senate only HIS bill. He is ignoring the will of the House of Representatives and putting in its place the will of Butler and King.

"We must bring back the House resolution for Philadelphia. We must ready a plan for it to win. A resolution requires only one voting, not three like a bill. So, tomorrow, and perhaps tomorrow only, we have a chance to move this Congress from disagreeable New York to Philadelphia. In comfort there, we can resume the tug-of-war concerning the permanent capital.

"We know who our enemies are and how many—13. They know who we are and how many—11.

"But we all know that two of their men are sick abed—Governor Johnston of North Carolina and Dr. Johnson of Massachusetts. They will not attend tomorrow. So tomorrow we must capture the Floor

first thing and bring forward the House resolution adjourning to Philadelphia."

Senator Lee of Virginia interrupted.

"Butler will strongly object. He will claim, as he did in our committee meetings, that committees don't have to report out resolutions—'they're only resolutions, not bills,' he says, and he further says if the committee chooses not to report it out, the resolution is dead."

A rumble of comment from all 10 Senators greeted this revelation. Robert Morris called loudly to Senator Lee, "Since you served on that committee, Senator, tell us who said what."

Lee nodded and proceeded. "Mostly it was Butler talking a mile a minute, and loud, with the two other Senators nodding in agreement. I was resisting at every step.

"Butler dressed up his logic in pretty speeches to us, but the creature underneath is this: He wants the usual tussle to break out between North and South members. Local ambition, he says, will kill any move to bring 'adjourn to Philadelphia' back to life. He will then put 'Potomac' in the blank for permanent seat, expect to make a vote-swap between the Southerners and Northerners, and keep Congress in New York four or more years.

"If Potomac supporters refuse to agree to endure four more years in New York, then back to the tussle, and the Northeast men will take any offer to team up with New York."

Morris declared loudly that if the New Yorkers treated Potomac men the way they treated him about Delaware Falls, "your river will never see Congress!"

Senator Lee banged his hand on the table. "What most offends me is the contempt Butler and his crowd show for an action of the House!"

With that, the famous "fuse-lighter Lee" who made the motion in 1776 to write out and send to the King a Declaration of Independence, stood up and said vehemently, "Gentlemen, I move that we enemies of New York agree to stick together on a plan of action, and carry it out tomorrow when 11 votes can win!"

Eleven voices cried "Yea!" Lee offered a plan. "First, we move to postpone Butler's bill, then we call for the House resolution. If Butler manages to withhold it, and get his bill on the floor anyway, we force a stalemate by voting as a BLOCK against EVERY motion so that nothing his men bring up will win!"

Morris exclaimed, "By God, I would vote against my own Falls of the Delaware if that would stop the rascals!"

"Or against Germantown?" asked Carroll.

"Especially against Germantown!"

Lee proposed a resolution, and it was adopted unanimously: "That as the business of a permanent residence is brought forward by our enemies evidently with a design of dividing us, we will uniformly vote against every plan named for the permanent residence."

"Now for the order of action," said Lee. "I will gain the Floor before Butler can, and I will move that the Butler bill be postponed so that the House resolution can be taken up."

"Excellent!" "We can win that! With Johnston and Johnson sick, it's 11 to 11—and Adams, friend of Philadelphia, will make us 12!"

"Who will second my motion?" Langdon of New Hampshire, an old friend of Morris, volunteered and the course was set.

"Senator Few of Georgia, one of Butler's recruits, is a little lame," said Senator Bassett of Delaware, his voice ringing with hope. "Maybe he'll stay home, too, and we won't need Adams's vote."

SCENE 5
THE PRESIDENT'S FISHING PARTY

PLACE: East River, within a half-mile of a wharf by Cherry Street, aboard a sizeable yacht, a sloop on loan to President Washington recuperating from his recent illness.

TIME: Wednesday, June 9, about 5 p.m.

George Washington in a floppy-brim straw hat, his gardening clothes, and a plain wool jacket, sat in a yacht chair enjoying the sun, sea air, and company of Thomas Jefferson. Sailors and the captain attended the sails and rudder, tacking in a light wind. From the cabin, which had bunk rooms, a galley, and a dining area, a sailor brought a tray with cups and a pot of the President's favorite hyssop tea.

American Ships of Colonial and Revolutionary Period (J.F.Millar)

The sloop had taken the President on his first outing since his narrow escape from death three weeks before. He and Jefferson had spent three days anchored mostly on the fishing banks called Sandy Hook just beyond the tips of Manhattan and Long Island. They caught sea bass and blackfish daily, giving Washington the pleasure of eating his favorite food for breakfast, dinner, and supper.

Private Affairs of GW (Lear/Decatur)

The sea air and change of scenery, the conversations with Jefferson about their days in Williamsburg when both served in the Virginia House of Burgesses before the Revolution, about Jefferson's experiences in Paris and his concern for the growing violence of the Revolution in France, about farm crops and implements, architectural features they had added to their homes—everything except office work, people, and problems on shore—made Washington feel stronger, and Jefferson's migraine headache abate.

Gazette of U.S., June 12

The weather all three days and nights had remained perfect. Washington was particularly grateful, remembering how he had suffered from seasickness during his one voyage abroad, a trip to

GW Vol.1 (Freeman)

Two Senators—Dr. Johnson of Connecticut (left) and Gov. Johnston of North Carolina (right)—sick with flu but brought from, or in, their beds to vote, arrive in the second-floor Chamber. Without their votes, New York would lose in one of the many tussles between that city and Philadelphia for the temporary capital.

Barbados when he was 18. He had accompanied his half-brother who had the coughing disease and believed Barbados would be good for his health. It did him no good, nor George either, for he spent most of his time there confined indoors with a mild case of smallpox.

As the yacht came closer to shore, the two men on deck saw a small crowd on the wharf. "They always seem to know where and when I am going to appear," Washington remarked. "I cannot leave the house or return to it without finding a little crowd lined up to watch."

"And applaud," added Jefferson.

They watched for a few minutes—then noted that one, no, two men were waving large white handkerchiefs. "It's Madison—and Lee," said the President. "I had suggested that they join us at sea to give us a private and frank account of House and Senate news. Our reprieve from government business is over."

The President called to a crewman and requested anchoring the ship where it was "for an hour or so, and bring out two more chairs for the men now approaching by row boat."

In a few minutes, Madison and Lee were clambering up the rope ladder and crewmen were pulling them aboard.

Rowboat and rowers gone, crewmen busy tending the sails, and tea cups taken away, Lee began his report on the behavior of the Senators during the past three days in regard to funding and the seat of government.

"Mr. President," began Lee, laughing and looking a little embarrassed, "I would be loath to tell you the absurdities of yesterday's Senate session—except that they are so excruciatingly hilarious.

"You know the set of characters—South Carolina's Senators Butler and Izard, the Vice President, Rufus King of New York, Gunn of Georgia, Oliver Ellsworth of Connecticut, and others. Butler had to

While no record tells of Lee and Madison joining Washington and Jefferson on the sloop to describe the actions of Congress, there is a record of the fishing trip, and of Madison, the President's man in Congress, reporting to him regularly. Senator Lee would have been the member to report on Senate action. Maclay's Journal gives details that fill in the bare outline in the Senate Journal for June 8, 1790.

think of a way to block a vote on a House resolution that called for Congress to adjourn to Philadelphia. You have heard, no doubt, how Butler hates Quaker preaching against slavery, and how friendly he has become with New Yorkers and other assumption pushers in New England.

"Well, Butler's way of killing the House action was simple—his committee threw it aside as 'just a resolution' and reported HIS bill instead! Its main purpose was to keep Congress in New York.

"As enemies against remaining in New York, 11 of us—Senators from Virginia, Maryland, Delaware, Pennsylvania, New Jersey, and New Hampshire—met and agreed on a counterattack.

"Yesterday I arranged with Mr. Adams to recognize me first when the session began, to present a routine matter—and I held the floor to move that Mr. Butler's fill-in-the blanks bill be postponed so as to take up the House resolution to adjourn to Philadelphia.

"Both Butler and Izard jumped out of their seats and began to shout, 'You are insulting the committee! You can't call up a resolution from a committee all on your own! The committee decided NOT to call it up! You are forcing the will of the minority—your position—on the Senate!' And much more. Izard talks louder than Butler, and, when he chooses, in a fluent gutter style. Butler constantly leaps from his chair to add something to Izard's flow, then sits on his chair-edge, ready to spring. They moved to postpone my motion.

"Finally we came to the vote. A tie—11 to 11. Mr. Adams, as we expected, voted with us to call up the House resolution.

"Izard and Butler went at it again, this time demanding a recess, saying they had been taken advantage of, and the vote wasn't valid since two of their men were on their way to vote. Adams actually called a recess and let them go out to 'hurry' their men! We knew they were in bed sick with flu

in nearby rooming houses.

"A half-hour later, Izard and Butler and some roustabouts brought them in! First was Johnston of North Carolina in his nightcap and gown, all wrapped in a cloak. Izard hung onto him at one side, Butler at the other, pulling the poor man along. He's been in bed a week and looked bearded, dull-eyed, and feeble.

"But the big spectacle came just behind him—four men carrying his bed! They set it down in the chamber, then took it to a committee room so Johnston could get into it between votes.

"In a minute, here came four men bearing a sedan chair! Dr. Johnson of Connecticut climbed out of that, helped by the agitated Butler. Johnson had on plain clothes, a head shawl topped by a tricorn—he's only half-well from flu. Senator Few of Georgia limped in by himself, just in time for the vote. Being somewhat lame in the leg, he looked as if he might fall into a heap.

"All this spectacle of getting the sick men in their places, and their beds and conveyances installed provided high entertainment."

By this point in the story, the President and Jefferson were laughing heartily. Lee paused to laugh with them. Madison, who had heard the story several times, snickered, still finding it amusing.

"The debate was noisy," Lee went on, "the talk back and forth argumentive to rowdy, at times sounding like a fish market. As soon as the vote was finished, and we had lost, Butler was up, reading his committee report, and calling for a vote on its first recommendation—that we fix the permanent seat. The vote was 12 and 12. Adams voted 'Nay!' with us.

"That quieted them down while they looked around at the man who had jumped from them to us—Mr. Ellsworth, Connecticut!

"It was a short pause, for Butler leapt up again and ignoring our vote against fixing the permanent seat, brought up his bill fixing the permanent seat! He had filled in the blank with 'Potomac'—hook and lure for us.

"We expected Adams to remind Butler of our vote not five minutes before—but instead, the Vice President ordered Butler's bill taken up!"

(Head-shaking and frowns from Washington and Jefferson.)

"So off the Senate went in noise and confusion through a briar patch of talk. When the vote was called, I gave the signal for our 11 to carry out the plan of action we Friends of Philadelphia had agreed upon the night before—to vote 'Nay' as a group, on everything, but EVERYTHING that was put before us.

("Ah ha, ha, ha")

"First was Butler's 'easterly bank of the Potomac.' I voted AGAINST it. Carroll voted against it. It was a strange feeling! All our 11 voted against it! So did Ellsworth! And both Dalton and Strong of Massachusetts! The faces of Yorkers, South and North Carolinians, and Georgians, sick and all, looked stunned.

"What next? we wondered.

"They wanted to postpone for two weeks. We voted 'Nay.' Izard tried Baltimore in the blank. We voted 'Nay'—17 to 7! They tried Wilmington. Only four voted for it—the sick and Butler, the blind. They decided on a sensible retreat—postponement, generally. NAY! Postpone til next session. NAY! Throw out Potomac and enact the bill with a blank—an absurdity. NAY! Adjourn! We were so set up to vote NAY! on everything, we voted NAY! But then in the ruckus, I got the word around that when I called 'Adjourn!' our 11 should vote FOR it. So we ended the uproar, which was fast moving toward a fracas.

"Butler, glaring and raging, face red as a turkey wattle, flashed his black eyes at us and twisted his mouth around some vile names that we abstained from hearing. The sick looked sicker, were helped to bed or sedan, and sent home."

Washington's expression had changed from hearty laughs to a smile of incredulity, to a pained frown, and a headshake. Jefferson had leaned forward, his mouth open, his face set in an amazed expression, his large, slightly protruding light-brown eyes focused upon Lee.

At the end of Lee's story, Jefferson leaned back to laugh, and to inquire, "What was Adams doing all this time?"

Madison answered with his imitation of the Vice President—his perfect portrayals of Congressional characters always made Jefferson laugh until tears ran down his cheeks. This time, in deference to the President, Madison subdued his mimicking of Adams' mannerisms—watery smile and call for order, helpless gazing at the antics of the Senators, decision to rise, decision not to rise, twisting lips but no words issuing, intent study of the floor or of lint on his breeches.

Jefferson and Lee could not stifle their guffaws, and even Washington did not suppress a broad smile. That many in Congress saw Adams as a comic figure whose pomposity and mannerisms seemed to spring from vanity, was known to all of them.

Washington could not forget that Adams in the Continental Congress during the war had held back support from him and his needy army, fearing, Adams said, to put so much power in one man's hands. But the President respected the office Adams now held, and with a small gesture ended the levity about the man.

Quickly, Madison switched his report to the House side of the Congress.

"Late this afternoon," he related, "we had the honor of hearing Mr. Gerry announce that HE has a bill placing the permanent seat somewhere on the Jersey bank of the Delaware. (Noises of dismay and exasperation) To quote Mr. Gerry, 'Tomorrow

J.Madison (Brant)

J.Adams (P.Smith)

Jefferson and the Rights of Man (D.Malone) p260

Hist.Cong., House Journal, June 9

(pause), some-t-time tomorrow (pause), I expect first thing tomorrow (pause), I will call up my motion (long pause).'

"There arose a rumble of exclamations in the House. Gerry is putting forward in the House 'somewhere' on the Delaware?—which in the Senate Robert Morris would surely convert to Falls of the Delaware! Could Gerry be so naive as to think that the river's little rapids would protect the virtue of Trenton and Lamberton from the lord of Morrisville on the opposite bank?"

The men laughed and shook their heads. "But we newly organized Friends of Philadelphia in the House," Madison declared, "will make a move tomorrow that could save New Jersey from learning the answer to that question. We have ready a repeat of our Butler-suppressed 'adjourn to Philadelphia' resolution!

History of Congress, House Journal, June 10

"The one we passed last week won 38 to 22. However, if this week our House opponents repeat the Senate opponents' tactics by throwing in BALTIMORE, I sense that our Maryland Friends of Philadelphia may suddenly prove to be better friends of Baltimore."

The four men gazed at each other silently for a moment.

"What of funding and Assumption?" inquired the President suddenly.

"Well," Lee answered, "the Senate has been too occupied with the entertainment of bickering over the seat to take up the funding bill passed by the House."

Washington frowned.

Maclay's Journal, June 9

"But I heard this afternoon," Lee went on, "that Ellsworth of Connecticut will make a move tomorrow to tie Assumption back onto the funding bill. Apparently, it's the same resolution Gerry tried some weeks ago, then Boudinot tried again, but no one in the House was interested."

"Is the Senate likely to accept it, and pass a two-part bill?"

"Mr. President, the vote on the Hamilton plan is split as evenly as the vote on the seat of government—and the maneuvering to tip the balance will call forth as much temper and ingenuity."

Still frowning, the President looked toward the town of New York. For the next few minutes, he seemed to be studying the low buildings in the mile-long skyline, and pondering what deals might be taking place that very moment in some of them.

CHAPTER 19

Capital Deals at the Top

SCENE 1
A HAMILTON-MORRIS TALK IN THE PARK

PLACE: Battery Park, tip of Manhattan.
TIME: Saturday, June 12, at 5 in the morning, three days after Washington's fishing trip.

Scene and quotes drawn from Maclay's Journal, June 14.

Left:
From the roof of the President's house (bottom right), the view down Broadway past Bowling Green and the parade ship "Hamilton," stretches through Battery Park to Elizabeth Town on the Jersey shore of the Hudson. In June 1790, Treasury Secretary Hamilton paced these blocks of Broadway and the Battery to beg Senator Morris one Saturday and Secretary of State Jefferson the next for help to push his federal finance plan through Congress.

A rather small, slim man with auburn hair, deep-set eyes, long nose, slightly jutting chin—a gentleman dressed in blue silk suit and white, ruffled shirt—paced back and forth on a gravel walk among the trees in Battery Park. He tried to appear casual, not watching or waiting for anyone, not worried nor nervous.

As he walked north toward the town and away from the sea, he saw on his left in the early morning light the elegant rowhouses lining Broadway as it sloped upward toward Wall Street. On the right, in a small, oval park, "The Bowling Green", where early Dutch settlers once played, a weathered parade ship sat among the trees. Faded paint on its side said, "Hamilton."

"It's falling apart—like my finance plan," observed Alexander Hamilton, for the early morning pacer was he.

As always when he saw that relic of a great day in his past, he thought of his good friend Pierre L'Enfant. The energetic, very talkative French architect had planned the events, including the parade and a spectacular outdoor banqueting fairway when, two years ago, the city lauded the Constitution—and Hamilton for his ongoing fight for ratification.

Hamilton turned and retraced his steps. Creaky wagons and loud-talking workmen passed and stopped nearby, ready for another day's work on

the foundations of the presidential mansion replacing old Dutch Fort.

Hamilton wanted the mansion to rise fast and lend weight to the reasons the federal government should remain in his city. He had promised when he was struggling for ratification that New York would become the capital, at least for a few years.

He wished his friend Robert Morris wasn't eyeing the same few years for Philadelphia to be the capital—long enough to seduce Congress into staying forever. Morris's "Adjourn to Philadelphia!" idea had all but stopped the crucial debates in the Senate and House on the Hamilton finance plan.

What an exasperating three weeks this had been! What a lot of time he'd spent rounding up votes and devising counterattacks and strategy! First, while Senator King was negotiating a swap of Potomac-New York for Assumption votes Senator Butler would lure from the Southerners, Morris broke loose with his "Adjourn to Philadelphia" move. Nothing to do but wave Delaware Falls at him to draw him away. His inevitable anger at the deception seemed less important than Southern Assumption votes.

But Morris's anger produced an "Adjourn to Philadelphia" resolution in the House! Even one of Butler's South Carolinians had joined other Southerners to pass it. Ominous!

In the Senate, Butler's committee first killed it,

A.Hamilton (M.Hecht)

Maclay's Journ., May 24

Hist.Cong. House Journ., ,May 31

Maclay's Journ.
June 7

then (helped by the sick and lame) stopped its resurrection. But angry "Friends of Philadelphia" block-voted to cut down Butler's bill for Potomac and implied New York. Ominous!

If it had only stopped there! But no, the House took up a new "Adjourn to Philadelphia" resolution and had the votes to pass it!

Maclay's Journ.
June 11

Hamilton, teeth clenched, shook his head irritably. Burke of South Carolina had agreed to amend, substituting Baltimore. In the vote yesterday, Maryland men broke away, as hoped, from the Philadelphia block, and Baltimore won.

"Next, the Senate will wrangle over Baltimore!" grumbled Hamilton. "It will reject it in the end.. But what I want—need—must have NOW—is a STOP to this back-and-forth about the seat!"

Hist. Cong., Senate Journ., June 14

He had worked all yesterday evening toward that end, rounding up 13 votes for postponing Senate action on the Baltimore resolution. Monday, his father-in-law would make the motion for a two-week delay.

"Two weeks!" Hamilton smiled. "For two whole weeks, the Senate CAN'T talk about the seat! It MUST talk about funding—and Assumption—the two rejoined, I hope. The House, waiting for Senate action on Baltimore, WON'T talk about the seat, and so MUST get on with the tax bill—money for my finance plan."

Hamilton (M.Hecht)

Hamilton took a deep breath. He was very tired. He had worked night and day for months to construct the plan, to explain the plan, to send out "gladiators" (as someone had told him Senator Maclay called his contact men) to find votes for the plan, to make deals for enacting the plan. Six months of deal-making and he still needed five more House votes to get Assumption accepted, and one more vote in the Senate, for funding and (with luck) Assumption rejoined to it.

Maclay's Journ.
June 14

Who could help? What reward must he offer or humiliation bear to get those votes?

Well, if he didn't find an answer to this question in the next two weeks, he would simply resign as the $3500-a-year Secretary of the Treasury and go back to his $10,000-a-year law practice.

Hamilton turned to walk back and saw the person he had decided could get him the needed votes. Coming toward him was a tall, overweight man with a round, pink face, and loose, gray hair. Relieved to see him, Hamilton quickened his pace.

Maclay's Journ.
June 14
(Morris's account)

"Good morning, Senator Morris! How fortunate for me that you take early morning walks!"

"Good morning, Mr. Secretary. A brisk constitutional before the heat of the day sets in! A pleasure to find you here. You and I are excessively busy these days. I never exchange a word with you any more. 'Tis a fine garden we have here—the President's favorite walk. Let's get on with our exercise (he lowered his voice considerably) and hear what it is you wish to propose to me."

Hamilton wasted no time with a description of the situation—Morris knew it only too well. "I need for the financing plan ONE vote in the Senate, and FIVE votes in the House," said Hamilton. "I want them before the end of two weeks. If you procure me these votes, I am offering—I am guaranteeing you—enough votes for the PERMANENT residence to be located at Germantown or the Falls of the Delaware—whichever you choose. Paired with New York, it will win."

"Good Lord!" said Mr. Morris. "That is an extremely valuable offer you're making, Mr. Hamilton. I personally lean toward accepting immediately. But of course I must confer with many others. In the Senate—well, there is Mr. Maclay. No use to ask him. His principles, you know. And his spleen. Perhaps George Read of Delaware will be pliable. I will take him for an outing tomorrow—we'll drive the 'the 14 miles around Manhattan.'

Maclay's Journal,
June 11

"Actually," Morris quickly added as they made a turn and started the walk next to the sea, "you need more than one Senate vote. A trial vote yesterday on an amendment to rejoin Assumption to the funding bill produced only NINE 'yeas.' But add my vote—I said 'nay' yesterday to keep the amendment from sinking the funding bill. Add Read, if he succumbs to my blandishments. That makes 11. The other side has 13."

Hamilton nodded briskly, "Yes, I know. But let us add Rhode Island also. Having ratified the Constitution, its legislature has appointed two Senators. They should arrive in a few days and be open to my persuasion. That's 13—a tie. I hate to leave it all to Adams. I want my own margin of safety—one more vote."

Morris laughed heartily. "Ahh, Mr. Adams! He's your bugabear! But he likes your plan—though he's still mad at you for his low electoral vote."

They walked on, quietly.

Morris began with, "As for the House...you know that five out of eight Pennsylvania Congressmen are now dead-set against Assumption. Also, in the past, they have had some memorable disappointments dealing with you New Yorkers. They now lean toward scorning Northeast deals."

"Uhm. Yes, I know," answered Hamilton.

"In addition," Morris slowly added, "their price likely will be something more realistic—umm, less RISKY—than a promise to secure the PERMANENT seat at Germantown or Falls of the Delaware."

"Less risky?" said Hamilton apprehensively.

"Exactly—too big a variety of opposition to those two places—too many members throwing their votes this way today, the other way tomorrow. We Pennsylvanians have voted to push hard for the temporary capital in Philadelphia."

Hamilton stopped and looked with dismay at Morris's pleasant though serious face. The young Secretary took a deep breath, as if he were about to reply—but instead, he began to walk on slowly in silence. Neither man spoke for several minutes.

At the end of the walk, Hamilton said in a low voice, "I don't know whether my friends will give up New York as the temporary residence or not. I will try to persuade them. I will let you know their answer day-after-tomorrow—Monday noon. Thank you for coming."

Morris nodded. "One more thing I myself must have, or I may vote against funding as well as Assumption. (You shouldn't look so shocked!) I want SIX percent interest on the new federal certificates that replace SIX percent old certificates, national or state! I cannot fathom why you imagined that dropping interest to FOUR percent would not dismay your supporters!

"And one more small request, my dear friend. PLEASE send no stand-ins to discuss this business with me—as you did yesterday. I will not talk to Tench Coxe, your new Assistant Secretary, or even Major Jackson from the President's family. I must do my talking directly with you."

They shook hands, one smiling pleasantly, the other ruefully, and parted.

Maclay's Journ., Mon., *June 14 recording of Morris's account of this talk with Hamilton on Sat., June 12*

Alexander Hamilton

SCENE 2
HAMILTON-JEFFERSON BROADWAY TALK

PLACE: West sidewalk of Broadway, from Battery Park to Wall Street (three blocks).
TIME: A week later, Saturday, June 19 at 9:45 a.m.

The rather small, slim man with auburn hair, deep-set eyes, long nose, slightly jutting chin—a gentleman in rumpled blue silk suit and limp white ruffles—was beginning to sweat as he paced back and forth, up and down the few blocks of sidewalk. His clothes looked as if he had slept in them, which was the case, but only an hour or two out of the past 24, and that in his office.

TJ Papers, Vol.6 (Ford, ed.) Jefferson account in 1793. Also his ANAS 1818, and a letter to GW.

His worries had multiplied since last Saturday's walk with Robert Morris. On Monday he had sent a note to Morris telling him that New York and New England members would not hear of giving up New York for temporary capital, and particularly would not give it to Philadelphia. Ever since, the hottest kind of arguments had gone on between him and Morris about the interest rate on replacement certificates. Hamilton's plan said four percent; Morris pressed for six. He was a double-sided man, Morris—one over-generous, the other pigiron-hard.

Hamilton greatly admired "The Man's" abilities. As finance officer for the Old Congress, Morris had taught young Hamilton the intricacies of government finances. They, with Madison, had devised a debt funding and bank plan to remedy the states' economic chaos. Congress said "nay." Seven years later, the plan guided Hamilton in devising his Federal finance program. He deliberately did not inform Morris.

But even as he worked out the details, rumor said Morris was buying debt paper and selling it in Europe for large profits. Promising full redemption, he was assuming—or so it seemed—that Hamilton would use their earlier plan. That he did not "assume" but KNEW, Hamilton had learned only recently. William Duer, Assistant Secretary of the Treasury, terrified of debtors' prison, confessed to Hamilton that last autumn he had told Morris the secret and was a partner in European sales.

Hamilton shuddered involuntarily, remembering the April day when he directed Duer, a close friend, to resign. Since then, prison inched closer to Duer every hour that Congress stalled on Assumption, for the debt paper market stalled with it, and speculators reaped no profits to pay high interest on borrowed money.

"But I warned my staff over and over that profiting from insider information inevitably led to their doom!" Hamilton reminded himself.

He had stopped in front of Number 1 Broadway, the Spanish Legation. He wiped his brow, his grainy eyes, and dabbed at his neck. He had paced this sidewalk for a half-hour, watching and waiting for Thomas Jefferson, who (the clerk at the State Department on Maiden Street had said) had an appointment with the President at 10 o'clock.

So far on this hot morning, Hamilton had the street to himself. He sauntered back towards the President's mansion. Halfway there, he suddenly saw ahead, at the crest of the slope near Trinity Church, a tall, slim figure moving toward him in Jefferson's loose, rhythmic, unmistakable manner.

Hamilton perked up and advanced up the slope quickly, tensely. Just past the President's door, he said breathlessly, "Mr. Jefferson! I have been waiting for you! I must speak to you a few minutes on a most urgent matter!"

"Of course, of course. You do look as if dreadful events have struck you. Your face shows evidence of much distress."

Hamilton, conscious of his over-night beard and untidy clothes, apologized for his poor condition. "I am tortured by the resistance of Congress to my finance plan. I know you well understand how indispensable it is for the preservation of our country. But Congressmen and Senators with their state and regional interests and jealousies can see no farther than the totals in their local accounts!

"I have been negotiating for the past week with Morris for five more House votes—Pennsylvania, anywhere—for Assumption. I have tried to give him a good trade: Germantown or Delaware Falls, permanent, with New York temporary.

"But they want the impossible—not only higher interest on new federal certificates, but also to ADJOURN TO PHILADELPHIA without naming a permanent seat, thereby leaving New York with nothing! I cannot! I cannot! The New Yorkers, who are the backbone of the Assumption vote, will not agree to deny our city the temporary seat, especially in favor of Philadelphia!

"I have threatened Morris with switching to Potomac, permanent, and New York temporary. They swear THEY will switch to the Potomac-Philadelphia combination if New York will not give in. AND—mark this!—they add that the government will never leave Philadelphia once it moves there."

Jefferson cocked his head, smiled, and said, "Morris threatens a Pennsylvania-Virginia deal? You will find it interesting that last Tuesday, I was requested by someone, whose name shall remain unspoken, to send word to Morris that 'there is a disposition of having the temporary at Philadelphia for 15 years and permanent at Georgetown on Potomac.' But nothing has come of it yet since I was not at liberty to tell Morris WHO could accomplish this deed."

"Oh." Hamilton's rapid-fire calculations replaced his rapid-fire talk for a silent 10 seconds. "Well, Virginia in combination with NEW YORK and New England could ALSO win," he declared. "Whoever combines with whom, there is no time to lose. Both houses have started a move to ADJOURN July 15! In the face of that, the Senate all this week has refused to decide anything about the funding bill, and last Monday refused Ellsworth's attempt to tie the Assumption bill to it! In one more week—next Monday the twenty-eighth—they'll haul out the seat of government business, and pfft—!

"I tell you they are planning to put off the financing plan until next March when a newly-elected Congress convenes! Look at the House—laying Assumption aside, picking at the whiskey tax with the intention of killing it next week so the finance plan, if ever passed, would have no money to implement it!

"They will also start final debate next week on the bill for settling wartime accounts between the states and Congress—a bone they could gnaw on

til adjournment!

"I swear I shall resign if Congress fails to approve my finance plan as it stands! Somebody else can preside over the collapse of our great dream of a Constitutional Republic!"

Jefferson's light-brown eyes glistened with alarm at the younger man who passionately threatened to abandon the Constitutional government for which he had so recently fought to ratify and bring to life.

"You must not resign!" Jefferson declared sternly. "That would throw the country into a financial crisis—one the new government might not survive. So high are the feuds excited by rejection of Assumption, the Eastern members particularly, who with South Carolina, are the principal gamblers in these scenes, threaten secession and dissolution if Assumption is not voted. For the sake of the Union, it is necessary to yield to the cries of the creditors—and save us from the greatest of all calamities, the total extinction of our credit in Europe!"

Hamilton replied quickly, "Then we should make common cause, Mr. Jefferson, to save the Union!"

"What do you need, Mr. Hamilton?"

"Five more Assumption votes—NOW—in the House, three in the Senate since the Rhode Island men won't arrive for another week. If you could speak to Madison, who leads the Virginia delegation in strongly opposing my plan, we COULD make common cause, supporting one another in this great effort of launching our new government."

"Yes, of course." Jefferson nodded. "The success of the government is paramount. I think the best way to proceed is to bring you and Madison together at my dining table. Will tomorrow be soon enough, and 3 o'clock convenient for you?"

"I would come at dawn if you set the time at dawn," said Hamilton.

"Madeira so early might tipsy our calculations," Jefferson laughed. "I'll see Madison in an hour or so. A messenger will bring my note with news to

Maclay's Journal
June 15.

Also, *A.Hamilton*
(F.McDonald) p184

Hist.Cong.,Senate,
House,Journals, and
Maclay's Journal
June 14-19

C.Carroll (E.H.Smith)
p160 Jefferson quotes.
Also, *TJ (Flexner)*
p248, and *TJ*
Papers(Boyd)

your office. Or to your home, if you will be there the rest of the day."

"Thank you, Mr. Secretary. Your support greatly relieves me. I shall go home to rest, and hope nothing hinders your plan. Please give my warm regards to the President—and to Mr. Madison."

Jefferson swung away to the President's door, and Hamilton crossed Broadway to Wall Street. A block from Federal Hall, he stopped before entering his own door to glare and lift a fist at that meeting place of the First Federal Congress just down the street.

SCENE 3
DINNER AT JEFFERSON'S

PLACE: Dining room in Thomas Jefferson's rented house on Maiden Lane.
TIME: Following day, June 20, about 4 o'clock.

Exact date not recorded but events before and after point strongly to Sunday, June 20

TJ's Cookbook (M.Kimball)

Ency.Brit. 11th ed. Fr.Rev.in early 1790

Three men—Thomas Jefferson, James Madison, and Alexander Hamilton—had just finished the main course of roasted loin of veal with herbs in wine sauce. During the previous hour they had sat at the fine mahogany table enjoying soup of small roots, broiled sea trout with onion butter, and string beans with wild mushrooms picked by the chef. The smell of sauces and fresh-baked rolls perfumed the air, enhancing each bite of food. An excellent vintage of French white wine, chilled in ice from the President's storage pit, had filled and refilled their stemmed glasses.

The conversation had kept to news from France—the King and Queen virtual prisoners in the Tuileries Palace in Paris ("Mirabeau predicts their death!"), the National Assembly radicals making decisions. "However," reported Jefferson, "they divided France into 80 local areas and gave local, elected officials

the power to run their own affairs! Result—locals levy taxes and keep all the money! How ironical! While we strive to establish a strong central government supported by a strong central financial plan, the French revolutionists to rid the country of the abuses of centralized power have marched in the opposite direction!"

Hamilton nodded vigorously. "The price for France will be no effective national government—the very weakness we combat here with our new Constitution and financial plan!"

Jefferson pushed his chair back and stood. "Gentlemen, a toast! To the good health of our Constitution and Republic!" Madison responded, "To the good health and long life of President Washington!" Hamilton raised his glass, looked straight at Madison and said, "To far-seeing judgment, benefiting the future!"

A black man brought in frosty glasses of chocolate mousse and poured strong coffee, all worthy of conversation. At last, having consumed imported cheese and local fresh strawberries, Jefferson opened the conversation that all three had been mentally rehearsing for 24 hours. "The object of our coming together is to find some temperament for the present fever in Congress. I am persuaded that men of sound heads and honest views need nothing more than explanation and mutual understanding to enable them to unite in some measures which might enable us to get along."

Hamilton again nodded vigorously. With a smile, he recalled that, since Madison himself had originated the idea of the central government assuming state debts—"1783, remember, when we offered the Continental Congress a plan to deal with our financial crisis, and were turned down"—Madison knew all the arguments for it.

"Your opposition now to Assumption has greatly surprised me," Hamilton said. "I thought you of all people would support it—though I did wonder at

TJ quote from his 1793 account

"Speculators vs. Veterans" (I.Brant) p87

Hamilton and the National Debt (G.Taylor, ed.)

Content of conversation reflects Jefferson's account, and the evidence of monetary and policy concessions to Madison, as described by Dr. E. James Ferguson in his definitive study, Power of the Purse, of Hamilton's finance plan.

Thomas Jefferson, Secretary of State (center) hosts the dinner in mid-June, 1790, at which Secretary of the Treasury
Alexander Hamilton (left) and Congressmen James Madison of Virginia (right) make their seat of government-assumption
of debt bargain, a compromise necessary for national stability.

your lack of response to my letter last fall asking for suggestions."

Madison replied in his soft, slow manner, "If the interests of Virginia had been protected by amending your original plan as I tried to do in early Spring, I could have agreed to Assumption."

Hamilton's eyes widen. He smiled.

Madison continued, "Virginia ought to receive credit in some manner for the war debts our taxpayers have paid. In addition, we should receive credit for millions of dollars the state expended of its own funds during the war and which Congress ought to repay."

"You know—" Hamilton began, but Madison hurried on. "All these claims should be settled under lenient policies—and NOW, hand-in-hand with Assumption accounts. Instead, your plan DELAYS these accounts until AFTER Assumption is completed. Many of us suspect that means NEVER!"

"Why, Mr. Madison," responded Hamilton, his head cocked, hands on hips, "you know that Commissioners have worked steadily for eight years—and still work—to verify and pay whatever Congress is responsible for!"

"Yes," nodded Madison, "for eight years these commissioners have contemptuously dismissed a great number of our claims for lack of 'proper' receipts or requisitions.

"A prime example is the cost to Virginia to send George Rogers Clark and an army to the west without waiting for orders from Congress. He saved the Northwestern Territory between the Ohio and the Great Lakes for the United States—and we are blamed for not having done correct paperwork.

"Other examples are locales where the British attacked, and our citizens sold for promises the food and supplies our soldiers needed while beating off the enemy. These turned-down claims deserve another hearing and greater leniency—which will require an extension of the time for filing."

Hamilton leaned toward Madison. "Are you suggesting that Virginians would vote for Assumption if settling accounts proceeded at the same time—if more leniency were allowed on claims—if time to file were extended?"

"That would begin to warm their attitude and sweeten the taste of Assumption," Madison replied.

"BEGIN to warm?! BEGIN to sweeten?! Good Lord, Mr. Madison! Those claims will add up to an amazing compensation for Virginia! What is YOUR estimate, Mr. Madison?"

"About double the $10,000,000 the Commissioners and Board have allowed us so far."

"DOUBLE! And even $10,000,000 more only BEGINS to sweeten your men toward Assumption?" Hamilton clasped his forehead.

Madison answered, "It is a measure of the injustices dealt us."

Hamilton, frowning, looking thoughtful, suddenly lifted his arms and hands in a gesture of acquiescence. "Very well. Many of your points are already in the Settlements Bill, the third part of my original plan, which the House is on the verge of voting upon. I will help it there, and through the Senate. Perhaps in the Senate it can be strengthened, clearing the way for LIBERAL handling of claims. If needed, I can later direct the Treasury Board to grant ALL demands to reconcile differences—for I will need speed in gaining final figures for Assumption if we are to set our country on its economic feet by early 1792.

"You will see then that our debt, backed by creditor trust, has become our national treasure—a national blessing! Paper of no value has become valuable—acceptable as money to expand commerce and industry!"

Madison began to shake his head and say, "I have never been a proselyte to the doctrine that public debts are public benefit—" and was interrupted by Jefferson addressing Hamilton.

Power of the Purse (E.J.Ferguson) p323-325

Hist. Congress, House Jour. Feb.11, Madison speech

"We are pleased to hear your agreement and your promised support on this matter, Mr. Secretary. As Mr. Madison said, the news will warm our delegates in Congress several degrees toward voting for Assumption."

"SEVERAL DEGREES?" Hamilton repeated with a frown. "Only several degrees? You are suggesting that even MORE is required to heat them to a vote-switching temperature?"

Madison, nodding his head, said, "You have set Virginia's portion of the Assumption Fund at $3,000,000—"

With a slightly sardonic smile, Hamilton interrupted. "How much more will you ask for?"

Cooly, Madison said, "About $500,000."

Hamilton laughed. Jefferson, smiling broadly, remarked, "A small price, Mr. Secretary, for a finance plan you say will save the country. Since a major benefit of Assumption will be to give people drawing interest from new federal certificates a powerful motive to work for success of the federal rather than a state government, it must be evident that benefits will greatly exceed any costs."

"But think of the uproar in Congress if we begin reapportioning the $19,000,000 debt total!" Hamilton said. "States losing in order for you to gain—"

"Since you see debts as a blessing," Madison said, "the debt total should be enlarged a million or two. After all, it's only an estimate. Virginia is not the only state that will ask for a bigger portion. North Carolina and Georgia, which, like Virginia, have redeemed much of their debt, surely will also ask for enough to come out even when all the sorting, adding, and subtracting is complete for accounts and Assumption."

Hamilton leaned back in his chair, folded his arms in front of his chest, and appeared to study the edge of the table. His companions could hear an agitated foot tapping the floor.

After a minute, he sat straight up and said, "It could be done in the Senate committee presently considering the Funding bill passed by the House. I have asked for an amendment adding Assumption to the bill, and I will recommend raising the debt total to, say, $22,000,000. Virginia's portion, based on population, would be about one-sixth, or $3,500,000, which will include the extra $500,000."

"New York's portion could well increase, too," Jefferson added in an amused tone.

Hamilton shrugged and barely smiled. "Now, how warm does this concession make the Virginians for Assumption?" he asked.

Quickly Madison replied, "Virginia Congressman Alexander White, whose district borders the Potomac River near Georgetown, and who is one of our prospects to switch his vote, will offer the most resistance. Marylanders in Potomac districts will respond in varying degrees of warmth. They are all incensed that speculators have robbed our people of Continental Congress and State wartime certificates, and taken that wealth to northern cities. The compensation that would warm even Alexander White to the switching-point for Assumption is the capital on the Potomac.

"Nothing could with more certainty sweeten the bitter pill of Assumption they are asked to swallow than the $500,000 in trade and commerce the seat of government will bring to the area every year," Madison said emphatically.

Hamilton had started, then looked quickly from one man to the other as Madison spoke. Now he said tensely, "Could you possibly be suggesting a New York-Potomac combination?"

"No, Mr. Hamilton. We are asking that you support Philadelphia for temporary capital."

Hamilton stared at Madison, his mouth open in a twisted smile. He turned his gaze on Jefferson, who smiled back pleasantly.

"I mentioned to you yesterday," Jefferson said, "that significant moves were going on between the

Pennsylvanians and Virginians."

"But you indicated," broke in Hamilton, "that Morris hardly showed interest in Philadelphia 15 years, Potomac permanent—despite a faint signal that the offer came from the President himself!"

Jefferson rearranged his legs under the table. "Overnight the situation shifted," he said firmly. "Let us say that Morris became satisfied that the offer came on good authority. At the moment, we are seriously negotiating the terms. We have little time. The Potomac-Philadelphia matter MUST be settled BEFORE Assumption or we will lose our converts."

Eyes held on Jefferson's pleasant face, Hamilton appeared taken aback by the words wrapped in the Virginian's soft voice.

Madison leaned toward Hamilton. "We must complete our plans during the coming week for the Potomac-Philadelphia debate during the week after—let's say by July Fourth. Virginians are acting in good faith. We trust the Pennsylvanians will also—no sudden moves for permanent capital at Germantown or Delaware Falls, with the temporary in New York. No jumping for temptations dangled by New York or New England."

Hamilton had glanced back and forth, Madison to Jefferson, his lips compressed. Then as Madison talked on, he had looked straight into the Congressman's eyes and listened intently.

"We desire," Madison declared, "that you, Sir, announce that YOU have given up seeking the temporary capital for New York! You will thereby reduce, perhaps eliminate, the amusement of New Yorkers and New England men who enjoy pairing New York with this or that place for permanent whenever either House takes up the residence question. A ruckus follows. Votes scatter. Sudden switching at critical moments prevents a decision—thus assuring that Congress will convene in New York next session."

Hamilton's fingers drummed the chair arm. He leaned forward, to the right, to the left. A man keenly alert, high-strung, intense, his turbulence at the moment was beginning to look explosive.

"Jupiter," Jefferson called calmly, "we are ready for the cognac." Turning back, he said to Hamilton, "You must be as painfully aware as we of the sizeable chance that neither Assumption nor capital will gain a decision in this session of Congress. But I believe your powerful influence on the New Yorkers and New Englanders would go far in bringing both matters to a successful conclusion. For example, if they are persuaded that further efforts to hold Congress in New York will hurt the prospects of Assumption, it will have the effect of releasing South Carolina's votes from your city. They would then vote for Potomac, despite its being paired with the Quaker City of Philadelphia."

Jupiter came with the cognac. Pouring, passing, and sniffing the aromatic liquid broke the tension.

All at once, Hamilton demanded, "Who are the votes Virginia and her friends can produce for me? You named Alexander White—who are the other four?"

Madison, with a look at Jefferson, hesitated. Jefferson quickly said that none of the men had been approached, but Madison had strong reason to assume they could be persuaded.

"The 'strong reason,'" Madison said, "is that three of the four susceptible House members represent Congressional districts on the banks of the Potomac River by Georgetown—namely, Alexander White and Richard Bland Lee of Virginia, and Daniel Carroll of Maryland. George Gale's district on Maryland's Eastern Shore faces Potomac's entrance into Chesapeake Bay. In the Senate, Maryland's Charles Carroll of Carrollton owns a 20-square-mile plantation on the Potomac above the falls."

"Ah—Carroll!" Hamilton said. "With the two Senators Morris has converted, I have the three votes I need in the Senate. But in the House," said

A.Hamilton (M.Hecht)

Hamilton sharply, "I may need five votes. You named only four. Who is the fifth House vote? Yourself, Mr. Madison?"

"We have a good prospect in another delegation," said Madison. "In view of how severely I have spoken against your finance plan, I cannot entirely withdraw my opposition. I will not vote for Assumption myself—yet, I will offer no strenuous arguments, but leave it to its fate. You will have enough votes without mine."

Jefferson's account

Hamilton stared into his brandy glass intently for a moment, sat it down firmly, and said, "YES! I will agree to everything you ask for. I must. I have no choice."

He paused, taking a deep breath. Looking past Madison to a window, he declared, "But I cannot promise you votes for your Potomac, and surely I cannot influence anyone to vote for Philadelphia. The Northeast is as stubborn about keeping Congress in New York as Morris is for absconding with it to Philadelphia.

"I regret," he continued, turning his gaze upon the two men, "I sorely regret—that I must give up keeping Congress in my city a few more years. But it must be. It is just as I must tell Rufus King, my father-in-law Philip Schuyler, and the New York delegates in the House: If we want Assumption and funding to save our stability, our credit abroad, and the fortunes—even the personal freedom—of those dealing in debt speculation (many of them solid citizens bulwarking this country) they must give up their rankling to keep the capital in New York. I will inform Morris that I have given up seeking the temporary for New York. I may or may not be able to restrain any Northeast man from trying on his own to capture it for our city."

GW (Flexner) p247

"Thank you, Mr. Secretary," Jefferson said.

Madison nodded but his expression was stern. "You have made mention of speculators, Sir. I wish to repeat, Mr. Hamilton, that the outrage Virginians feel at the speculation in war debt paper, accounts for much of our resistance to Assumption. We are bitterly aware that 22 outsiders—wealthy Northern speculators—own $1,000,000 of Virginia certificates, most of them soldiers' pay—"

A.Hamilton (F.McDonald) p178

Hamilton interrupted, grimacing and shrugging his shoulders. "Mr. Madison, it is a natural part of the process—it is regrettable but it cannot be helped."

"So!" exclaimed Jefferson before Madison could reply. "Potomac and Philadelphia will gain the long and short-term capitals, the country will gain a financial base, and New York will have to be satisfied with what it has already had. Gentlemen, a toast in this exquisite cognac to a compromise destined to have far-reaching consequences!"

GW (Flexner) p248 TJ letter to Monroe

The three men rose to their feet.

"To success!" said Jefferson. "To national strength!" added Hamilton. "To the power of compromise!" said Madison.

"Compromise?" said Hamilton thoughtfully, placing his brandy glass on the table. In the blunt, challenging manner he sometimes indulged in, and was thereby noted for offending others, he added, "No. Hard bargain."

Not answering, Madison began to move from the table. "We have several hours of daylight for me to begin locating the men with the votes," he said. "With Congress champing at the bit to adjourn, I must make the most of every hour."

Hamilton also moved away. "I have another hard bargain—one with Morris—to work out," he declared, "or rather, some slight-of-hand to perform with interest rates: making his six percent today add up to my four in the long run."

Hamilton

To keep his bargain with Hamilton, Madison (at table) calls together the four Congressmen and one Senator whose votes if changed from "nay" to "yea" will bring victory to the federal finance plan— and the permanant capital to the Potomac. Congressman Richard Bland Lee and Alexander White of Virginia, and Daniel Carroll of Maryland all represent districts on the Potomac. Senator Charles Carroll's Carrollton Manor borders Potomac above the falls. George Gale's district on Maryland's Eastern Shore of Chesapeake Bay faces the mouth of the Potomac.

CHAPTER 20

Switching the Voters

SCENE 1
POTOMAC'S MEN

PLACE: Parlor in Thomas Jefferson's rented house on Maiden Lane, New York City.
TIME: Monday, June 21, about 9 o'clock, the morning after the "Compromise Dinner."

No record exists of the Virginians' meeting, but Jefferson recorded the reaction of some members to the request that they switch their votes. In only one of his 3 versions of the event (1792, 1793, 1818) did Jefferson say that several members of Congress attended the dinner; more likely his memory merged two separate events—his dinner for the policy makers, and a subsequent meeting of the prospective vote-changers, probably at his house also.

"Compromise of 1790"
Wm/Mary Qtr.
(K.Bowling) Oct.1971

Pale, balding, very serious James Madison, standing beside Thomas Jefferson, watched the expressions of the five men listening to their host's brief description of the urgency of the matter—nay, matters—at hand. Senator Charles Carroll of Carrollton whose thin face wore his usual benign expression, also looked wan, tired, and motionless, except for eyes roving restlessly, inquiringly, behind half-closed lids. He already knew from Madison the details of the ongoing deals, one with Morris, another with Hamilton, and had warmed up the two Maryland Congressmen whose House votes might bend in the direction he had decided to bend his own in the Senate.

One of the Congressmen, his distant cousin Daniel Carroll of Upper Rock Creek near Georgetown, sat beside him on a sofa with deep red damask cushioning. Daniel, robust though in his 50's, twisted mouth and brows in his plump, round face as he twisted his body in his seat, responding to the interesting information he was hearing.

The other Marylander, George Gale of Somerset County, on the Eastern Shore of Chesapeake Bay, opposite the mouth of the Potomac, had the eager look of the young politician excited to find himself attending a confidential meeting with his friend, Senator Charles Carroll, and other famous leaders.

The two Virginia Congressmen's districts bordered the lower shore of the Potomac River. Richard Bland Lee, not quite 30, represented President Washington's own district centering on the towns of Alexandria and Leesburg. Attorney Alexander White, 52, whose plantation and mansion "Woodville" were near Winchester in northwestern Virginia, represented a district reaching to the Ohio. The expressions on their faces showed exactly opposite thinking as they heard Jefferson reveal in concise and eloquent phrases that their votes for Assumption and funding at full value would save the Union. Without both, "our credit in Amsterdam will burst and vanish, and the states separate to take care every one of itself."

Their votes would support a revised Assumption bill that recognized and rewarded Virginia's having paid most of her war debts. There would also be another, special benefit. "But I leave that happy news for Mr. Madison to tell you."

Lee beamed. White glowered.

"Now I will excuse myself," Jefferson concluded, "for this is Mr. Madison's meeting. I am only providing a private meeting place. In addition to being outside the legislative branch, I have just recovered from two months of migraine and am far behind in my reports on weights and measures. Good day, Gentlemen. I will return when your meeting is over."

Creating the Federal City (K.Bowling) (Octagon Research Series)

TJ letter to James Monroe June 20, 1790 (quote)

Madison plunged immediately into the story of the developing drama. Hamilton wanted the Assumption bill to pass; the President wanted it to pass; Robert Morris wanted it to pass. "And now, even I want it to pass," added Madison. (Exclamations, much exchanging of glances.)

"I want it to pass because Hamilton has agreed that settling accounts between states and federal government will proceed hand-in-hand with assuming state war debts. (Hand clapping and a rumble of approval.)

"This means Virginia has a good chance to come out even. (Murmur of approval from the two Virginians) Probably Maryland has a good chance, too—for Hamilton promises LENIENCY, approving ALL claims! (Hand clapping, cries of 'Well done' 'Bravo, Mr. Madison!') He will help these changes through the Senate—and extend the time for submitting claims. In addition, he will recommend raising the total of state debts to be assumed by a few million dollars, which will be allotted to us and others who deserve more than now allotted them in his plan."

"Amazing!" exclaimed Bland Lee. "Hurray!" White looked at him with disapprobation for his outburst.

Madison hurried on. "I am well aware of the negative votes you have cast against the Assumption measure in the past. Although I despise the vultures who are gulping down the body of our state debts, and who will profit by millions of dollars, the fact remains that the new federal government must have a solid credit rating at home and abroad. Faith in the word and money pledges of the new government are essential.

"Now that changes in the bill will allow us a fair deal, I have promised Hamilton to propose to you gentlemen that you use your vote to support his funding and Assumption plan."

Alex White, one finger scratching a sweaty spot under the edge of his wig, his face frowning ferociously at Madison, began struggling to rise as he spluttered, "I am ap—"

Madison raised his voice and one hand while rapidly saying, "For this, we will be further rewarded! Another dramatic development will come out of this!" White, still frowning, stared at him, but settled back.

"We who want Potomac for the federal district," Madison confided, "have a pledge from Hamilton concerning the seat of government—IF, of course, you vote his plan. It is this: He will drop his campaign to keep the temporary capital in New York, and he will urge the Northeast men to do likewise.

"He will tell them it is the only way to enact Assumption—which, as we all know, will keep some of them out of debtors' prison. (White began vocalizing a question and again struggling to stand.)

"Assuming they follow his lead, they will make no attempt to undercut an agreement we are working to conclude with the Pennsylvanians for the temporary seat in Philadelphia, and the permanent seat on the Potomac!"

"Ahhhh!" "How sensible!" White settled back into his chair.

"We all know how important this is," Madison continued. "How many times have the Northeast men dangled in front of Morris the lure of permanent capital—with New York the temporary!

"How close—within a split second—have they come to success, as in the case of Germantown!

"The plan now working between Virginia and Pennsylvania could bring a decision during the next two weeks for Potomac and Philadelphia. ("God bless you, Mr. Madison!")

"The President has... knows about it," Madison added cautiously. ("Bravo! Bravo!" "This is truly it!")

"The action in both Houses should move much easier than any before—Hamilton will discourage the Northeast men from conniving to displace Philadelphia with New York, or throwing in the names

Daniel Carroll
of Rock Creek

Power of the Purse
(Ferguson)

216

of other towns when our bill is debated.("Good! Good!!")

"BUT!" Madison wagged a finger. "I hasten to remind you that in return, Hamilton must have Virginia, Maryland, and Pennsylvania votes for his financial plan. So—we cannot have a Potomac capital unless we support Assumption.

"I believe Mr. Hamilton will keep his pledges, for he is desperate for Assumption to pass before adjournment next month. I am now asking you—Senator Carroll, Daniel Carroll, Richard Bland Lee, George Gale, Alexander White—to yield Hamilton your votes for Assumption. To win, he says he needs three Senate votes and five votes in the House—"

"Does that mean you yourself will give him the fifth vote, Mr. Madison?" asked White.

"Pennsylvania will provide that vote, Mr. White," Madison answered quickly. "I think you will agree that a switch in my vote—I, the Congressman who has most resisted Assumption the past six months—would raise troublesome questions. My job, therefore, will be to work on the Pennsylvanians. So far, Morris tells me he will convert Read of Delaware, and one other Senator, unspecified."

For a moment a thought-filled silence held the floor. Daniel Carroll looked at his cousin Charles whose eyes seemed focused on his folded hands; Lee looked at White and nodded and smiled; Gale, smiling, looked around at all the others before nodding enthusiastically at Madison. Charles Carroll of Carrollton then spoke. "Mr. Madison, you mentioned to me that the offer to Morris was 15 years for Congress to remain in Philadelphia—"

"FIFTEEN YEARS!" cried White. "Who on earth ever made that outrageous offer!"

Senator Carroll responded, "The President." With his gaze turned to Madison, he added, "This fact these men will know sooner or later. I doubt any of us will spread it—certainly no more than Morris or Hamilton, who know it."

White, quite subdued, stared open-mouthed at Carroll. Cautiously, he said, "But 15 years!"

"Yes, Mr. White, it sounds too long to me also," said Carroll. "I seriously doubt that those who support Potomac will consent to 15 years of waiting. On the other hand, it must be enough to satisfy Morris with second place for Philadelphia. We could try for 10."

"Suppose Pennsylvania won't accept 10," asked young Lee. "Suppose they SAY they accept but turn tricky and greedy on the Senate or House floor?"

Madison grimaced and threw up both hands. "We have one, possibly workable, alternative: a deal with equally tricky Northeast men for Potomac and New York. But I feel convinced Mr. Morris realizes that, for Philadelphia, it's second place or nothing—and that he must have the South for Assumption or that will be nothing, too. Getting neither will kill him."

"There are those who would not grieve," mumbled Lee, then quickly added, glancing at his neighbor, "Mr. White and I would hope for—expect—some direct benefit to our districts in return for our Assumption vote. Our state legislature just six months ago has said the same. In short, the bill must NOT specify Georgetown, Maryland, on the Potomac, as it often has in the past."

Daniel Carroll began expostulating, "I don't see–" but White, half rising, loudly interrupted. "We must tell Congress to think WEST—upriver from Georgetown and tidewater—and to include Virginia land. Gentlemen, I would like to help compose the language of the bill. We ought not to disregard our western brethren nor the words of the Virginia act of last December offering $120,000 and a 10-mile square AT A PLACE on Potomac where Virginia and Pennsylvania as well as Maryland can participate. That place is 100 miles upriver from Georgetown.

"That place is Hancock, only a few miles from the town of Bath. It's a settlement known through-

Papers of Thomas Jefferson, Vol.19, Editorial Note p9, 19 (Boyd)

Berkeley Springs, W. Va.

Papers of James Madison Vol. 12 (Hobson/Rutland) p427

out the country as a natural crossroads of trails east and west with trails north and south on the Maryland bank of the Potomac. Sitting as it does on the three-mile-wide waist of Maryland, Hancock would be the center of a 10-mile square extending north into Pennsylvania and south into Virginia. How fitting it would be for the seat of government to rest at the crossroads of the Potomac flowing to the ocean, the Tuscarora Path joining north to south, and the wagon trail connecting the East with the Ohio Valley!"

Senator Carroll had become more and more alert and attentive as Congressman White's voice and words had warmed. Leaning forward, hands resting on his knees, Carroll interrupted when White was catching his breath.

"I, too, favor a site above Georgetown," Carroll said in a firm, almost stern tone, "for Carrollton Manor on the Potomac at the mouth of the Monocacy, 40 miles upriver from Georgetown, has all the requirements of soil, climate, and beauty for a capital city.

"HOWEVER! To offer a Potomac bill that does not even permit consideration of Georgetown, the long-known preference of the President, is not only an unacceptable rebuff to him, but also will offer to our enemies the means to divide us. Our goal must be to name the Potomac—ONLY the Potomac! When that is secure, it will be time enough to thresh out the exact place on the Potomac."

"But, can we afford a rebuff to the Virginia legislature? $120,000—" countered White.

"Yes—if Virginia demands the unthinkable or proposes the impractical!" declared Daniel Carroll of Georgetown, Maryland.

George Gale pitched in, "Hancock is just a crossroads, not even a village, behind four ridges of mountains! The nearest town is 40 miles east— Hagerstown, just this side of the Conococheague Creek. Is it reasonable to ask Congressmen to travel into wilderness, across mountains and streams three days beyond the closest town to Hancock?"

Every man began voicing an opinion. Madison, rapping his knuckles hard upon the tabletop called, "Gentlemen! Gentlemen! If it is agreeable to all, I will meet after dinner today with Senator Carroll, who will introduce the Potomac bill next Monday and guide it through the Senate. I believe we can draft and present to you tomorrow morning a bill acceptable to both the Virginia and Maryland delegations, and their state legislatures."

When the five men had voiced agreement, Madison returned to the main business. "I have asked you to yield your vote to Assumption, else we have no chance for a Potomac capital. What say you gentlemen? Senator Carroll, Sir?"

"I am ready to take my vows," Senator Carroll of Carrollton announced. "In view of all that is involved, I pledge my vote for Assumption—provided that the Potomac-Philadelphia bill is taken up and completed FIRST. ("It will be," Madison interrupted.) I want to be sure we get the seat before I hand over my vote on Assumption.

"One fact that has helped me decide to switch is the loose talk—which I take seriously—that those in Congress who have much to lose in speculations will, in revenge, vote against ALL of the finance plan if the Assumption paragraphs are lost. That will damn the whole country and union to failure. Therefore, I will say 'yea' to Assumption, a necessary evil."

"I, too!" declared Gale, his round face flushed.

"And I," said Lee. "My cousin, Senator Richard Henry Lee, who is bitterly opposed to the Hamilton plan, will deplore my switching to support it— BUT my constituents will approve my reason for doing so. The national capital situated on the Potomac will generate much wealth for the area— and the South. That is a fair price for a finance plan amended to assure Virginia her just due."

Charles Carroll

Maclay's Journal, June, 1790

R.B.Lee letter to Theodorick Lee

"And you, Mr. White? What say you?" Madison prodded.

Alex White rubbed his nose, sighed, and answered, "Everything I have thought and said for the past six months has been against Assumption and the accompanying speculation. The only time I made even a gesture toward approving it was my amendment in February, which was voted down. Perhaps with all the money adjustments Mr. Madison has squeezed out of Hamilton, I can justify to my people why I have switched my vote.

"I can say the adjustments satisfied my worst objections. But I hate to give the appearance of a man who has abandoned his principles. So, with a revulsion of stomach almost convulsive at the possibility of appearing in any such light, I pledge my Assumption vote for the good of Virginia and the country."

Jefferson accounts of the event

"Thank you, Gentlemen," Madison said solemnly. "We must now move very quickly. The action in the Senate will begin next Monday, the twenty-eighth, when Butler's postponed bill and the House's Baltimore bill are both brought forward. I will proceed today to tell Morris we offer 10—not 15—years for the temporary. Assuming that the Pennsylvanians accept that, we will present to them the Potomac-Philadelphia bill which the Virginia and Maryland delegations will, by that time, have agreed upon.

"One thing more before we disband. I ask everyone on good terms with Senator Butler of South Carolina—is ANYONE?—to persuade him to relent on his dislike for the Quakers of Philadelphia and vote CONSISTENTLY for Potomac. Remind him that Assumption will now pass because of US, not the New Yorkers—that South Carolina will get more money from the Assumption plan because of US, not the New Yorkers—that a vote for New York is a vote against the South."

Power of the Purse (EJ Ferguson) p330, 333

"Can Butler be trusted not to tell every detail of the Potomac-Philadelphia plan to his dear friends the New Yorkers?" asked White, hoisting himself from his chair.

"Yes, if he is not told any detail beyond those that come to the Yorkers from Mr. Hamilton!"

Just then, the door opened and Jefferson's sunny face appeared. "Oh, you're on your feet—I trust all went well?"

"Yes," replied Madison, "Mr. White with a convulsive revulsion, Mr. Lee with an eye on the wealth flowing from a Potomac capital, Mr. Gale with enthusiasm, Mr. Carroll of Rock Creek and Georgetown with hope, and Senator Carroll of the manor on Monocacy, have pledged their votes for an adjusted Assumption plan, for 10 years at Philadelphia, and for the glory of the Potomac!"

"Not worth a Continental," Americans said of paper money issued by the Continental Congress. The $6-bill above was worth only 60¢ soon after its printing. In 1790, under Hamilton's finance plan, the federal Treasury redeemed the bill for close to the dollar value on its face.

Pennsylvanians at a dinner meeting to act on Madison's Philadelphia-Potomac offer, pause briefly while Senator Morris catches his asthmatic breath at an open window. The vote becomes a unanimous "Yea!" when Senator Maclay pledges to vote "Yea" in the Senate, in line with the majority vote of the Pennsylvanians.

SCENE 2
PENNSYLVANIA'S MEN

PLACE: Brandon's Tavern where the Pennsylvanians have dined before a business meeting.
TIME: Three days later, Thursday, June 24.

All the scene from Maclay's Journal, June 24, p296-301

Rapping his spoon against a wine bottle, Speaker Muhlenberg quieted the dozen men at the table and announced in his commanding voice, "Senator Morris is recognized to speak!"

Senator Morris slid his chair back and stood to look about the table at the familiar faces of Pennsylvania's eight House members, Senator Maclay, and three visitors. "Fellow Pennsylvanians and neighbors—Senators Read and Basset of Delaware, and Senator Elmer of New Jersey!" Morris bowed slightly toward the senators. They bowed back, one of them through encircling clouds of bluish cigar smoke.

"During the past few days, I have let all of you know that Hamilton has given up New York for temporary seat of government. (A scattering of applause—but an outburst from Senator Maclay— "Hamilton's hand now in the residence means his foot will be in it before the end of the session!")

Morris, unperturbed, continued. "The way cleared for a Philadelphia-Potomac pairing, I have since Monday afternoon been negotiating with the Virginians. The fact is, Virginia's House delegates have cut down the first—uh—unsubstantiated offer of 15 years. They say 10 only—it's that or nothing. They'll turn to New York. Our interest is to keep this deal with the South alive. If we do not, the temporary residence will, one way or another, remain in New York, the permanent one way or another will go to Potomac, and Pennsylvania will be left with nothing—cheated of its just due! As I have told most, I think all, of you already, and heard a unanimous but informal expression of agreement

("Not mine!" cried Maclay) I will be satisfied with 10 years for Philadelphia. So, the business has been settled at last! With our concurrence today, Senator Carroll will make the motion TOMORROW, Friday, for Potomac and Philadelphia! He wishes to make his move before Butler makes his on Monday."

Maclay called out, "What happened to the committee appointed last week to draw up our reasons for rejecting ALL of Hamilton's proposals—and we should not be reduced now to groveling after the TEMPORARY seat! I consider the PERMANENT residence itself ought to belong to Pennsylvania, no matter from what point of view it is considered—geographically or politically! To deprive us of the seat is in my opinion a species of ROBBERY!"

His large, plump face flushed with exasperation, his voice wheezing and labored, Morris declared, "Senator, we did reject all Hamilton's offers. If you thought such things about the temporary, you should not have agreed to our contract last Saturday with the Virginians for 15 years temporary."

"What contract?" Maclay demanded. "I never entered into any agreement!"

A clamor of voices (Morris, Fitzsimons, and Speaker Muhlenberg) declared, "Yes, you did! I remind you, sir—I remember distinctly, we all agreed! Indeed, sir, don't deny—" but not drowning out Maclay's, "You're concocting nonsense! I never agreed to any number of years for temporary—I wrote out my arguments for sticking with permanent—I gave them to Hartley! Colonel Hartley, show them that paper!"

Congressman Hartley, all eyes upon him, screwed up his face, rubbed his chin, glanced across at Maclay and over at Morris. "Oh, yes, you did give me such a paper, Mr. Maclay. Actually, on that occasion, we only discussed—we made no contract for anything." Morris's face flushed redder. He tried to speak. Instead he began gasping for breath. Clymer in the next chair jumped to his feet, ex-

Robert Morris

Maclay does not mention Morris's having an asthma attack at this meeting. Morris was subject to them, however. Description of an attack in R. Morris (Oberholtzer) p286

claiming, "Asthma attack! It's the cigar smoke! Open the door! Let me help you to the window, Bob!" At the window, Morris lifted his shoulders and chest up and down, breathing in a moaning gasp, his arms working as if he were "pumping water from a ship's flooded bay."

R. Morris
(Oberholtzer) p286

At the table, the smoker snubbed out his fire, and a waiter hurried away the offending tobacco. Another waiter fanned the air with his coat, driving smoke out the door, while a third rushed in with a large mug of strong coffee—"Makes him breathe easier, he's told us!"

During the few minutes' wait for Morris to return to normal breathing, Congressman Scott quietly said to Maclay, Hartley, the Speaker, and Senator Elmer, "I must confirm Colonel Hartley's statement: No contract was ever made for any specific number of years. We only discussed a tentative offer."

Speaker Muhlenberg drew himself up, forced a smile, and said, "Well, we have one now, and a unanimous consent is desirable. I think we should take our vote—is Mr. Morris able to vote now?" he called to the two men by the window. "Good! Stay where you are! No need to sit at the table to vote! The question is, Shall we vote for a bill giving the temporary residence for 10 years to Philadelphia and the permanent residence to Potomac? All in favor say 'yea.'"

"YEA!!" from all directions.

"All opposed, 'Nay.'"

"NO!" boomed Maclay.

Dead silence, all eyes directed at the contrary voter. "Senator," said Speaker Muhlenberg, "does that mean you will vote against Philadelphia and Potomac in the Senate? If you do, we could lose this chance by your ONE vote. New York would rejoice. But Pennsylvanians would remember you as the one-man minority who overruled your delegation majority. Is that the role you wish to play? Or will you join our majority vote when you vote

Frederick Muhlenberg

in the Senate? We have been offered the temporary seat—and we can work to make it permanent. In both acts, we serve the public good. What is your answer, Senator Maclay?"

In the silence, the question hung about the shoulders of the gray-haired Senator, sitting regally and glumly in his chair. Abruptly he rose, tall and straight, his white linen suit setting off his lean, once-handsome face. Lips tight, without turning his head, he looked at each face about the table. "Since we have come here to consult the public good—" (several men took a deep breath and closed their eyes) "I am willing to be governed by republican ideas, and will stand by the vote of the majority, as a house divided against itself cannot stand."

Instantly, the other 12 men broke into cheers and applause, pushing their chairs back and standing to clap harder and to reach for a handshake. "A toast to the Senator from Harrisburg!" called Muhlenberg. Glasses raised, the Speaker said, "To Maclay the Republican! A man of iron-clad integrity, fearless independence, and lofty ideals!"

"To Maclay!" the men shouted, and the meeting broke up in noisy pleasantries.

At last, when Morris, Clymer, and Fitzsimons were outside and out of sight, Morris stopped and clasped his two friends on the shoulders. "By God, I can hardly believe it! Old cranky Maclay actually gave it to us! I almost had another asthma attack when he said he would go with the majority! Well!" he added as they walked on, "so Carroll will open the show tomorrow to get a three-day jump on the House resolution for Baltimore, scheduled for Monday the twenty-eighth. Carroll is absolutely the best man to take the lead for our bill. We should win easily—shouldn't we?

"With almost every Senator south of New York voting with the Potomac crowd—though Butler of South Carolina will play hide and seek with his vote—we can say 'to hell with New York!' Then

William Maclay

George Clymer

Hist.Cong., House Journ. July 26 vote

A.Hamilton (F.McDonald) Note 20

after 10 years to work on it, 'to hell with Potomac!' But! (Morris stopped to wag a finger at his two friends) IF our Virginians try any tricks in the Senate or House, to hell with this deal! On to Germantown and New York!"

"EXCEPT—" Fitzsimons began, and Clymer carried on, "as the three of us know, without the votes of our Virginia and Maryland friends we lose the other prize—ASSUMPTION!"

Morris gave a wheezy sigh. "Ah, yes. We must bear that in mind. We do need them. I have worked on our neighbor-state Senators who just sat with us, and we have enough votes in the Senate. In the House, it's not so certain—nothing seems capable of causing five of our own men to switch THEIR votes. Have you tried talking to them again this week—Hartley, Heister, Scott, General Muhlenberg, Wynkoop?"

Fitzsimons nodded. "Wynkoop seems to be softening. The others spoke to us as roughly as Jackson of Georgia spoke to the House gallery the other day, though without drawing pistols the way he did. 'Begone!' I heard Jackson's big voice boom at a pair of talkative characters, 'Begone, uncouth peasants, lest I shoot you dead, sirs, dead!'"

A New York cartoonist loads all the blame on the back of Robert Morris of Philadelphia, money bag in hand at left, for depriving New York of temporary capital. On Morris's travois ride 13 happy Senators—the majority—who voted with him for Philadelphia. Behind them, the "manority", 12 grumbling Northeast Senators, trudge at the end of Morris-held leashes tied to their noses.

CHAPTER 21

Raucous Final Votes

SCENE 1
POTOMAC AND—NEW YORK!!

PLACE: Senate Chamber, Federal Hall.
TIME: Four days later, Monday, June 28, 1790

Maclay's Journal combined with Senate Journal for June 28, 1790

Building details from "Federal Hall Revisited" (Louis Torres) Journ.Soc. Arch.History. Dec.1970

Senator Charles Carroll of Carrollton passed close to Senator Maclay's desk and motioned him to come outside the Senate. With the clerk clattering through long readings of Baltimore's attractions and accommodations, all described by eager citizens excited that Congress was considering their town for the permanent capital, the two Senators walked out to the "Portrait Gallery" lobby around the head of the marble staircase.

Carroll led Maclay past Trumbull's life-size portraits of Washington and Hamilton, to a far corner. Underneath a gilded frame holding Governor Clinton on canvas, Carroll stopped and looked up at Maclay's large blue eyes.

"Senator Maclay," he said, "I have a favor to ask of you—but it's one I think you might enjoy doing."

"What is that, Mr. Carroll?"

"In regard to the postponement I just sought and won for the House resolution attempting to put Baltimore into the PERMANENT seat—"

"Yes—?"

"I am going to call up immediately, after our return to the chamber, the bill I introduced on Friday for Potomac as the permanent seat and Philadelphia, the temporary."

"Yes—the one Bonny Johnny on Friday pretended he heard a call to postpone! I am incensed that after we voted 'nay,' Adams allowed Izard's 'recon-

sider,' and gave him time to run outside, grab Rhode Island's new Senators, and make them vote for postponing. I saw Izard pull them to their feet and all but hold them up. They had no notion what they were voting for."

"The very bill," Carroll smiled. "It begins with 'be it enacted,' and goes on to say 'a 10-mile square for the permanent seat, to be located at'—and here we have left a blank to be filled."

"Yes—with Potomac."

"I would appreciate your moving to insert BALTIMORE in that blank, Mr. Maclay."

Maclay looked down at Carroll in puzzlement. "Baltimore? But you just sought and won a postponement on the House resolution for Baltimore as permanent! We want Potomac, not Baltimore!"

"Yes, we want Potomac," Carroll said, "but if a Baltimore RESOLUTION requiring only one reading and one vote had passed by a stroke of luck, the Senate would have been committed to Baltimore. My bill requiring three readings is much safer—but we must use it at first to get rid of Baltimore, freeing Maryland and Carolina Senators to then vote for Potomac—and Philadelphia. We need their votes."

Maclay drew his tall frame up straighter and stiffer, and looked at Carroll indignantly.

"Why would you think of asking me to do such a

Maclay's Journal, June 28, 1790

Maclay's Journal, June 28

thing? It has the sound of tricky business afoot. I will have nothing to do with it."

Carroll's eyes continued to hold Maclay's. "There is nothing tricky about it—it's just common sense strategy. I am told that you will vote with us—is this not so?"

"In a weak moment I DID commit myself," Maclay admitted, "but that did NOT include advertising the weakness in advance."

Carroll's smile broadened. "Thank you, Mr. Maclay. I will find someone else to name Baltimore."

They walked back to the Senate and took their seats. In another few minutes, the clerk's readings done, Carroll called up his bill. Izard of South Carolina rose.

"Mr. President, I move to insert the town of BALTIMORE in the blank for the permanent seat of government!"

The vote came quickly: NAY! Four Southerners who voted for Baltimore now had only one Southern location to favor—Potomac.

Carroll caught the eye of each one—Butler and Izard of South Carolina, Johnston of North Carolina, and Few of Georgia—before he began to read "..10-mile square..on the river Potomac, at some place between the mouths of the Eastern Branch and Connogochegue.."

Hist. Cong., Senate Journal, June 28

That vote came quickly, too: YEA to Potomac. Butler, Izard, Johnston, and Few were among the 16, and so were Maclay and Morris. Three out of four Senators from Pennsylvania's neighbors, Delaware and New Jersey, were part of the score, but from farther north, only two votes—one each from Rhode Island and New Hampshire—escaped to the South.

Nine losing New York and New England men glumly whispered among themselves. Slowly, slowly, for the next three hours, Carroll presented amendments to his bill and heard them debated,

Maclay's Journal, June 28

then accepted—Commissioners for the District, $100,000 borrowing right for land and buildings, and December 1800 for Congress's moving day from wherever it was temporarily sitting.

Where would it be temporarily sitting? An open blank waited for that place name. Izard grabbed the floor.

"NEW YORK, sir!" (Groans and cries of dismay from Virginia and Pennsylvania men.) For the next few minutes, tempers flashed and words clashed in hot duels. New Yorkers pressed claims, Maclay and New Hampshire's Langdon struck back for Philadelphia. Virginians alternated accusations with passionate reasoning. ("Where are Hamilton's controls on the New England and York men?" murmured Carroll to himself.)

At 3 o'clock, the question was put. Butler, Izard, Johnston, and Few clung to the side of New York—AND VICTORY! 13 to 12! Cheers and applause reverberated all the way across the lightwell to the House public galleries on the same level as the Senate floor.

"Adjourn! Adjourn!" cried New Yorkers King and Schuyler. New England men joined them in the joyous chant, and then in the backslapping all the way out the door.

Maclay waited at his desk until Carroll was passing, and joined him. "Let them enjoy their one-vote victory," Carroll responded to Maclay's growl. "Tomorrow, Butler will be back with us on the second reading."

"How do you know?"

"He will. You'll see. We'll remind him how much he needs us for other things he wants. He'll jump back."

"Butler has only one vote. That means a tie."

"Your Bonny Johnny likes Philadelphia."

Hist. Cong., Senate Journal, June 28

Maclay's Journal, June 28

Hist. Cong. Senate Journal June 28

SCENE 2
PENNSYLVANIA WILL NOT BE CHEATED!!

PLACE: Senate floor, Federal Hall.
TIME: The next day, June 29, about noon.

*Maclay's Journal and
Hist. Cong,. Senate
Journal, June 29, 1790*

"Are you convinced?" said Carroll to Maclay. They had strolled from their desks to the passage between Vice President Adams's red damask canopy and the arched windows.

"I heard and saw Butler switch back to our side, and that both Massachusetts men and Georgia came with him. The New Yorkers—and Izard—lost by four votes the seat they won yesterday, and bounced in surprise," Maclay growled. "But I am not convinced any of them is abandoning New York."

Carroll said softly, "I'm told that Hamilton has put a squeeze on Massachusetts—"

*Building details from
Journ. Arch.History,
Dec.1970 (L.Torres)*

Maclay snorted. "I do not doubt that he squeezed Senators Dalton and Strong, but I predict they will soon appear fully reinflated. They, and Gerry in the House, talk about 'fairness to New York' for beautifying the halls of Congress."

Abruptly Carroll said, "I see Adams returning from the call-of-nature recess. Let's go. I'll ask ahead for recognition to call up our bill next. I hope I've allayed your nervousness about our strategy."

*Maclay and Senate
Jour.*

Maclay answered irritably, "I will feel a lot better about your strategy when you finally introduce Philadelphia, and for 10 years. You've taken your time."

Within minutes, Carroll was offering Philadelphia for 10 years as temporary seat.

Senate Jour.

Immediately Schuyler and King of New York tried to salvage something for their state.

Maclay Jour.

"Four years for New York, six for Philadelphia!" they cried. Long speeches accused, pleaded, complained, and (Maclay perceived) threatened.

"I heard you say that moving the seat from New York would convulse the nation!" he shouted at King. "I never said that!" King shouted back.

Senator Morris, sitting beside Maclay, said loudly with irritation, "No, he didn't!"

Maclay barked at Morris, "You're taking sides AGAINST Philadelphia, Senator, after two days of saying not a word FOR Philadelphia! Other Senators heard the phrase 'convulse the nation'—"

"I heard it!" called out Wyngate of New Hampshire. "He said it!" came from another corner.

King stood up and tipped his hat to the Senate. "If a number of you heard it, I may have said such—but it was not my intention nor my thought, and I withdraw any such phrase anybody thinks he heard from me."

*Maclay and Senate
Jour.*

Schuyler and King's motion drew a 13-13 tie vote. Adams voted against New York.

Senate Jour.

Suddenly Butler was on his feet calling again for four years in New York—followed by six years in Baltimore! It failed with a hard thump—16 to 10—both sides glaring at him. Butler, undaunted, tried again: "Two years? New York deserves that for all the expense it went to for Federal Hall. Philadelphia should be satisfied with eight years."

*Maclay and Senate
Jour.*

Again, a tie vote! Again Adams voted "Nay."

Maclay sent Carroll a note: "Notice how Massachusetts voted to steal six, or four, or two of our years?"

Senate Jour.

At last came the vote on Carroll's original motion for 10 years in Philadelphia.

A tie AGAIN! Butler and Massachusetts were sticking with New York.

*Maclay and Senate
Jour.*

All eyes and ears turned to Adams. Without his usual lecture, he said flatly, "Nay," for the third time that day.

Senators bounced out of their seats exclaiming—delighted surprise from Northeast men, consternation from those of Pennsylvania, Virginia, and Maryland. "My God! Adams killed Philadelphia! What's wrong with the man!?"

Adams looked up at the commotion, his head

"Don't you tell me how to vote, Sir!" shouts Pierce Butler of South Carolina at Robert Morris. Butler had voted for New York in the last Senate vote of the day, creating a tie. Vice President Adams misspoke "Nay" to break it—and suddenly Philadelphia had lost the temporary capital. Angry Morris suspected a plot to scuttle his city. With dire threats of revenge, he stormed, "Pennsylvania will NOT be cheated!"

cocked questioningly, his dimpled half-smile working around his mouth.

Carroll called frantically, "Mr. President! Mr. President! Mr. President!" Adams tapped the desk with his silver pen and recognized him. "I move that we now have the third and final reading of that part of the bill that was earlier approved!"

"NO! NO! NO!" a chorus shouted. "Not Potomac alone!"

Adams frowned with uncertainty. He did not respond to Carroll's motion, the cries against it, or the commotion on the Floor. Virginia Senator Richard Henry Lee, an old friend of Adams, shouted over the hubbub, "Motion to adjourn!" The Vice President had only to nod and the vote came loud and fast—"YEA!"

Senator Morris, his great round face crimson with anger, strode across the chamber to catch up with Senator Butler. Just outside, in the vast "audience room" surrounding the head of the east staircase, he grabbed Butler's arm and confronted him.

Wagging his forefinger rapidly in Butler's indignant face, he shouted, "YOU, sir, YOU—have betrayed us again! What do you mean, Senator Butler, voting AGAINST Carroll's motion for Philadelphia and Potomac!? Your vote alone would have saved us from a tie and Adams' silly 'Nay'! What kind of a man is it who swears he will stick with you on the big votes even if he rambles on the in-betweens—then renegs when he's needed most!? You have tricked us to play your old game for New York—keep-Congress-just-where-it-is! Sir, you have jumped back and forth one time too many!"

Pushing Morris's hand aside, Butler shouted, "Don't you tell me how to vote, Senator! I don't have to explain my votes to you or anybody else! If I think it's unfair to give New York nothing for all the trouble and expense it's been put to, that's what I'll vote and damnation to what YOU think!"

Hands on hips, feet wide apart, Morris stormed

Scene derived from Maclay's Journal about the behavior of Morris during these days in the Senate, and by discerning from the sequence of recorded events what unrecorded confrontations probably took place.

back, "I think you Southerners have put together a treacherous scheme to cheat Pennsylvania out of having anything—not the permanent, not the temporary, just NOTHING! You got our votes for Potomac in the two readings! Then you played it foxy, with Adams helping you, making it look as if HE alone killed Philadelphia!" ("No, No, Senator! Not so! Never, never!" voices called from the ever-enlarging circle.)

Morris's flashing blue eyes scanned the gathering. "Look at what Carroll did! He jumped up the instant Adams said 'nay' to Philadelphia temporary, and called for the third and final vote on the permanent-seat paragraphs—the Potomac part! That shows bad faith—"

"If it was the will of the Senate—" broke in Virginia Senator Walker.

"Will of the Senate like hell—TRICK of the Potomac crowd, conniving behind the canopy with the New Yorkers!" Morris's face had grown beet red, his blue eyes glared, his expression was mobile with fierce anger.

Senator Carroll stepped forward. "No trickery on our side," he said calmly. "But there were peculiar moves on yours—disturbingly like those we've seen on other votes for the seat during the past few months—for example, not offering a single word of support during the present debates—"

"But I VOTED with you!"

"You also took the part of New Yorker King yesterday against your fellow Pennsylvanian Senator Maclay" (Morris grimaced in disgust) AND in the background we heard over and over that you were telling the world you would never let go of the seat, 'just wait until Congress meets in Philadelphia, there are ways and means to hold it there, it will never get to the wilds of Conococheague'— and the like. That is far from reassuring, Sir!"

"BUT I VOTED WITH YOU!" Morris fairly screamed. "It was your Southern brother from South

Pierce Butler

Maclay, June 30

Carolina—where is he? The coward has slunk away! HIS vote killed Philadelphia! Or perhaps that tie vote was planned! Then the Massachusetts man in the chair gave the final blow! YOU grabbed the loot and tried to run off with it! We now have every right to leave you and Potomac!"

Carroll's thin lips had compressed to a tight, straight line. "Senator! Such accusations are unwarranted! There was no such plot! There was no intent to forsake Philadelphia—no matter the uneasiness your behavior gave us. I knew that, in the next moment, we might nail down Potomac—but we could lose it if we waited through the heat of a long debate on the temporary question. However—the moment has passed. Tomorrow, we will ask for a reconsideration of the Philadelphia paragraph."

Carroll's gaze fastened upon Morris's, until Morris announced in a steely, calm voice, "We had a bargain with Virginia. We kept our bargain. Unless Philadelphia is reconsidered tomorrow and given the 10 years, Pennsylvania will NOT vote for Potomac on the third and last reading. That is final."

Senator Walker of Virginia burst out, "You will only drive us to the New Yorkers. With all our votes—the Carolinas and Georgia are definitely with us—and New York-New England—Pennsylvania will get nothing, nothing!"

Maclay, June 30

"You may THINK you have all those votes," replied Morris hotly, "but we all know that moving words around in a bill can move votes around, and we have many 12-to-13 tallies besides. But if you should succeed in that devilishness, if you finally cheat us by such treachery, Pennsylvania can and will kill the whole finance bill, funding, assumption, and all, come what may to anybody, including myself. South Carolina can then wallow in its debt. You can have your capital on the Potomac but no government to sit there. You Senators speculating with borrowed money can face ruin and prison. PENNSYLVANIA WILL NOT BE CHEATED!"

With that, Morris drew his grossly overweight body to its full six-foot height, swept a flinty glance around the group of Senators, and strode away.

"Well, Gentlemen," Senator Carroll said as Morris's broad back, then his head and long, ungathered gray hair moved out of sight down the marble staircase, "I, for one, have several important visits to pay. First—to Mr. Adams, who, I believe, is in the clerk's office. Next, to Mr. Butler, who might even be in hiding."

SCENE 3
RECONSIDERED YEAS AND NAYS

PLACE: Senate Chamber, Federal Hall.
TIME: Next day, Wednesday, June 30

A chastened Pierce Butler rose from his seat to speak in place of Charles Carroll, yesterday's loser in the vote on Philadelphia, and so ineligible under the rules to ask for a new vote. "I move," said Butler in his calmest voice, "that the Senate reconsider the paragraph struck yesterday from the seat of government bill." He and 13 others voted "Aye" for his motion and once more Philadelphia for 10 years as temporary capital became the business at hand.

Maclay's, and Senate Jour., June 30, 1790

Senator Morris looked across the room at Senator Carroll and made a small bow.

Once more Schuyler and King tried to split the 10 temporary years between their city and Philadelphia. Butler stuck with Philadelphia. The move failed.

Schuyler and King persisted. They moved for only two years. Butler unstuck and gave them a tie. Adams now had his chance to begin correcting his bumble of yesterday.

Maclay's Journal, June 30

But first he must make a little speech.

"Before I cast my vote to break the 13-13 tie, I

wish to pay my compliments to the people of New York City." (Morris clamped his teeth together and leaned forward, frowning.) "No people in the world could behave more orderly, more decent, than they, especially those who sat in the House Gallery to listen to the proceedings." (Did that mean he was once again going to vote so that Congress would remain here? Both Carroll and Maclay watched Adams' every move, ready to jump to their feet.) "They are polite to the members of public bodies... (In this pause, Walker and Lee half-rose from their chairs) and always observe proper decorum. But be that as it may (Morris bit his upper lip) I will go to Philadelphia without staying here a single hour more, if Congress so directs. 'Nay' to amending the paragraph to favor New York."

A rumble of grumbles among the New York and New England men, relaxed sighs from Carroll and Virginians, and a whisper from Maclay to a relieved Morris, hand shielding his brow. "Bonny Johnny got his 'yeas' and 'nays' sorted out right today," said Maclay. "If he hadn't," replied Morris, "and we'd lost two years to New York, I would also have lost all faith in Carroll and the Virginians, and that would have finished our deal.

"NOW, will Butler stick with us on today's last vote on the whole bill?" whispered Morris.

He did. He stuck with keeping $100,000 in the bill for land and building—but the Virginians and Marylanders saw fit to let it go. On the last vote of the day, he stuck with them to take the third and final vote on Potomac-Philadelphia the next day.

Afterwards, he hurried out the door and down the stairs and around the corner of the building to escape a lambasting from King of New York, a lambasting he knew would be as hot as the one Morris, then Carroll, had given him the day before.

SCENE 4
LONG-AWAITED, FINAL, FINAL SENATE VOTE

PLACE: Senate Chamber, Federal Hall.
TIME: Next day, Thursday, July 1.

"It is evident that the Northeast men have planned to spend the day at this," Maclay remarked to Morris. "First they tried the useless amendments they concocted—changing Conococheague to Hancock 40 miles beyond, changing December 1800 to the next May, and restoring the $100,000. Delay, distraction, and irritation! Now talk is following talk, some with theatricals. Listen to King's act."

Having related the sins of the anti-New York crowd in the Senate, King was wiping his eyes, putting a wail in his voice, and once emitted a sound like a sob. Then he scolded for 15 minutes, railed for 15 more, and accused everybody—then nobody—of bargaining, contracting, vote-swapping, for a half-hour.

"All of this for a decision in favor of a location for the seat of government that will dissolve the Union!" he cried out.

("Where, oh where, is Hamilton's control?" Carroll moaned to himself.)

From every corner of the room, Senators objected. King begged pardon. He began to describe men who swear to support a cause, and in the next hour swear to give their all for another. He went into long and damning detail of someone who could be no other than Butler of South Carolina.

For such a public lambasting Butler was ready, and when King at last sat down, mopping his sweaty brow as well as his moist eyes, Butler answered, "although I feel sure the Senator was not talking about me." On this theme he played in a long, philosophical wandering—until Senator Johnson of Connecticut could stand it no longer.

"Adjourn!" he interrupted.

Maclay's Journal and Senate Journal, July 1, 1790

Rufus King

"Question! Question!" re-echoed from different quarters of the chamber. Adams, looking as if he had roused from a little daydream, put the final question of Potomac and Philadelphia. As soon as the second name, Butler, was called, and his "Aye!" resounded through the room, the tension of the event disappeared.

Potomac and Philadelphia, 14 to 12, was by dinner time in the hand of a fast-walking Senate secretary on his way to the House of Representatives.

SCENE 5
LONG-AWAITED, FINAL, FINAL HOUSE VOTE

PLACE: House of Representatives, Federal Hall.
TIME: Tuesday, July 6 - Wednesday, July 7 - Thursday, July 8 - Friday, July 9, 1790

Hamilton had kept his promise to talk to Yorkers and Northeast men about giving up New York for temporary seat. He also advised them against making offers to Pennsylvania or Virginia in the hope of prying the pair apart.

All the scene from History of Congress, House Journal, July 6, 7, 8, 9, 1790 (Gales/ Seaton)

But even his father-in-law, Senator Schuyler, had heeded not a word Hamilton said about abandoning New York. That fair city deserved some of the glory and prosperity of a seat of government—and, by God, in the Senate they had been victorious twice (each for 24 hours) and lacked only one vote for victory three other times! House members took up the battered New York banner.

With a little luck, they might do just a few votes better in the House and win for keeps.

They went over and over the arithmetic: 22 they had—11 more needed to win. South Carolina loved them and hated Philadelphia Quakers—add five votes. New Jersey would have benefits with the seat in next-door New York—add four votes. Where

could they find the other two?

Maryland? In the Senate, Carroll and Henry had voted straight through for Potomac and Philadelphia. But in the House, half of the six Marylanders passionately favored Baltimore for permanent over Potomac. A deal was possible there!

"Then, there's the one vote of the delegate from Baltimore's close neighbor, Delaware," said Roger Sherman of Connecticut. "That could push Baltimore and New York over the hump."

When the Potomac-Philadelphia bill from the Senate was opened up in the House on Tuesday after Independence Day, the plan was ready. The bill was hurried through two readings without debate. On the third reading, Sherman of Connecticut led off with, "Strike Potomac! Insert Baltimore!"

"Baltimore?!" cried Alexander White of Virginia. "That town has been repeatedly rejected in the Senate! If we strike Potomac for Baltimore, when the bill goes back to the Senate, we shall end this session with neither temporary nor permanent seat!"

Young Richard Bland Lee added, "Inserting Baltimore is calculated to destroy the entire bill and delay the decision!"

"No! Baltimore is simply a better choice!" Burke of South Carolina shouted. "A populous place is better than building a palace in the woods of Conococheague! As for moving from New York to Philadelphia, that move will excite the most turbulent passions in the minds of the people! And you'll see—Congress will never leave Philadelphia! Commissioners will incur no penalty for neglecting their duty to build a new city! Besides—a Quaker state is a bad neighborhood for South Carolinians! Another thing: There's no public gallery in the Philadelphia house proposed for Congress! An open gallery is a very important check to the Legislature! Here in Federal Hall, the House if not the Senate has a gallery!"

John Laurence of New York declared that 10 years

delay in moving to Potomac "or that Conococheague place" meant the People disapproved of dragging the Government to so undeveloped a spot. They particularly disapproved, he added ominously, of the sad fact that funding and other important matters must wait "until the seat is decided in favor of Potomac!"

When Michael Stone of Maryland rose to speak, the House quieted, all sides listening with hope and nervousness.

"Both Baltimore and Potomac are in my state," he began. "I would vote for Baltimore had that name come from the Senate. But—the Senate sent the name of Potomac, and I will not be drawn from voting for Potomac by any amendment, motion, or modification of the bill whatsoever! I consider the locating of the seat of government as one of the most painful and disagreeable subjects that can be agitated, and wish to have the business finally and unalterably fixed!"

Thin and bony Elbridge Gerry of Massachusetts stuttered, "But this b-bill holds out the possibility of fixing the government at Conoco-co-cheague. This cannot be, ah-h-h, serious! I doubt anyone ever had any intention of going to this Indian place! It must rank as a mere maneuver!

"P-people will ask 'Where in the name of common sense is Conco-no-chick,' which they cannot even pronounce. I do not believe that one person in a thousand in the United States knows there is such a place on earth! You would sound more in earnest to insert Mississippi, Detroit, or Winnipipiocket Pond!

"Baltimore holds out the only prospect of a permanent seat of government in the South! For the temporary seat, New York came into an unconditional adoption of the Constitution on the promise of the seat. Should this bill pass, what c-can the promise to New York be denominated but a d-d-deception sanctioned by us?"

"Sir!" answered Hartley of Pennsylvania. "It is the fault of the New York Senators last year that they did not vote for a four-year residence in their own city with the permanent one at Germantown—which their votes could then have secured!"

John Page of Virginia informed the House that any unprejudiced, disinterested man in the world, looking over the map of the United States, would put his finger on the Potomac and say, "This is your place, Sir!"

Gerry, with much shaking of the head, disagreed. "Taking so southern a position will amount to a disqualification of many Northern members—who will forego their election rather than attend the N-National Legislature on that river!"

Finally, James Madison had his say just before the vote on Baltimore was taken. "We ought not to risk this bill by making any amendments. We should hazard nothing! If the Potomac is struck out, are you sure of getting Baltimore? Is it not probable we may have Susquehanna inserted, perhaps the Delaware? Make ANY amendment, Sir, and the bill will go back to the Senate. Will it come back into our possession again? I religiously believe that if Baltimore is inserted, the amended bill will never pass the Senate. A Southern position will vanish forever!"

"Question! Question!"

The vote was taken. Baltimore lost 37 to 23. It was a portent of votes to come.

Burke of South Carolina tried to squeeze from the 10 years not quite two years for New York. For one reason, he was worried lest he had to pay rent in two places, having signed a lease in New York that had another year or so to run. Gerry was worried that New York's heavy expenses for beautifying and rendering more convenient Federal Hall for Congress had not been reimbursed. "Will it not be considered the height of ingratitude to quit the place under such circumstances?"

The House members decided 32 to 28 it was not

Elbridge Gerry

the height of ingratitude.

On Friday, July 9, the fourth and final day of talking, Elias Boudinot made a last-ditch stand for Falls of the Delaware, Fisher Ames offered Germantown, Smith of Maryland "between Potomac and Susquehanna."

All failed.

Sherman, Laurence, Tucker, Burke, Smith of South Carolina, Smith of Maryland each tried to strike or add words or whole sections.

All failed.

Running out of changes, they attempted to block the final vote—"until Monday!" NAY! "Until tomorrow!" NAY! "Adjourn now!" NAY!

The voting began. In 10 minutes, Potomac had won—by three votes.

Among the 32 "yeas" were all of Pennsylvania's and Virginia's members, most of Maryland's, half of New Jersey's, Delaware's one, and South Carolina's only South-supporter, Thomas Sumter.

At long last, Mr. Madison had the action for which he had labored with much art and patience during five years in both Continental and Federal Congresses. It was an answer that would please President George Washington, and not displease his arch rival for the national capital, his old friend, Robert Morris.

In the lower gallery on the front row, two of the President's aides had risen to their feet, were applauding vigorously, and leading a few other spectators in joyous cries. "Well done, Sir! Well done, well done!"

Behind them, glum New Yorkers began silently departing, their glances at the cheering party dark with envy and disappointment.

Victorious 14 Senators with Captain Carroll directing helmsman Morris, while Maclay, perhaps, shouts "Huzzah for Philadelphia!" embark from New York on the ship Constitution. Twelve losers, noisily accusing the "Controller" of signing the bill for self-gratification, crowd a rowboat tied to the ship. All head for disaster at the Devil's waterfall. Three Philadelphia looters wait to plunder the wreckage of "a majority and the Treasury." In the far corner, trees cover a Potomac River site labeled "Congressejig."

Part Four
Washington Chooses the Capital Site
September–December 1790

Waving farewell to New York and officials on August 30, 1790, Washington departs with his family for Philadelphia. Congress adjourned after approving Potomac and Philadelphia for the capitals, and after approving Hamilton's finance plan. In a three-month recess, Washington had to resettle in the third Executive Mansion, travel to Mount Vernon and attend its business, and ride horseback nearly 100 miles up the Potomac to choose a capital site.

CHAPTER 22

Washington Family Departs New York

PLACE: Whitehall Slip by the Battery, East River, New York City; then the Jersey road to Philadelphia.
TIME: Monday, August 30, 1790, from 6 a.m. until noon the next day.

Details in Private Affairs of GW, p150 (Lear/Decatur)

G. Washington (D.Freeman)

Washington After the Rev. (W.Baker)

The President's barge, specially built the year before at the expense of the leading men of New York to bring him from Jersey to his inauguration, would now, 17 months later, take him back across the Hudson River to the road to Philadelphia.

Its 11 oarsmen waiting on the ready, the handsome vessel strained against dock ropes during the last bit of Presidential ceremony.

President Washington, dressed in a dark gray suit, stood on the pier bowing to the small crowd on the wharf and street. He had hoped for—requested—a leave-taking without ceremony. But at 6 o'clock that morning, when he was rising from the breakfast table, Governor Clinton, Vice President John Adams, Jefferson, Hamilton, Knox, and Randolph, Chief Justice John Jay, the mayor of New York and other city officials, the Sheriff, marshals and constables in their colorful insignia, the church ministers, and a little crowd of citizens arrived at his front door on Broadway.

In procession, they walked with the President's party of 15 down Broadway, and past the Presidential Mansion a-building, to Whitehall wharf. Tall President strode slowly beside short Lady Washington; Nelly Custis, age 12, so pretty in her long dark curls, held on to her brother "Wash"; that lively 10-year-old skipped and frisked, enjoying every detail of the occasion. Behind them followed an orderly column of two maids in starched white aprons and caps; four white servants; four black servants; and the President's aides, Major Jackson and Thomas Nelson.

At least the crowd at this early, unannounced hour was small, and the officials had agreed not to make speeches. Only the cannon spoke, BOOM! 13 times while the President's family boarded the barge. All spectators and all taking their leave were only too aware that the town of New York was losing the excitement and prosperity as well as the honor of being the seat of government.

In the quietness after the cannon ceased, Washington, last to board, stopped, turned to remove his hat and bow deeply to the crowd. Handkerchiefs went to teary eyes rather than to wave rapturously overhead as they had when Washington arrived in April 1789.

NY Daily Advertiser Aug.31, 1790

"Farewell, Mr. President!" called the Governor, saluting. Washington, tears glistening in his eyes, bowed again, slowly, holding his hat over his breast. When he looked up, he saw men and women with full hearts who could not restrain their tears. He did not speak, but when his tearful eyes met those of his executive officers, his facial expression and slight nods to each revealed how deeply this last mark of esteem had touched him. With one final bow, he turned and stepped onto the barge.

The coxswain shouted orders to heave the ropes, signaled the rowers to ready position, and began the count for strokes. The barge moved away from the wharf. Still standing, Washington lifted his hat in a last salute. "Farewell!" he cried. A chorus from the crowd answered him, and hands waved and waved until he was out of sight.

Hist.Cong., Senate/ House Journals, July 16, 1790 (Gales/ Seaton)

The seat of government bill he had signed into law July 16 directed Congress to sit in the temporary capital, Philadelphia, when it next met—December. Immediately the 60 or so Congressmen, 26 Senators, four department secretaries with their staffs, and the diplomatic corps began packing to leave New York as soon as Congress adjourned.

Assumption, re-united with funding, and expected to total, with the extra allowances, almost $100,000,000 in federal debt certificates at six percent but evolving in time to four, passed in the Senate July 21 by two votes (Carroll and Read). The House passed the bill July 26 by six votes (two Maryland, two Virginia, three Pennsylvania).

Hist.Cong., Senate/ House Journals, July 21-Aug 12 (Gales/ Seaton)

Congress adjourned on August 12. The next day, the President signed a treaty in Federal Hall with the Creek Indians, departed on a week's visit to Rhode Island (avoided the year before when he toured New England since the littlest state had not yet ratified the Constitution), then directed the packing for the move to Philadelphia. When the Washingtons departed on August 30, Tobias Lear stayed behind to see to the shipping by sloop of all goods and records, except personal baggage.

The rowing pilots dipped their oars and pulled to the rhythmic call of the coxswain. As the 47-foot barge glided swiftly across the calm waters of the harbor, the two grandchildren stood to point and exclaim at the dolphins leaping in nearby water, and at the sights on Manhattan Island.

Washington took his last look at Battery Park where he had walked so many times; at the houses next to it facing the Bowling Green; at the new Presidential Mansion in which no President would ever live. He could even glimpse just this side of Trinity Church a corner of the mansion he had lived in, so roomy, elegant, and comfortable. Would they live in one so suitable in Philadelphia?

He turned and voiced his question to "dear Patsy," who was still wiping her eyes with her handkerchief and did not answer.

Now Manhattan Island and the small town at its tip passed from their view and their lives—forever, as it turned out.

The oarsmen with a heave and ho, pressed the vessel through Hudson River current surging between Manhattan and Jersey. In the distance, on a shore below low, green hills, a crowd waited at Elizabeth Town Point, the village wharf. Officials and townspeople, and a company of militia and mounted officers, strained to see on the water the tiny speck that was bringing their hero to their town.

GW (Freeman)

Already the baggage barge bearing the Presidential coach, a chariot for the maids, a baggage wagon, and 16 horses, had arrived and been unloaded. At last the President's barge approached close to the Point, and the band began to play. Cheers and applause greeted Washington and his family as they stepped ashore.

But no speeches, nor a parade and program. Tobias Lear, the President's secretary, had sent word that the President had requested no more ceremony than what was absolutely necessary to gratify the people, that long displays were very fatiguing to his family. On arrival, Mrs. Washington and the children were escorted to the home of Elias Boudinot in the village, while the President mounted a horse to review the local militia and constabulary. At the tavern, he mingled with the important men of the village, and drank a glass of Madeira.

GW (Freeman) p278

The family dined with the Boudinots, spent a quiet evening, and went early to bed. Late the next morning, as the roomy "Penn coach" (the state of

GW (Freeman) p278

Presidents on Wheels
(H.Collins) p22-23

Pennsylvania had presented it to Mrs. Washington 10 years before) drawn by four white horses rolled away from a cheering, hand-waving crowd, "Patsy" sighed, "Well—it does some good to request less ceremony. The town did exactly enough."

"Wash" disagreed. "Next place, I want to stay with Grandpa and ride a horse to see the soldiers!"

Outside the coach window, they could see and hear mounted officers from Elizabeth Town riding alongside Major Jackson. More rode in advance of the coach, stirring dust so thick that all the venetian blinds had to be closed tight. An hour out of the village, the escort, with a little show of ceremony, turned back home. Much relieved, the Washingtons opened all the blinds, while the drivers and postilions jumped from the coach to brush the dust from their hats and new white, red-trimmed suits. The servants in the chariot, and the drivers on the baggage wagon flailed their clothes, wiped their faces—and the faces of the horses whose eyelashes, even, were loaded with dust.

"We will stop to dine and sleep at New Brunswick," the President said when they proceeded. "The inn is quite respectable there. It's a sizeable village, too, but Lear wrote to them, as he did to Elizabeth Town, to plan no ceremonies. We will go leisurely this first day since some of the horses are young, and the teams have been lacking hard exercise. Besides that, your 'Penn' coach, my dear, is not in the best of condition, being rather old. I'm very fond of it, and shall take it to Coachmaker Clark in Philadelphia for an overhaul. I will rent a coach and team to take us to Mount Vernon."

Private Affairs of GW
Lear/Decatur

Lear/Decatur p170

The children immediately wanted to know what would be changed. Their Grandpa's description had them clapping their hands and exclaiming happily. "I want it totally renewed," he began, "and refurbished handsomely—but simple and elegant. See how soiled the lining is? It must be replaced. The ceiling will be leather. All eight Venetian blinds

The President, Lady Washington, and grandchildren Wash and Nelly Custis say their last goodbyes to hosts in Elizabeth Town—just as they would in Burlington and Trenton after overnight stops. From Philadelphia to Mount Vernon, 160 miles south, required six more days of living in a coach.

Presidents on Wheels
(H.Collins) p22-23

will be replaced, and the windows fitted with silk curtains, festooned. We need glass in the front (the children squealed with pleasure), new folding steps, new leopard skins for the coachman's box, new harnesses with ornaments of plated silver handsomely executed. Outside, the coach must be painted and highly varnished. I would like my coat of arms on the door panels, perhaps, but certainly the pictures of the seasons must be repaired."

"Will there be any tassels?" asked Wash.

"Most probably," said his Grandpa. "When we get to Trenton tomorrow, I will ready a list for the coachmaker in Philadelphia."

"Grandpa! When we get to Trenton," said Nelly, her dark eyes sparkling, "Can you tell the girls and ladies to meet us and sing the way they did when you were going to the inauguration?"

"And throw flowers at us?" piped up Wash.

Grandpa smiled and said, no, he hoped nothing much would happen at Trenton so that they could go straight to Vandigrift's Inn, have dinner, then retire to a good night's sleep.

"But," he added, knowing that this was one of the grandchildren's favorite stories, "I will point out to you the creek bridge that had a big arch covered with greenery—an arch as wide as our barge of yesterday, and twice as tall as our coach here. On the front was fixed a very large paper sunflower, and a sentence painted on a long strip of cloth. It referred to Christmas Day in 1778 when our Army crossed the icy Delaware River and took Trenton from the Hessians—Germans hired to fight for the British.

GW Diary April 1789

"Recalling that affecting moment on the bridge, surrounded as I was by the crowd of Trenton people, brings back exquisite sensations of memory," Washington said. "The astonishing contrast between the day of battle and the ladies' ceremony at the same spot, the elegant taste with which the bridge was adorned for that ceremony, and the innocent appearance of the white-robed choir who met me with congratulatory song, made impressions on my memory that will never be effaced. I still have that song in my Letter Book."

"Tell us how it starts!"

"You know already!" he said.

"Let me! Let me!" Wash said in his shrill little voice. "'Welcome, mighty Chief! Once more welcome, to this grateful shore!' Then the cannon goes BOOM!"

"Good, Wash! Good! There may be some cannon booming when we arrive in Trenton, and you can count on hearing some in Philadelphia."

Martha Washington joined in to say she did dread to start all over again house hunting, unpacking, arranging furniture, putting up curtains. "Three times in little more than a year! And SO expensive! Papa, do you think that Tobias can make a good settlement with Mr. Macomb about our rent on his house? I was so surprised when he sent word that he did not desire to cancel the remainder of the year's lease! We should at least get an allowance for the stables and washhouse you had built." Wash added, "And the cows, too!"

Washington nodded and reminded his family that Tobias Lear was a most competent man, especially now that he had his bride Polly to help him. "He told me as we were leaving—I did not mention this to you, since we won't know definitely until we arrive in Philadelphia—that Robert Morris has offered his home to us. He's moving into his other house, next door, which he has just renovated."

"Oh, but Papa!" Mrs.Washington said. "As much as I have enjoyed visiting the Morrises in their home, the house is not anywhere BIG enough to accommodate 20 people, your office, and public rooms for entertaining! We will be as cramped as we were in the Cherry Street house in New York!"

Washington replied in a tone of resignation that although it was the best free-standing house in Philadelphia, "you are right, Patsy. Without build-

GW Letter Book

Private Affairs of GW
(Lear/Decatur)

GW (D. Freeman)

ing additional rooms for servants and services, it is entirely inadequate to the commodious accommodation of our household. If this is the house selected for us—and I think it will be—I will immediately draw up plans for the changes and necessary additions. Tobias can execute them while we are at Mount Vernon these next three months."

Mrs. Washington sighed. "I am so looking forward to being at home again. I wish you were not obliged to be away those two weeks when you ride up the Potomac. It does seem such a waste of time. When for years the name of Georgetown has been proposed over and over for the seat, why do the Congressmen now require you to ride a hundred miles upriver to look at a creek with a name they cannot even pronounce right?"

(CON-o-co-chig)

"It's not quite a hundred miles, dear Patsy," Washington answered, patting her hand and smiling. "I will not complain about this small political price I must pay for the help that brought the seat to the Potomac. Besides, I haven't been up the Potomac to Conococheague for 30 years, nor seen the canal project around the falls near Georgetown for two years. I am pleased to have the requirement to visit upriver Potomac—Wash, my boy, take care not to kick your Grandpa's knees."

Martha's thoughts had wandered as soon as her husband began "canal talk." She wondered about life in Philadelphia—would etiquette keep her as housebound as she had been in New York?

After a minute or so, she ventured to make a request she had been thinking about during the past month. "Papa, don't you think I could be more free to pay social calls in Philadelphia, and stay home less than I did in New York? Philadelphia has many respectable families and sociables. The Quakers, for all their agitating us about our slaves, are good people. It's a very cultured city with not nearly so many foreigners as New York."

Private Affairs of GW
(Lear/Decatur)

Washington looked at her fondly and said, "I believe we can relax some on the etiquette now, my dear, especially since Mrs. Morris will be living next door, just through the garden, and willing, I expect, to accompany you if you like. I know you have felt like a state prisoner in New York, and were bored and lonely. But we have many old friends in Philadelphia, and I think relaxing our strict etiquette there should offend no one.

1789 letter,
M. Washington

Private Affairs of GW
(Lear/Decatur) p194,
195

"However, when you return visitors' calls, go in the early afternoon before dinner to avoid the tea-and-cards events. I hear that gambling for high stakes—three or four hundred dollars lost at a sitting of a game of loo—takes place in every drawing room after dinner. There are other more appropriate entertainments in Philadelphia. Its Southwark theater is open now, and the company we saw in New York will present the plays we liked so much. We can attend informative lectures at the Assembly. There's a circus ('A CIRCUS?' squealed Wash) and I hear that the portrait painter Mr. Peale has opened a museum of natural history in rooms added to his home. In his yard and stables, he keeps curious animals."

Philadelphia: Portrait
of an American City
(E. Wolf 2) p111

"Grandpa, may we go soon as we get there? Can we, Grandpa?" both children begged.

"Not then, but after we return from Mount Vernon. Grandpa expects we will stay only one night at Mrs. House's establishment before starting for Virginia. When we get home next week, I must inspect the plantation to see the state of crops and people. In a few weeks, I must ride to Georgetown to look at farmland next to it, go upriver to look at farmland on Monocacy River, and many miles beyond to see the valley of Conococheague Creek. On one of those farms, Wash and Nelly, you will one day see a great city—the United States capital!"

Writings of
Washington Aug., 1790
p100 (Lear letter)

Wash looked at him, puzzled. "But Grandpa, you've already told us Georgetown is the best." Washington smiled. "Yes—much better than Falls of the Delaware, Susquehanna, or Germantown."

To Georgetown's Potomac wharves in 1790, ships from the Atlantic seaboard, West Indies, and Europe bring manufactured goods, sugar, and rum to trade for grain and tobacco. Beginning as a tobacco inspection warehouse and a dock, the town was laid out in 1751 by order of the Maryland Assembly and named for two objecting landowners with the same first name. Uphill from the wharves, the town's 2500 residents of 1790 had a splendid view of Virginia's heights opposite and the river at the head of tidewater.

CHAPTER 23

The President Begins His Potomac Journey

SCENE 1
FARMS AND RIDGES BY GEORGETOWN

PLACE: Georgetown, Maryland, and adjacent flatlands and low hills bordering the Potomac.
TIME: Saturday, October 16, 1790

Suter's Tavern
Georgetown, Md.

Details of tour reconstructed from contour maps (Ellicott, Hawkins), histories, early autobiog., canal reports, and Washington diary of his 1785 trip along the same route. Dr. Stuart as companion and prospective commissioner, is probable. Abingdon site: S. edge present National Airport near Four-Mile Run junction with Potomac.

On this fine autumn day, crisp dry air clarified the light to vibrant brightness, unveiling the sky's bluest blue. Objects on earth seemed edged in luminous light. It was an ideal day for President Washington's visit to the flat farmland and wooded terraces adjacent to Georgetown, first candidate on the Potomac for the location of the Federal District.

Washington, accompanied by Major Jackson, had left home the day before to begin the upriver journey Congress required. Two miles beyond Alexandria, they stopped at "Abingdon," a frame house where the mother of Wash and Nelly lived with her second husband, Dr. David Stuart, their regularly enlarging brood of children, and two Custis daughters in their early teens.

Washington needed to talk confidentially to Stuart, whose company he would enjoy as a traveling companion. Now slaves added Stuart's small trunk to Washington's on the packhorse. Major Jackson hurried ahead to tell friends at Georgetown, Seneca Creek, and Frederick Town the President's travel plans.

For the President and Stuart, it was less than an hour's ride from Abingdon to the ferry that crossed the Potomac from the end of the Alexandria Road by Mason's Island to Georgetown. Ferrymen poling the bottom and hauling on a great chain stretched across the river brought them to the

Georgetown dock close by the foot of Water (High) Street. Proceeding up the steep, rutted way for two blocks, they arrived at Suter's tavern, or Fountain Inn, in time for dinner.

A message was sent to Mayor Robert Peter inviting him and Georgetown's principal men to next day's breakfast before accompanying the President on a tour of the area between Georgetown and the Eastern Branch. The President and Dr. Stuart stayed the night at Suter's, which had beds for six or eight gentlemen.

The dazzling morning light illuminated the long table in the private meeting room of the tavern where the nine men were about to rise from a breakfast of quail, river fish, corn bread, grape hull preserves, and coffee.

Shortly, they were mounting their horses and clopping a block or so uphill to Bridge, the main street, on their way to ride through farms and woods that might soon be surveyed into a 10-mile square for a city.

"We go straight out Water—High Street after it crosses Bridge—turn east in a few blocks onto the upper Post Road. We'll go this way, fording Rock Creek, Mr.President," Mayor Peter said, "because Congressman Daniel Carroll is on his way there from his farm, and will join us for the tour. Besides that, the road along the embankment above the

Early Recollections of DC (C.Hines)

Portrait of Old Georgetown (Ecker) p14

Ecker p30

Portrait of Old Georgetown (G.Ecker) p25, 27, 30

Ellicott's topographical map 1792, and 1987 extension by Don Hawkins.

Hist.Natl. Capital (W.B.Bryan) p.41, 49, 55, 74, 83, 100, 101

Portrait of Old Georgetown (G.Ecker) p.16, 17, 89

M Street

Wisconsin Ave.

P St.: Hist.Nat. Capital (W.B.Bryan) p62-3

Ecker p216-217

Hist.Nat. Capital (Bryan) p62-3

ford is on a ridge so high, you can see across the area to the Potomac, a mile or so away."

In addition to being principal men of the town, the Georgetown men were also some of the principal owners of the farms and woods they were escorting the President to see. Washington knew all of them well—venerable Mayor Peter; first settler George Beall of "Dumbarton House"; Thomas Beall of George, his banker son; the 50-year-old export-import merchants, General James Lingan of "Prospect House", and Colonel William Deakins, Jr.; the less than 40-year-old merchants, Benjamin Stoddert of "Halcyon House", and Uriah Forrest, a fairly recent Georgetowner.

Six of the farmers living on the "Flats" had also been invited but did not come: Newly married young Daniel Carroll of Duddington was away; Notley Young, 55, had injured his back when a horse threw him; David Burnes, 53, who lived closest to Georgetown, was too busy; brothers Abraham and William Young, and Anthony Holmead, who lived miles away near the Eastern Branch, failed to show up.

Crossing Bridge Street, the horsemen proceeded two blocks up the gentle incline of High Street—a "rolling road" for horses pulling barrels of tobacco rolled to market—and downhill two blocks to a road turning east toward Rock Creek, almost a mile away. Shortly, they met the twice-weekly stagecoach coming from Bladensburg and Baltimore, horses straining and steaming, trotting on the mostly level road at the foot of another long, gentle rise.

Farther on, the gentlemen riders stopped to let turkey-herders guide a flock of several hundred birds past them; and near the creek crossing they stood aside for a drove of cattle.

Rock Creek lay between steep banks. To reach the ford of the post road, the President and his escorts zigzagged down the slope. They splashed through the stream, and zigzagged up the opposite bank. The road continued to rise, passing among great trees, green but dotted with color—red, gold, magenta, rosy orange. The men rode in two's and three's, saying little in the midst of such a scene, and in such company.

They stopped on a knoll where Carroll's route from the far northwest joined the post road, and waited for him to appear. Through an opening among the trees, they could see across cleared fields and lower-level woods to the river, a ribbon of silver sparkling in the sunlight.

"There's the Congressman!" announced Mayor Peter, and waved in the opposite direction to the horseman hurrying down the wooded hill.

Daniel Carroll had been riding from his plantation about eight miles almost due north of Georgetown. If Washington chose Georgetown, a 10-mile square edging the river would reach two or so miles beyond Forest Glen, the Congressman's home and farm on upper creeklets of Rock Creek, in an area abounding in bubbling, "silver" springs.

He was ready with his speech glorifying the Potomac site by Georgetown.

"Mr. President," he began as soon as the pleasantries had been done, "you are looking at the perfect geography for a capital city! Here a crescent of wooded terraces step down to flat, open fields and the river—an amphitheater specially and particularly made for the seat of Empire! Below, on the flats, the Federal officials at work. Up on the terraces, the People viewing the power and glory of our constitutional government!"

"Hear, hear!" "Bravo!" "Plain, good sense, Congressman!" the Georgetowners applauded.

"It is a most pleasing scene," Washington answered. "I have admired it from this road a number of times when traveling to and from the north.

"In my youth I admired it from the river while canoeing and fishing. Most assuredly, it will receive my serious consideration. But I must temper your

Present, about Connecticut Ave. and Florida

Present Forest Glen, by Beltway/Georgia Ave., between Silver Spring and Wheaton, Md.

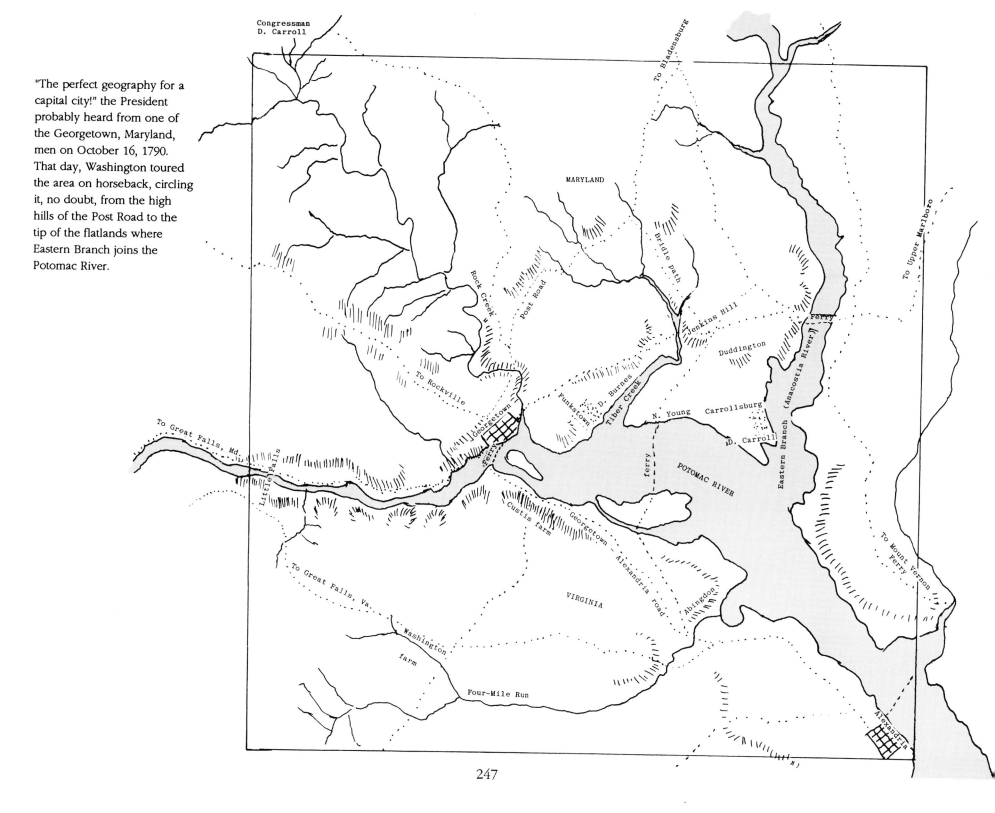

"The perfect geography for a capital city!" the President probably heard from one of the Georgetown, Maryland, men on October 16, 1790. That day, Washington toured the area on horseback, circling it, no doubt, from the high hills of the Post Road to the tip of the flatlands where Eastern Branch joins the Potomac River.

Congressman D. Carroll

To Bladensburg

MARYLAND

Bridle Path

Rock Creek

Post Road

Jenkins Hill

Duddington

To Rockville

To Upper Marlboro

Georgetown

Funkstown

D. Burnes

Tiber Creek

N. Young

Carrollsburg

D. Carroll

Ferry

Eastern Branch (Anacostia River)

To Great Falls, Md.

Little Falls

Ferry

ferry

POTOMAC RIVER

Custis farm

Georgetown - Alexandria road

To Great Falls, Va.

To Mount Vernon Ferry

Washington farm

VIRGINIA

Abingdon

Four-Mile Run

Alexandria

Bryan p37

Bryan p109

Ellicott 1792 topographical map of DC

Present Rhode Island Ave./Brentwood N.E.

Bryan 61

solicitation with the reminder that Congress has deleted all funds with which to buy land or raise buildings. Even with the contribution that Virginia promised, and that Maryland is about to grant, money will be scant for this great undertaking."

Robert Peter quickly spoke up. "Mr. President, I remind you that those of us here who own substantial portions of Georgetown flats have already put on paper an offer to sell our acres—a paper you have now in your possession. As we said, we are not asking for inflated prices—only the price or terms you determine as reasonable."

"That's right, Mr. President." "We've all signed it, Excellency!" the others said.

The President nodded, tapped his horse, and led the procession away at a lively gait. The road kept to level land at the top of a long ridge, crossed wooded areas, occasional fields of shocked corn stalks, and creeklets. At frequent openings in the woods, Washington caught a glimpse of the river, and heard the beauties of the site extolled.

The post road began to ascend a high ridge marking a third of the nine-mile road between Georgetown and Bladensburg. At its crest, the men looked out upon all the features of the land—the two rivers, a triangular area between them descending ridge by ridge to its flat point. "Mr. President, there can be no more beautiful or suitable place in the whole country than this for our seat of government!" said Carroll.

"Amen!" sanctioned Mayor Peter. Washington recalled having his driver stop the coach once when he came this way, in order to admire the view from this height. The Georgetowners exchanged smiles of rising confidence.

"From here," said Carroll, "we can continue toward Bladensburg before turning back on the Anacostia ferry road—or we can shortcut on a bridle path to a small lane leading to Jenkins Hill. There, you will be looking down on Goose Creek and the flatland farms of Davy Burnes and Notley Young."

Washington chose the bridle path. In single file with little talking, they climbed again and descended to a flattish valley that led straight to the lane going to Jenkins Hill.

The lane rose so gently, it was hardly noticeable, for it crossed less than two miles of a plateau ending at the highest point of Jenkins Hill. During the ride, the President kept his usual silence. His face and alert interest, however, assured his companions he was enjoying the wild woods, the fragrant air, cornflower-blue sky, and even the startling covey of quails that suddenly rose, rumbling like thunder beside him.

Among the trees and brush of heavily wooded Jenkins Hill, the President gazed down the long slope to the scene 90 feet below. A horseman was fording Goose Creek and proceeding on the beaten path. It angled right, across David Burnes' field toward a low ridge pointing west to Georgetown.

Goose Creek itself soon turned sharply west paralleling the road and flowing toward the Potomac. It broadened as it passed along the low side of David Burnes' farm, and flared into a sizeable bay where it joined the river. Giant sycamores, their huge and ancient roots protruding from the earth, lined the high bank next to Burnes' tobacco patch. But on the low, south side of the creek, rising tidal water was spilling into the land and marshing a width of Burnes' cow pasture.

All at once, a great flock of mallards flying along the river from the northwest turned into the broad mouth of the creek. As they settled, a huge brown spot grew and grew until the water was covered from bank to bank. The rhythmic sound of tens of thousands of squawking ducks floated the mile or so to Jenkins Hill.

Washington began to relate stories he had heard about the Indians who had once camped in several spots in this neighborhood. "They had no need

Don Hawkins topographical map of 1790 District of Columbia

From the vicinity of the junction of Florida Ave. Northeast, Maryland Ave., Benning, and Bladensburg Rd., to Capitol Hill via Maryland Ave.

C.Hines p45

From the top of Jenkins (now Capitol) Hill, Washington and the men from Georgetown two miles west look down at wide-mouth Goose Creek flowing west to the Potomac. To the south, farmland comes to a point a mile away where waters of two rivers mingle and head downstream 100 miles to Chesapeake Bay and the Atlantic.

for snares. They could stand on the creek bank and catch ducks by hand. Fish were equally plentiful. Every day when the tide went out, a number of catfish from the swarms in the creek would lie stranded in pools on the marshy bank. Indians paddled their canoes alongside, filling their baskets with fish." The Georgetown men declared they had done this when they were boys, and Georgetown boys were still doing it.

"However," the President added, "marshland and tidal flooding, as well as gullies I can see cutting across ridges and cropland, mean water problems for any city built here. While it is essential for a city site to have an adequate water supply—and I know there are numerous and excellent springs in these acres—some provision would be necessary for confinement of the creek and for drainage."

He paused. In the next few seconds of uncomfortable silence, Congressman Carroll walked his horse next to the President. "Mr. President," he said, "no site will turn out to be perfect. While we acknowledge that this site here and there is too well-watered, that is a fixable fault. But what other site can offer ports, an expanse of high riverside flatland, the most desirable for laying out a grid of streets? What other has natural embankments rising behind it, guarding the city by land? What other has a thriving town adjacent, a comfortable base for the builders of the new city? What other is easily accessible by land and by water?"

The other men exclaimed their agreement. "Right! Right! Hear, hear! Well said, Carroll!"

Washington gave his old friend a favoring smile, but did not comment. He pulled at the reins of his horse, clucked it into moving, and began to turn away. "Might Mr. Burnes, whose house I see under the big trees near the mouth of the creek, be at home today?" he asked.

"Most likely, sir," answered Uriah Forrest. "He is the least interested of any landowner in having this site chosen, dreading to give up his fine fields and his family home."

Washington replied that he thought few, perhaps no families, would lose their home.

"Probably the amount of land the government will purchase for its buildings and grounds will be small—a few hundred acres. The rest of the site will be owned and developed into a town privately. On government-owned land, if a house sits where it is determined that a public building must sit, it seems reasonable to assume that the owner would be given ample time to find another dwelling."

Turning back to Carroll, he added, "I hear that your nephew Daniel Carroll of Duddington is building a mansion on this height, perhaps very nearby."

Daniel Carroll II (Sister Geiger)

"My nephew-in-law, he is—his wife Ann is my niece, but I'm hardly kin to the young owner of Duddington, in spite of our bearing the same name. He's kin to Charles Carroll of Carrollton. As for the new house, it's about a half-mile away," the Congressman replied. "Daniel has chosen a high knoll sloping all the way to the Eastern Branch, much the way Mount Vernon's lawn slopes to the Potomac. He began digging the cellar six months ago. It's completed—and the foundations. He's been busy closing and covering them over for the winter. Usually he works there every day but he went to Marlborough on business and is not expected to return until tomorrow."

Hist.Nat.Cap. (W.Bryan)

L'Enfant and Washington (E. Kite) p80n

Mayor Peter added, "Mrs. Carroll sent word back last night that she would have a cold collation ready for us when we arrive at their house today. They're living in a house his father built and where, 20 years ago, he surveyed lots for a village—the same as Jacob Funk had done with 130 acres behind Davy Burnes' house. Carrollsburg and Funkstown! Or Hamburg as Funk called it. Funk sold all his lots—almost 300. Carroll parceled about the same number through a lottery. Hardly anybody built houses in either place—they're just paper towns."

Washington in Embryo (Faehtz/Pratt) Intro.

Washington, frowning, replied, "As many as 600 owners of those 300 or so acres?"

"I think nowhere near that many," answered Mayor Peter. "Many buyers, like me, took several lots." Washington's frown relaxed.

Bryan p119

Congressman Carroll, looking at a gold watch drawn from his vest pocket, interrupted to say that noon was too early to eat even the best cold collation. "We should ride up Ferry Road to Eastern Branch, Mr. President, and view the deep-water anchorages along the river banks as we go that way to Carroll's house."

Wash.Sun.Star Nov.24, *1946 article by J.C.Proctor*

On the south side of Jenkins Hill, they turned left onto the rough surface of the ferry road, chopped up by wagon wheels and horses' hooves.

Through leafy woods nipped by autumn, it brought them after three miles to an opening in the Anacostia's high bank where the Upper Ferry had just landed. They could hear shouting and horses neighing, and in a moment they saw several horsemen, a wagon, a coach and men with backpacks coming toward them.

Bryan p55

Across the river, on the opposite bank, the road from which the ferry riders had embarked was easily discernible. Washington remarked that when he had no need to pass through Georgetown on his way north, his Mount Vernon ferry took him across the Potomac to that Maryland road which overlooked, first the Potomac, then the Anacostia, for a shorter ride to Bladensburg.

Almost interrupting him, Congressman Carroll exclaimed, "One of the horsemen from the ferry is our Daniel of Duddington!"

Waves and shouts brought him cantering to them. "Mr. President! What a lucky day for me! My business went well, I caught the midday ferry, and now happily find Your Excellency on the way to visit my house and farm!"

Washington replied that with Carroll as guide across his land by the Anacostia's bank, they would learn first-hand about the best deep water anchorages. "I've heard it said that along this bank could be some of the best harbors in the country."

Eagerly, Carroll declared, "Deep water! Oh, it's deep enough that four-masted ships from Europe can anchor with no fear of going aground. That's what it will take to make the seat of government a commercial success, not just a political center.

"But capital or no, I have just built a dock for big ships—Port Carrollsburg! Two ships from Glasgow have already contracted to load and unload here—they're due any day now. Large ships have much difficulty at present keeping out of the sandbars between Mason's Island and Georgetown—"

Several Georgetown men protested at the same moment. "Those sandbars are easily evaded, Mr. Carroll!" "Big ships use our channel every week, Mr.Carroll!" "Any ship that anchors here could as easily anchor at Georgetown!" Congressman Carroll, noting the President's attentiveness to this show of argumentive rivalry, hastily changed the subject.

"Mr. President, I believe I can see Christ Church spire in Alexandria from this high ground, today being so clear. And in another mile or so, we'll be close enough to Carroll's house to begin betting how many cold collations my neice has waiting for us. They will no doubt be served with warming spirits, eh, Daniel?"

Carroll replied "yes" to the spirits, but "no" to ease of getting to them. Gullies, ravines, and deep inlets cutting into the bank for the next mile south forced them to an inland trail. "We'll backtrack about half this road you came on, then cut south on a tolerable track leading past Port Carrollton to my house. Let's go, Gentlemen!"

The President followed his lead, tapping his horse into a trot, the others trailing.

Later, as the men ate roasted turkey, smoked fish, baked waterfowl, a leg of veal, applebutter, roasted peanuts, hot biscuits, and homemade wine ("Ev-

erything from this plantation, Mr. President!" Carroll said proudly), the young host announced that he would accompany the visitors as far as his building site. "It's about half way back to Jenkins Hill."

When they arrived at the fine knoll of the future Duddington mansion, young Carroll escorted the men around the hillside sloping to the Anacostia River. He exclaimed eagerly, "I believe I love this view as much as you love yours at Mount Vernon, Mr. President! And look! A fine spring of great volume by the new house—wonderfully cold and delicious water! In digging the cellar and foundations, we found many arrowheads, so it must be true that Indians built a village by this spring."

The house would be called "Duddington," he added enthusiastically, recalling that this plantation name still clung to the flatland section adjacent, inherited by his step-uncle Notley Young. "You said you planned to stop by his place?"

"Yes, of course," laughed Congressman Carroll, "so that I can see my sister, Mrs. Notley Young, and further confuse anybody trying to determine the kinships among us."

It was late afternoon by the time the President and principal men of Georgetown had splashed through the shallow James creek and marsh, crossed a half-mile of wheat field and drunk tea with ailing Notley and his wife Mary. They talked about the President's tour, carrot crops, the advantages of a new seed drilling plow the President had ordered from England, work on the bypass canals of the Potomac, and the cost of everything. "I would sure love to go with you and hear what Davy Burnes says, Mr.President. He and I are not only about the same age, we also feel much the same way—he wishes the government would stay away from us and set up at Conococheague or any other far-away place!" Young said as the party left.

To cross Goose Creek, the men rode nearly a mile back to the foot of Jenkins Hill and passed

Bryan p60n

Present: Between 4th and New Jersey Ave.S.E., and D and F Sts. (Duddington house torn down in 1886)

Hist.Nat.Cap. (W.Bryan) p48

D.Carroll of Rock Creek (Sister Geiger) p15, 301

Present: L'Enfant Plaza high bluff area, overlooking Fish Market and Marina on Maine Ave. east of 14th Street.

through the ford. Leaving the path that angled toward Georgetown, they cut straight across Burnes' field, soft from disking-in tobacco stalks. Shortly they halted their horses in the yard of his cottage.

Burnes, his curly hair a mixture of white and red bushing out from under a tall, felt bowler, had seen the horsemen coming across his field, and made himself ready to receive them. He knew who they were and what they wanted. He had seen Washington a number of times, but still felt stirred as he watched the President's approach. "Damn good horseman, that he is," he said aloud.

Present: Pan-American Building site

"Daddy, can I stay out and see the President?" Eight-year-old Marcia Burnes looked up at her father, her long, dark hair hanging in loose curls about her shoulders. "We're going to talk business," he answered. She frowned and cocked her head. "But," he added, "I'm going to meet them out there under the big oak. You—and your mama, too, if she wants—can watch from the steps here." With that, he and two hunting dogs stepped away and took their places just as the horsemen entered the yard.

They did not dismount, but all spoke and lifted hats respectfully to the farmer known for his forth-rightness, honesty, and independence. He lifted his bowler briefly, greeted the President, gave the others a nod. Congressman Carroll, as agreed beforehand, did the talking. "The President has been sent by Congress, as you know, Mr. Burnes, to examine likely land along the Potomac on which to build a seat of government. We have shown him the lay of this land—and we hope he views this site with favor. Aside from the honor, the presence of the seat of government will bring prosperity to the entire area forever!"

"Hear, hear!"

"That was a good sales talk," said Burnes. "Mr. President, I am honored that you have stopped to see me at home. I am 53 years old —five years younger than you—and recall clearly the day some 35 years ago when you and General Braddock and dozens of other officers landed at the creek mouth, and set up big tents almost all the way to this house. It was the most splendid sight I'd ever seen in all my 16 years! This house had just been built—I've lived here since then, farming. I'm a better farmer than magistrate, my other job, or ever was as an army Lieutenant, so I canNOT tell you, Mr. President, that I am overjoyed at the prospect of giving up my family's farm, house, barns, slaves, livelihood, and view of the river and land. I will sleep sounder when I hear that you have picked Conococheague or any other Indian place—or even your step-grandson's plantation just across the Potomac."

The President flushed, his face stiff. The other men tensed and glanced at each other, shocked at Burnes' audacity.

Recovering quickly, the President asked politely, "How many acres do you own, Mr. Burnes?"

"Five hundred and twenty-seven. They go from the boundary of Funkstown behind the house there to the foot of Jenkins Hill—a full mile.The width is from Notley Young's boundary on the other side of Goose Creek all the way to the crest of the first ridge—a good half-mile. It's a fair piece of land, and I'm proud of being its master."

"Quite valuable, too," said the President, "with or without the seat of government. Your river view I can well appreciate as having particular value. Good day, Mr. Burnes."

The horsemen splashed through the water rising in a tidal inlet behind the Burnes house and followed a trail across higher land, lightly wooded. "Not much to see in Mr. Funk's platted village," remarked Peter. "The grid of streets—five on five—his laborers cut in the woods has grown up in alders and brush. Funk 20 years ago sold us on the idea of big growth and appreciating land prices on account of river traffic. But as you know, traffic from the west has yet to happen. Funk built a house,

Col.Hist. Soc.Records, 1919, p128-on. Also 1969-70, "David Burnes, Ancestors and Descendants," p110, on.

Funkstown: Present 23rd St.on west, 19th on east, H St. on north, Constitution Ave. (Tiber Creek) on south. (Proctor)

sold it, now lives next to Frederick, Maryland, 40 miles northwest, in another Funkstown."

The horsemen climbed the slight grade nearly a mile to arrive at the corner of a high, thinly wooded rock bluff that marked the creek's entrance into the river. Through open spaces between the trees, they looked toward Georgetown. Where the river began to bend, a quarter-mile distant, the mouth of Rock Creek was visible. Past the river bend rose Georgetown's high slopes and terraces. Their buildings stood higher even than "Braddock's Landing."

Present: Heights between Constitution Ave.(Goose or Tiber Creek) and Kennedy Center

"This is the first time I have visited this place since the day described by Mr. Burnes," Washington remarked. "Many of the officers who camped here then, and half of the army that camped around Georgetown, fell in the French and Indian ambush in the Alleghenies a few months later."

All was silent except for horses blowing and a whippoorwill calling far away. Abruptly, the President broke the reverie with a brisk question.

"Mr. Peter, how soon could a survey of the area between Georgetown and the Eastern Branch—the Anacostia—be made and sent to me in Philadelphia?" The question was passed around until Deakins volunteered his brother's surveying skills and predicted December first. "In the meantime, does anyone have an old survey I could borrow?" the President asked. "I do, Sir, and I will bring it to you at Suter's," responded George Beall.

Bryan p115

"I am much obliged to you, Mr. Beall, for I must study all three possible sites on the Potomac and render a decision in a matter of weeks. I am much indebted to you Gentlemen for your escort today. I shall journey to the Falls and Seneca tomorrow and would welcome the company of any or all of you.

Bryan p101

"Now, Mr. Stoddert, since we are already an hour late for the dinner you invited Dr. Stuart and me to share with you, we should proceed the shortest way to Georgetown."

Reining their horses to head toward Rock Creek,

and urging them to a trot, the horsemen in a few minutes approached a wooden bridge recently installed at the foot of the long slope leading to Georgetown's main street, and thundered across.

Bryan p62

Present M St.

SCENE 2
BOATING ACROSS POTOMAC TO SENECA AND GREAT FALLS CANALS

PLACE: Georgetown to Little Falls, Seneca, and Great Falls of the Potomac.
TIME: Next day, Sunday, October 17.

Uphill a minute's ride from Suter's front carriageway, President Washington, Dr.Stuart, and six of the principal men of Georgetown guided their horses into a left turn. The street there changed its name from Bridge to Falls, and pointed the way to Little Falls three miles upstream, and Great Falls nine miles beyond.

Present M Street

On the deserted street early Sunday morning, the only sounds came from the rhythmic thump of eight horses' hooves on the earth, and a few words of conversation among the riders. Two blocks later, they had an unobstructed view on the left of the wide river lapping at the foot of a steep rockbank. Benjamin Stoddert remarked, pointing to the steeper rock hill on the right, "From the top floor of my house on Prospect Street up there, I can see my ships coming around the bend!"

GW's Canal at Great Falls, Va. (T.Hahn) p8

On the bankside road, the river was always in sight, sometimes within reach, sometimes unreachable behind boulders and stony strips. After three miles, the horsemen saw the first signs of the work begun on a canal to bypass two miles of rapids, "Little Falls."

Guide to Architecture of Washington (Am.Inst.Arch)

Superintendent James Smith was waiting for them on his horse. Unhatting and bending in

Looking down the Potomac toward Georgetown from high bluffs near Little Falls.

*Columbia Historical
Society Records, 1909*
(Bacon-Foster) p176

numerous bows, he pulled his mount alongside the President, who, it was evident, wished to consult with him about canal problems. As they proceeded along the surveyed route of the canal, and two hours more to Great Falls (heard, then seen from a high ledge) and finally by noon to Seneca, the Superintendent kept up a stream of news as rough as the cataracts.

He enumerated, described, related whys and wherefores for all manner of delays, difficulties, haps and mishaps.

*GW's Canal at Great
Falls, Va.* (T.F.Hahn)
p15, 16, 17

"No, Sir! Laborers will not consent to labor! An indentured man the Potomac Canal Company bought a year ago ran away—and took my best suit with him! He was caught and whipped, his head and eyebrows shaved. Yes, Sir! We rented a slave from General Light Horse Lee in Virginia at Great Falls, and every day that slave said he was sick, stayed in bed, nothing could move him. We sent him home, got no refund, no replacement. Last week, our best powderman poured too much powder and blew himself up along with a hundred tons of rock. Yes, Sir! Work goes slow, very slow.

"To move faster? More money! Can't pay decent labor next to nothing and hold them. Need better weather! Men and gunpowder won't work in the rain. Need an engineer who knows how to build a wooden lock! Nobody in this country seems to know how, so the trench around Great Falls is just sitting there, empty."

The Superintendent's wail ceased near Seneca when Mr. Goldsborough, with former Governor Thomas Johnson, now Chief Judge of Maryland, and his brother James came galloping up, calling out their greetings and welcomes. Major Jackson had yesterday delivered to Goldsborough at Seneca Creek, and to the Johnsons in Frederick, the message that the President and Dr. Stuart desired to sleep Sunday night at Goldsborough's, and that the President would like Johnson to join him there with

Thomas Johnson
(E.Delaplaine)

enough horses for the rest of the journey to Conococheague.

"We did even better, Mr.President," drawled stocky, mild-mannered Johnson. "Two fine boatmen floated the old poplar dugout down the Monocacy from Frederick! You remember how, in '85, we shot Seneca Rapids in it and crossed over to Virginia!? Well, as President of the Potomac Canal Company, I want to take you through the first completed canal on the Potomac, the bypass of Seneca Falls. Then we'll continue on downriver to see the fine ditch skirting Great Falls. What we need there is a lock engineer."

GW Diary Aug.1785

*Columbia Historical
Society Records, 1909*
p175

"Yes SIR, that's what I've been telling the President!" burst in Superintendent Smith.

The President, looking very pleased, approved the dugout trip, and added, "Robert Morris has a crew working on canal plans to connect the Schuylkill to the Susquehanna, and has persuaded an English engineer to come and design—perhaps build—those locks. I will ask to borrow him, at least for some advice."

At Goldsborough's house, after a refreshing glass of Madeira and cold spring water, the Georgetown men—Stoddert, Deakins, Deakins' brother Francis, Forrest, General Lignan, and Mayor Peter—said their farewells and left for home.

*Columbia Historical
Society Records, 1909*
(Bacon-Foster) p180

In the long, narrow dugout by the creek bank, the President, Dr. Stuart, Smith, and the two Johnsons took seats one behind the other.

With a yell, the boatmen shoved the dugout from shore into the current, jumped agilely into it, and grabbed their oars to begin the big excitement of the day. At sluggish Seneca's mouth, the Potomac was a half-mile wide and free of rocks. The oarsmen headed straight across it toward the Virginia side. Currents angled the boat downstream just enough to bring it to the entrance of the Seneca Falls bypass canal.

Towpath Guide
(T.Hahn) p52

The sight of the canal, 25 feet wide between red

Columbia Historical Society Records, 1909 (Bacon-Foster) p172

Seneca sandstone walls, brought a broad smile to Washington's face. Here in this quiet passage nearly a mile long was the first realization of a dream he had been working on since the early 1770's. "Pretty good, eh, Mr. President?!" called Johnson, who had been an originator, then partner in that dream.

"A few boats are coming with goods all the way from Cumberland now. Not perfect navigation—takes a good pair, or quartet, of boatmen—but it can be effected as far as Great Falls despite shallows and rocks that need clearing out. The worst problem is low water. When traffic starts in earnest, if the water in the canals is too shallow—it's portage or stop."

Columbia Historical Society Records, 1909 (Bacon-Foster) p172-3-4

The President called over his shoulder to Johnson, "There must be a solution! For very important reasons connected with the locating of the seat of government on the Potomac, the navigation of this river ought to be pushed forward with all the celerity which the nature of the work will admit!"

Columbia Historical Society Records, 1909 (Bacon-Foster) GW letter, p179

"I agree!" answered Gov. Johnson. "We have to ask the company subscribers for another 10 percent increase in funds next month!"

With Washington looking extremely pleased, the dugout in a few minutes left the canal for the calm water downriver from Seneca rapids. The boatmen steered for several miles along the river bank. A flock of swallows led the way, wheeling time after time to skim and ruffle the water. On land, two heron watched the boat, twisting their long necks curiously. Always the rumble of the massive fall of water downstream grew louder. Suddenly, a boatman called out, "Skirting canal! All ashore!"

Nat.Geo.Mag. (R.Gray)

All seven men walked beside the deep, walled-in, empty ditch, 25 feet wide. A few feet away, the Potomac's rushing water rumbled steadily, tumbling over a river-wide ledge rugged with huge boulders. The waterfall crashed into a frothing turmoil 75 feet below.

GW's Canal at Great Falls (T.Hahn) p8, 36

"It'll take a lot of locks and a long canal to move boats and barges past the churning gorge!" Governor Johnson shouted over the roar.

Washington nodded vigorously and shouted, "Engineer—a must!" The short, stocky, red-faced, red-haired Marylander beamed at his stalwart old friend, commander-in-chief, President, and fellow dreamer. Abruptly, in a rare public show of affection, Washington briefly squeezed Johnson's shoulder with his huge right hand.

Towpath Guide (T.F.Hahn)

That night, warming up a cold bed in the Goldsborough's house, Thomas and James Johnson talked over details of the day's excitements. Thomas remarked that he had never even shaken hands with Washington, or seen him shake hands with anyone, or touch anyone, before today's shoulder clasp, a surprise.

"But Tom, don't you remember the last time we stayed at the Goldsborough's," James said, "back in '85 when the General and Canal Company officers went upriver together?"

Tom Johnson began to chuckle. James began to snicker. Both broke out in laughter. "Lord yes! I'll never forget that!" said Tom. "You and I were assigned to the General's room, the one he's in tonight, which has a proper bed and a lesser one. The General said, 'Come Gentlemen, who will be my bedfellow?' You looked at me, I looked at you. 'No,' I said, 'we brothers are used to sleeping in a lesser bed. You will rest much better without a bedfellow snoring in your ear, General,' I said.

The Ten-Mile Square (J.Elliot) p64

"And that's the way it went. Greatly as I felt honored by the unique distinction, the awe I feel in the presence of that admirable man will ever prevent me from approaching him SO NEARLY!"

Great Falls, great barrier to river traffic, tumbles from a rocky ledge 75 feet high. Washington's Potomac Company by late 1790 had blasted out on the Virginia side (left) a by-passing ditch—future canal that he would have visited on this river trip. But 10 years would pass before it became a lock-canal taking the place of horse and wagon portage around the falls to continue to Georgetown, 12 miles downstream.

Johnson's new iron furnace on a dammed creeklet of the Monocacy would have enticed Washington to turn off the Frederick road for a look. His long-time friend Thomas Johnson, would proudly have explained the state of-the-art technology—waterwheel with axle and rods to work two giant bellows for a hotter fire. Iron, lime, stone, marble, and timber, needed for building a capital, abounded in the Monocacy area of the Potomac.

CHAPTER 24

Monocacy to Conococheague

SCENE 1
CARROLL COUNTRY

PLACE: Monocacy River Valley, 10 miles up the Potomac from Seneca Creek.
TIME: Monday, October 18, 1790

Potomac Bottomlands Trail, Maryland and National Capital Parks and Planning, p91-93

Discovering Our Industrial Past (D. Weitzman) p45-53

Washington's route in 1790 is not fully recorded. Reconstruction based on his 1785 trip upriver recorded in detail in his diary. Also three 1790 newspaper items, and a letter in Oct.1790 to Lear.

Roaring and puffing smoke with every breath of its mighty bellows, the tall furnace built against the side of a high bank of Furnace Creek near its entrance to Monocacy River, threw out surprisingly little heat. President Washington and Dr. Stuart nevertheless stopped and looked questioningly at the noisy, smoking pyramid of stone 30 or so feet high.

The Johnson brothers, furnace owners and ironmasters, looked around at their companions and reassured them. "It roars and spits fire like a dragon, but it's harmless, General! More than 2,000 degrees inside the pot, but the walls are several feet thick!"

Washington nodded. Former Governor Thomas Johnson and his brother James knew what they were about, having run blast furnaces for 15 years and produced thousands of tons of pig iron.

All at once, red balls of fire flared out the furnace top, which rose a few feet higher than the top of the bank. With a great puff and roar, a black cloud of smoke sparkling with red hot cinders enveloped the fiery balls and tongues of flames.

"Quick! Under the shelter there!" shouted the Johnsons. "Cinders falling!"

Under the crude lean-to, Tom Johnson assured his visitors that nothing dangerous threatened. "But falling cinders—barely warm when they reach the ground—would spoil your clothing." To Dr. Stuart's question about what had exploded inside the furnace, Johnson said, "Nothing! You see, when red hot charcoal powder heats a layer of ore pellets to 2200 degrees, the ore liquifies, and collapses. The layers above it begin tumbling down. Up through the cracks fly sparks, flames, and smoke!"

"Quite a noisy place here," remarked Dr. Stuart. "The water falling on the wheel, and the sound of it turning, I can identify, but what is that creaking and swooshing apparatus attached to the wheel?"

"It's the newest thing—a pair of big bellows instead of one. Makes for hotter burning with quicker rises in temperature," said Johnson.

He led them to the accordion-like devices, each the size of a small house, each heart-shaped with their points stuffed inside a hole at the bottom of the furnace. SWOOSH! went the bellows squeezing air into the furnace. At the same time, the other bellows swelled full of air until the waterwheel axle, cranks, and shafts moved to squeeze it out, SWOOSH!

"Two of them pumping in tandem keep a steady blast of air going into the furnace," Johnson said. "Falling water from the creekdam does all the hard work, though—work always even, always steady, all day and night. Not men nor animals could do it, for a furnace this size needs giant blasts of air continually to run temperatures up to rock-melting

Visit to Johnson's furnace probable, considering their close friendship, Johnson's pride in his new furnace, Washington's interest in technology, and the road passing almost within sight of the furnace.

Thomas Johnson

heights and keep them there."

Washington, always interested in mechanisms, implements, crafts, tools—he had invented a seed drill himself—spent some time examining the bellows. The Johnsons then led him and Dr. Stuart away and up a ramp cut into the embankment, a road for oxen pulling wagons packed with charcoal, ore, and lime. "We'll watch the 'fillers' pour those materials into the mouth of the furnace."

In a storage area on top of the embankment, and near the furnace mouth, several men shoveled powdered charcoal, lime, and crushed ore from the wagons into wheelbarrows; other "fillers" pushed the barrows to the furnace mouth and dumped the material down its throat.

"We have to keep the fire going day and night for eight or nine months," Johnson said. "Breaking up the ore is done at the Point of Rocks mine. Charcoal is powdered at the burning pits next to Sugar Loaf Mountain where the trees are cut.

"Takes a lot of wood—400 cords a week for this one furnace! And we have five! But there are miles and miles of forests in this valley, you know, and we keep finding beds of ore."

From below, a man's voice shouted up, "Molders! Come down! The iron'll need running out within the hour! Be ready! Be ready to pour the pigs!"

"We can see that in a few minutes," Johnson said. "First, I'll show you the little mountain we're making of slag. It's a right big hill already—globs of melted rock and dirt. In the furnace, slag, like cream on milk, rises to the top of the heavier, melted iron, as you may know, and we just skim it off."

From the slag heap, they walked through the woods to a clearing on the creek bank where workers and their families lived in log cabins. "The crew you see tending the fire began work at midnight, right after the other crew poured iron. Comes noon, the crew present now will pour and go home, the other crew will take ahold, work 12 hours and

pour—and that's the way it proceeds every day. About once a year we let the fire die—so we can clean and repair the furnace.

"Now it's about time to see the pour. I love it when the red hot liquid rushes out the tap hole at the bottom of the furnace, runs down the iron channel, and begins to fill the pig-shape molds in the wet sand. There's a sizzling sound with sparks a-flying that is wonderful!"

Washington and Stuart agreed with the Johnsons a half-hour later when they saw and heard the orange-red liquid running into the wet sand molds on the ground by the furnace. "Only 20 bars?" asked Dr. Stuart.

Johnson laughed. "You never tried lifting a 'pig', did you, Doctor? Each one weighs a hundred pounds! That's a ton of pig iron lying here!"

Having greeted both the departing and arriving crews of astonished workers, the President, Dr. Stuart, and the Johnson Furnace owners remounted their horses and proceeded to ford the Monocacy.

From there, they cantered over a field of stubble in open, rolling country to find the wagon road going from the Monocacy's mouth, which they had inspected earlier in the day, to Frederick about 12 miles ahead.

"Of course, if you pick the Monocacy Valley for the seat of government and want our 2,000 acres, we will give them up, furnace and all," Johnson said. His brother nodded consent. "I expect that Charles Carroll of Carrollton Manor has told you much the same."

The answer was an unfathomable smile.

"Well, he has a lot to give up—14,000 acres!" Johnson added. "As you know, it starts with the Potomac river flats, and continues almost to Frederick Town on the north, and nearly to the Catoctin ridge in the west."

Thomas Johnson laughed. "I call this Monocacy 'my' valley but it's Carroll's. He's had it since about

Hist. Maryland
(J.Scharf)

Charles Carroll of
Carrollton (E.H.Smith)

Hist. Carrollton Manor
(W.J. Grove)

1765 when he came home from 15 years of schooling in France and England. He put 'of Carrollton' to his name since he was one of several Charles Carrolls. But all this you know. I hear now that his Carrollton rentals have developed so well, this manor pays him more than the family seat at Doughoregan. At five shillings a tillable acre—"

"So much!?" exclaimed Washington. "How can farmers afford to pay so much?" Johnson assured him that the farmers—mostly Germans—made a good living despite the rent. "With this rich red soil and perfect climate, the Monocacy Valley produces a million bushels of wheat a year—more than any other place in the land, I'm told. Keeps our 80 grist mills busy."

"You should tell the President that Frederick County now has more than 27,000 people, and that the town of Frederick is at least as big—maybe bigger—than Georgetown," James prompted his brother. Washington looked surprised.

Hist. Md. (Scharf)
p364

"In this valley," Washington began, clearing his throat (the Johnsons and Dr. Stuart all leaned toward the President expectantly) "and in Middle Valley over the Catoctin Ridge, much marble is to be found, is there not? and in all colors. (Yes, that's certainly true.) There is also much sandstone for building blocks, slate for roofs, limestone for plaster, gravel for streets and roads, the only glass factory in America—"

"Amelung's!" said Johnson enthusiastically. "John Frederick Amelung came from Bremen, Germany, a few years ago, and chose the Frederick area—actually the Sugar Loaf Mountain area—for its plentiful flintstone."

Hist. Carrollton Manor
(Grove) p86

"I have a strong interest in this glass-making community," Washington continued. "Hundreds of artisans came with their families, I have been told. Amelung's superior window glass, bottles, bowls, and glass ornaments are much valued in New York and Philadelphia. In addition to these resources and skilled workmen, the Monocacy Valley has copper and iron ore, furnaces, and foundries. These few square miles also have 400 whiskey stills, I hear."

Even solemn Dr. Stuart smiled. The Johnson brothers laughed noisily, especially after Gov. Johnson replied, "Yes, Sir, 400 KNOWN stills. We'll need them all if Congress settles here! We have paper mills too. It will take 400 of those to supply the clerks and speechmakers."

Hist. Md. (Scharf)
p369

With solemnity, the President asked for a survey to be sent to him in Philadelphia within a month, precisely marked as to the location of stills and paper mills.

"But I cannot help noticing that the valley is quite narrow," Washington said when the light-hearted moment had passed.

"Yes," admitted Gov. Johnson, "between the eastern sandstone ridge running to Sugar Loaf Mountain, and the western Catoctin Mountains, it's only three miles or so across the lower valley fronting the Potomac. As you go inland, however, the valley spreads wide like a fan—well, like a half-opened fan. If the Catoctins wouldn't be thought too much of a wall between our valley and Middle Valley, the two valleys together—each rich and beautiful—would make an admirable 10-mile square. The northern boundary would fall a few miles short of Frederick.

Dennis Griffith June
1794 Map of Potomac
River, Maryland

"My own main holdings would lie outside such a square. But no matter who else benefits, I feel so strongly about the suitability of Monocacy Valley for a capital serving East and West, North and South, I am compelled to recite its many virtues. These pretty hills and enclosing ridges, rich in ores and minerals, drew me from fancy Annapolis society and Maryland politics for good 11 years ago—"

Thomas Johnson
(Delaplain)

Scharf p24
Delaplain p352

"To the benefit of the Revolution!" Washington interposed. "The cannon and cannonballs produced in your Catoctin furnace and foundry made success in battle possible. Your ironworks as much as your three years in the Governor's chair, or your deeds as General of the Maryland militia, were indispensable during those troubled years!"

Diminutive Tom Johnson, so exceedingly plain in looks and manners that a Washington aide who did not know him had once called him "a little, insignificant-looking, swearing redhead," now glowed with pleasure at Washington's praise. He looked around at his brother and exchanged with him a smile of great satisfaction.

At Buckey's Town, half-way to Frederick, the men dismounted at the stone tavern within sight of the tannery of George and Michael Buckey. Ordering a round of ale, Gov. Johnson asked the tavern keeper whether Charles Carroll was at his manor house two miles west on Manor House Road.

Johnson had visited "Tuscarora" mansion, the center of a village of slave cabins, barns, stables, outbuildings, and a sizeable Catholic church with a fine steeple. The tavern keeper had visited it too, and was glad of an audience to hear him describe how well he knew the owner of it and of most of the land for miles around. "Oh, Mr. Carroll's coach and four," he said, "and a long parade of baggage wagons, landaus, chariots, a stable of horses, slaves, servants, relatives, hunting dogs, and who knows what, were seen turning out Manor Road, just there, yesterday morning about seven. They wheeled past here, heading to Frederick and the road to Baltimore. He's been at the big stone house by Tuscarora Creek for about a month. He comes here in harvest season to take his rents and check on his mills. Then he goes straight home, 40 miles in eight hours to Doughoregan Manor House. It's near Ellicott's Mill, 20 miles this side of Baltimore.

"You Gentlemen know him? He'll be sorry he missed you, I'd bet money. You've visited him before? You have? (to Gov. Johnson). I thought you looked familiar. Most everybody traveling this road stops at my tavern! Come again, Gentlemen!"

At a discreet distance up the rough, red wagon road, Washington laughed as heartily as his three companions. "I thought there was no person left in this country who could not recognize you, Mr. President!" declared James Johnson. Washington replied that if he had seen only portraits painted of himself, he would not recognize himself either. "There must be a hundred different portraits of me, and as Mrs. Washington says, they only succeed in looking like no one we know."

Near Frederick, Gov. Johnson led the party on his own private trails skirting the town, taking them four miles beyond it to his mansion, "Richfield." Major Jackson in bringing the request for Gov. Johnson to meet Washington at Seneca, had also brought his request for a quiet entry into Frederick, an evening without visitors or ceremony, and an early retirement hour. Even the cooks and house slaves had not known for whom the special dinner was being prepared.

In the fading light of day's end, Washington expressed a desire to take a walk with Johnson around his farm. Their conversation touched on Johnson's health (not as good as it had been, but tolerable); the road from Frederick to Georgetown by Rockville in winter (better than the trail they rode today but still impassable in the worst rain and snow storms); his wife's health (very precarious); the state of his business and finances (going well, but with so many furnaces, foundries, mines, farm renters, and mills, including a new sassafras oil mill, he was overloaded).

As they approached the spacious house on its grassy mound, Washington asked a question that gnawed at him. "My good and trusted friend, you have suggested there is a likelihood that low water in the Potomac may stop river traffic for much of the year despite the bypass canals. In the back of your mind, do you conclude that a capital built above the falls is doomed to failure?"

T.Johnson (Delaplain)

Steamboat Hist.
(J.Fitch) p159

Hist. Carrollton Manor
(W.J.Grove) p110/115

Grove, p21

Colonial Mansions of
Maryland
(J.M.Hammond)

"Tuscarora": At Buckeystown, turn west on Manor House Rd. from Rt. 85. Go 2 m. to dead-end. Turn left into house's drive. "Doughoregan": Route 144 (Md.) 5 miles west of Ellicott City, turn south on Manor Lane.

"Richfield": From Frederick: North on Rt. 15 four miles. On right, opposite Beckley's Motel. House is called "Birthplace of Admiral Schley" on historical marker.

Hist. C. Manor (Grove) p87

(Grove)p87

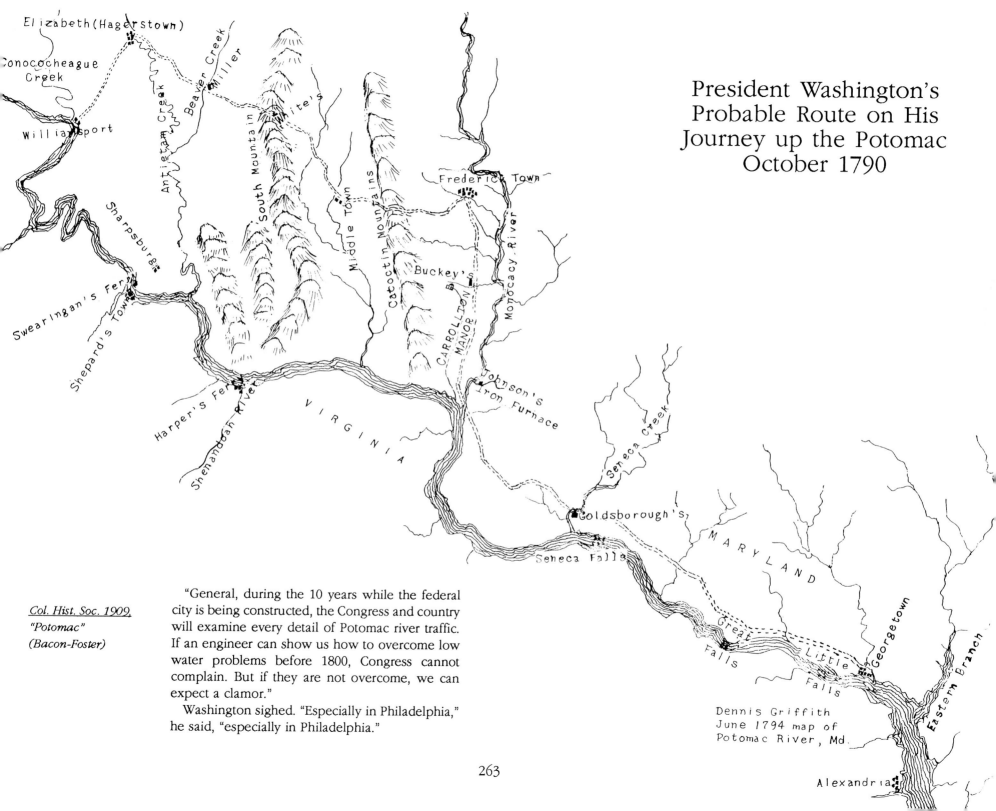

Elizabeth (Hagerstown)

Conococheague Creek

Williamsport

Beaver Creek

Miller

Antietam Creek

White's

South Mountain

Middle Town

Catoctin Mountains

Frederick Town

Buckey's

Monocacy River

President Washington's
Probable Route on His
Journey up the Potomac
October 1790

Sharpsburg

Swearingan's Ferry

Shepard's Town

Harper's Ferry

Shenandoah River

V I R G I N I A

CARROLLTON MANOR

Johnson's
Iron Furnace

Seneca Creek

Goldsborough's

Seneca Falls

M A R Y L A N D

Great Falls

Little Falls

Georgetown

Eastern Branch

Col. Hist. Soc. 1909,
"Potomac"
(Bacon-Foster)

"General, during the 10 years while the federal city is being constructed, the Congress and country will examine every detail of Potomac river traffic. If an engineer can show us how to overcome low water problems before 1800, Congress cannot complain. But if they are not overcome, we can expect a clamor."

Washington sighed. "Especially in Philadelphia," he said, "especially in Philadelphia."

Dennis Griffith
June 1794 map of
Potomac River, Md.

Alexandria

SCENE 2
40 MILES WEST INTO THE SETTLED FRONTIER

PLACE: Wagon trail from Frederick, Maryland, over Catoctin Ridge and South Mountain to Elizabeth Town (Hagerstown)
TIME: Tuesday and Wednesday, October 19-20.

Bicenten.Hist. Frederick Co. (W.R.Quynn)

From five o'clock when he awakened and watched the servant with his candle lighting kindling under logs in the fireplace, Washington nostalgically recalled a week or so he had spent in Frederick in his youth, and scenes along the route he would now follow again. As he dressed, he saw the scene, the people, heard the noises of an April day in 1755. He was arriving in Frederick Town, Maryland's most western village, to join British General Braddock's army as his aide. Benjamin Franklin had already arrived. For the first time, Washington, in his twenties, met the already-famous printer, writer, postmaster-general, a vigorous, ebullient 50-year-old. Franklin had just been appointed by the Crown to arrange for supplying Braddock's army, 2,400 men, about half colonials, during its campaign to drive the French from the Ohio River.

Hist. Cumberland (W.Lowdermilk) p114

Washington recalled the spark of interest and empathy that flew between Franklin and himself. He heard again Franklin describe General Braddock "storming like a lion rampant" when local farmers ignored his call for horses and wagons. He remembered Franklin's prediction of disaster when Braddock pressured the visiting royal governor into "selling" his splendid English chariot and four horses for the 200-mile ride through the wilderness.

Shaking off memories of the grim journey and horrifying defeat that followed, Washington descended the stairs to "Richfield's" dining room. Shortly, in the first streaks of daylight, he and his companions were riding across Johnson's fields west to the wagon trail leading to Elizabeth Town.

"It's the perfect week for such a journey, General," Johnson remarked. "Slow rains of the past week have stopped so the roads are dry but not dusty. With the first frosts, the flies are all gone, which makes the horses happy. They like the chilly air, too, especially for hard mountain climbing."

Washington answered that, if Johnson saw good weather ahead for a few days, he would like to hire at Williamsport a fast, maneuverable river boat and skillful boatmen to waft him and his companions downstream to Seneca. "I can thus view the banks of the Potomac, inspect the work done, or remaining to be done, that will permit easy navigation even in low water." The Johnsons knew some boats and boatmen and would attend to their hiring. "Two boats would be safer, Mr. President, the one to help the other in case the unexpected happens. In a three-day trip, there is plenty of room for occurrences."

From the undulating open fields ("Everything south of this road belongs to Carroll") the horsemen entered thick, virgin forests at the foot of the high Catoctins. As they passed beneath the intertwined branches of golden-leafed chestnut trees, they saw deer bounding through the brush, concentrating on each other, rutting season having begun in earnest. Foxes raced across the trail; once a black bear crashed through a thicket of red sumac, looked at the rearing horses, and fled.

The ascent of the mountain went slowly, particularly where every step required careful placing of each hoof on the rocks. From time to time, the riders let their horses stop to blow, catch their breath, before going on.

By noon, they viewed from the crest the taller, unbroken length of South Mountain facing them five miles away, the other wall of narrow Middle Valley. They silently compared the valley behind them with this rumpled patchwork of fields and woods—tan, light green, dark green, dark earth-

Travels of a Frenchman 1791 (F.M. Bayard) p27-41

red, with low, long creases of colorful trees where creeks and branches of creeks ran to the Potomac. On the middle branch lay a village of 25 houses, Middletown.

Within an hour, the horsemen were dismounting there in the yard of a large farmhouse where a friend of Gov. Johnson lived. An excited, flustered, thrilled farmer, his wife, and three children spread the news to the mostly German-speaking town— "Der Praesident Vashington, der General, ist HIER!"—and spread their dining table with food and cider. All hundred or so villagers gathered in the yard to watch, then accompanied the visitors to the creek ford, staring at the President, smiling, waving, and clapping their hands when he lifted his hat in farewell.

Ten miles later, half-way up South Mountain, Johnson was knocking at dusk on the log cabin door of farmer John White. A stalwart man in his mid-30's, musket in hand, cracked open the door, then swung it wide, exclaiming with much joy, "Governor Johnson! This is a great and wonderful surprise! Come in! Come in! What brings you into our wilderness?! You have companions—I can't believe it—Washington! SIR! Your honor—your EXCELLENCY! SIR! We are most honored! Come in, come in—my house is your house, Sir!"

That night, the President and Stuart slept in the front room bed, the Johnsons in the children's bedroom, while the Whites lay on quilt pallets spread upon the kitchen floor.

In early morning, the travelers began toiling up and easing down steep grades among rock formations of strange, gargolian shapes. But it was worth the tedious struggle, they agreed, to thrill at the grandeur and beauty of the scene below when they arrived at the mountain's top.

Such a valley! Such a morning to see it! Sunlight broke through a scattering of low drifting clouds and earthbound flimsy fog. Two almost river-size

creeks a few miles apart worked to the Potomac from the high Alleghenies. The nearer creek, Antietam, wriggled past Elizabeth Town and adjacent Funkstown. Six miles west, Conococheague looped down to Williamsport's almost empty grid of streets.

Beyond, across rows of green hills splotched yellow and red to the dark mountains on the horizon, all appeared wild, untouched.

On the precarious descent, Washington recalled the scene of General Braddock's English coach-and-four crossing South Mountain. "He damned the chariot all the way for jouncing him so hard on these rocky ridges. Throughout, over rough trails, through woods, across creek fords, his drummer beat the Grenadier's March for him and the body guard of light horse protecting both sides of the chariot. By the time he reached Fort Cumberland, 50 miles beyond Conococheague, he and the chariot were worn out, and he had consumed all the great store of food and wine that Franklin had crowded into the coach in Frederick."

In the valley, Washington observed that the land was more hilly and without the quality of the Monocacy or Middle Valley—still, much wheat must come from the thousands of acres planted here. The wagon road crossed several miles of such hilly fields, and brought the travelers to Beaver Creek, feeding into the Antietam.

Miller Newcomer brought them cold, refreshing cider. While James Johnson hurried on to Elizabeth Town, seven miles ahead, to announce the President's approach, the tongue-tied miller showed his homemade waterwheel and mill to his visitors.

At 2 o'clock, three miles outside Elizabeth Town, when they saw a dozen horsemen trotting towards them, Johnson said, "Well, from now on, it will be ceremony and speeches, Mr.President."

Hat-lifting and respectful bows accompanied greetings and introductions of the town's prominent men, all staring and smiling.

Hist. Wash. Co. (T.J.C Williams)

"We read in our newspaper—Hagerstown's own 'Spy', started up early this year—that Congress finally agreed on Potomac for the seat of government," the mayor said, "and that you would be coming upriver as far as Conococheague to look for the best site."

Scharf 1141

Scharf 1068

"A hearty welcome to our beautiful valley and our thriving town, Mr. President!" spoke Tom Sprigg, who was planning to run for Congress in an upcoming election. "Being deeply impressed with your illustrious character, and sensibly awake to your resplendent and innumerable virtues, we hail you, our beloved Chief! We thank you for granting us the greatest of all favors, your presence! We should think ourselves doubly blessed could we have the honor to be included within your more especial command and jurisdiction!"

When the other men continued to stare, saying nothing, Washington said his thanks and added, "I cannot better reply to your confidence than to assure you that the same impartiality shall be shown to all in the making of this, as in other, decisions."

Scharf 834

With another lift of his hat, the President made the move to proceed to Elizabeth Town. At its edge, just after crossing the bridge over the Antietam ("Braddock's men built this bridge, Mr. President") a company of militia, hastily assembled and uniformed, waited for the President and his escorts. By the roadside, cheering men, women, children, and barking dogs greeted Washington, the hero.

Hist. Wash. Co. (Williams)

In the midst of the procession of people, the President rode past dry goods and general merchandise stores, fulling-dying-coloring shops, joiner and cabinet makers, tinners and coppersmiths, the blacksmithy, nail and seed stores, hats and mantua shops, to arrive at the Globe Tavern run by Mr. Beltzhoover.

Scharf p1057, 1170

After the briefest of settling in, when bells of both churches began peeling fast, the town cannon booming (once), and the militia shooting off a volley of musket fire, the President, his fellow travelers, and escorts emerged to more cheers and applause from the waiting crowd. Walking briskly, nodding to the crowd, the distinguished guests and the men of the town visited the market house where a few wide-eyed, German-speaking farmers still had eggs and butter to sell; the bowling green; the cockfighting ring ("Our game cocks are renowed from New York to New Orleans!"); the German church; the English church; the Courthouse on its grassy square; the jail, stocks, and whipping post.

Scharf 1176

At 5 o'clock, dusk, and for the next four candle-lit hours, visitors and principal townsmen ate the mayor's banquet in the tavern dining room. Wine flowed freely with each of 13 toasts. The town cannon boomed 13 times.

Scharf 1068

Outside, crowds encircling great bonfires watched the dining room windows, buzzed with conversation, and applauded any activity they could see of the diners inside. At last, they saw the men rise, raise their wine glasses, say something in a chorus, drink, and begin moving away from the table.

The crowd cheered and applauded and wondered what was going on. "What did they say?" "Did the President tell them where it would be?" "If Conococheague gets it, will the Congress House be built here—we're only seven miles from the Potomac—or at Williamsport on the creek and river?"

Hagerstown newspaper

Inside, the President was going upstairs to his bedroom, and the Mayor and Tom Sprigg, watching him, were puzzling over his Potomac toast. "Did he mean the seat still can be snatched from Potomac? He said, 'May the residence law be perpetuated, and Potomac view the Federal City.' Do you think he's much worried?"

"Yes. He hinted that Philadelphia is plotting. He's hinting, too, that he must choose the least assailable Potomac site for the residence of Congress. That's Georgetown, below the Falls. You'll see."

"May the Residence Law be perpetuated, and Potomac view the Federal City!" Washington's toast at the Hagerstown banquet revealed he took seriously Philadelphia's—Morris's—plan to charm Congress into staying there forever. Frontier villagers, celebrating with bonfires the visit of the President, thought he might choose a western 10-mile square like their Antietam Valley and neighboring Conococheague.

SCENE 3
CONOCOCHEAGUE

PLACE: Hagerstown to Williamsport at the mouth of Conococheague Creek entering the Potomac.
TIME: Thursday, October 21

Washington, in the saddle, his heavy cloak draping his shoulders, heard the final command of the militia's drill captain, the boom of the town cannon. He then quieted his horse, waved his last farewell to the applauding townspeople gathered in front of Beltzhoover's tavern, and turned away.

In a clear sky, half of the sun was above the horizon, a late start. But the principal men of Hagerstown had prolonged breakfast with too hearty a repast and a speech of thanks and gratitude from each one of them—all topped off by a complimentary jigger of Beltzhoover's corn whiskey. As they rose from the table, four principal men of Williamsport arrived, necessitating a second round of Beltzhoover's generosity.

At last, all ceremonies performed, the President's party with its enlarged escort broke into a brisk trot. The seven-mile rolling road would bring them to Williamsport in an hour and a half.

Washington, looking at vast, open wheat fields, stretches of pasture lands, herds of cows, and only occasional sections of timber, was moved to comment when the horses slowed that it was 43 years ago when as a 16-year-old he first saw Conococheague. He had come to the frontier with a land surveying team. "It was entirely wilderness. We swam our horses over the Potomac from Virginia to the mouth of the creek. The only improvement on the face of the country was the stone hut or 'fort' of Colonel Cresap, Indian fighter, frontier settler and agent of Lord Baltimore. He guarded against land infringements by Lord Fairfax of Virginia, our employer.

"But the hut was abandoned. Cresap had moved farther west, and we tramped there, 40 miles of the worst road that ever was trod by man or beast. He took us in—Lord Fairfax's nephew George, myself, and a surveyor—for five days, until the weather improved. While there, I saw for the first time a party of Indians. A little liquor put them in a dancing mood. They did much jumping around a fire, rattling a gourd with shot in it, and beating a deerskin stretched tight over a pot of water."

Colonel Elie Williams, brother of the founder of Williamsport, declared that an old stone hut still stood on Conococheague Creek not far from his Springfield Farm, a mile from the Potomac. "It may well have been Cresap's! Since then, the area has flowered—Williamsport will surprise you! My brother, General Otho Williams, had it surveyed into streets and building lots three years ago!

"People are coming every month! The newest arrival has brought a manufactory! He buys hog bristles and horse tails and makes brushes. He also makes magic ink powder! It's guaranteed to make ink in one minute, and is equal to anything imported from Amsterdam, Rotterdam, or any other 'dam' wheresoever!"

When the other men saw the President smile, they let loose their laughs and titters.

As they approached the scattering of houses and stores, a tavern, and a warehouse with scales for weighing tobacco, more horsemen joined the escort. The President requested an inspection of the river bank, while Gov. Johnson sought out suitable boats and crews for the journey back to Seneca.

Standing on the high bank, he could see a mile upstream and a mile downstream. Below the bank lay mud flats several hundred feet wide. Mid-way the river rose small, dark mounds. Washington pointed to them. "Could that mean shallow water?" he inquired.

"Water is kind of low right now."

Hist. West. Md.
(Scharf) p1219-1224

Scharf 1223

Scharf 1057

GW Diary March 20,
1748

Cresap's stone hut or fort, still stands, say local historians, and is home for its present owner.

Source of all details about Williamsport:
History of W. Maryland (J.Scharf) p1219-1224

Nat. Park Ser.,
Dick Stanton,
Sharpsburg, Md.

Potomac Canals
(Hahn) p10

"How deep is the water when it's high?"

"Oh, say 10 feet."

"What is it now?"

"About five—but these long, flat-bottomed boats, the narrow kind such as you'll ride tomorrow, they don't need much water, even when they're heavy laden. Riverboats 60 and 70 feet long loaded with a hundred barrels of flour leave here almost every day for Georgetown. They have to hire wagons to portage around Great Falls, but as soon as the new bypass canal begins working, we'll be outmilling Baltimore!"

The other men, more than 30 by now, chimed in with assurances and reassurances.

"What is the lowest water depth you can remember?" the President inquired. Someone said, "A little above my ankles."

The President, silent, studied the current ripples, the wide river bend upstream, the heavily wooded flats on the opposite shore, the low hills, all aglow with autumn reds and golds.

At last he spoke. "I have traveled the river by boat only from Harper's Ferry to Seneca, and only in fairly high water. Tomorrow I will begin here a three-day journey in low water to view from the river the possible sites for a federal city.

"Governor Johnson, president of the Potomac Canal Company, and I, will note what further improvements can be made to facilitate navigation. I am pleased to hear from you that loads of grain and furs from Fort Cumberland 50 miles west are arriving here safely and regularly. ('Yes, yes! That's right!') Later, roads and canals connecting Potomac to streams farther west should bring the riches of the Ohio Valley to Williamsport. ('Lord be praised!') Your future in this beautiful and flourishing valley looks bright."

The men applauded, lifted their hats, cried "Hear! Hear! God bless you! Hurrah!"

Elie Williams spoke up to say that they all hoped the 10-mile square for a federal city would be located in this Maryland county recently named for Washington. "We are willing to make every contribution towards the necessary accommodation of Congress that can be reasonably expected."

Another voice called out, "Or that our circumstances can afford!"

After a three-hour tour of the mansions close by— Col. William's "Springfield," Major Van Lear's "Tammany"—the grist mill and cloth factory of Mr. Hershey on the Conococheague, the tobacco warehouse, the flour mills on the nearest plantations (5,000 to 10,000 acres), the President arrived at the tavern for dinner. A little group of women, children, youths, tradesmen, artisans, and laborers waited by the door to look at him. They shyly clapped their hands, smiled, and said "Hurray" when Washington tipped his hat to them.

Inside, the wives of the principal men, dressed in their Sunday best, waited in line to be introduced. When each had curtsied, thrilled to Washington's slight bow and his voice repeating their names, the large party settled on benches around long tables.

In the middle of eating large helpings of venison, turkey, smoked ham, river trout, baked apples, pumpkin pie, all washed down with hard cider, Elie Williams spoke discreetly to his neighbor, Major Van Lear, a rising young man Washington had earlier asked about the Yorktown musket ball in his leg.

"Did you hear," Col. Williams asked the Major, "the hints the President dropped that our town is high on his list? I'm going to write Otho in Baltimore, give him details—let him know Williamsport is fair to become the residence of Congress!"

With a skeptical grimace, the young Major replied, "If I know Otho, mostly likely he'll write back to you, 'It's all a hum, brother, all a hum!'"

When Gen. Otho
Williams replied, his
letter said exactly this.

Riding riverboats from Williamsport at Conococheague Creek to go "down that noble river which will be proud to waft him home,"
(as Hagerstown's newspaper said), Washington and companions could view both sides of the Potomac for more than 100 river
miles. At Harper's Ferry (above) where the Shenandoah (left) enters Potomac 80 river miles above Georgetown, they could inspect
boulder-clearing and enjoy a visit from brother Charles Washington of Charles Town.

CHAPTER 25

Wafting Down the Potomac

PLACE: On the Potomac from Williamsport to Seneca and Great Falls, then on the road to Alexandria.
TIME: Sunday, October 24, 1790, the third day of wafting down the Potomac.

*Boats: Hist.Travel in America (Dunbar) p41
GW's Canal (Hahn) p10*

Washington Spy newspaper, *Elizabeth Town, Md., Oct. 21, 1790: "He set out for Williamsport in order to take passage down that noble river which will be proud to waft him home."*

Before sunrise, the slow, dark waters of the Monocacy in muted light spread like black ink into the gray, rippling Potomac. Two narrow, 40-foot pole boats, partly canopied, their simple sails furled, glided out of the shadowy cover of bankside trees.

Their boatmen had paddled them a mile or so from "The Dutchman's" tavern on the Monocacy where the President, Dr. Stuart, Governor Johnson, his brother James, and the 10 boatmen had spent the third night of their trip after wafting down 60 miles of the Potomac.

Now one boat with its steersman and four polemen standing with long staffs of wood in hand, turned upstream, back toward home in Williamsport. To pole against the current, two boatmen at the bow thrust at an angle their sharppointed poles into the river bottom. By pressing down on the poles as they walked the running boards toward the stern, their poles pushed the boat forward. To hold the distance gained, two other polemen at the stern jabbed their poles into the river bottom while the bow men ran back for another push. Thousands of times they would push the poles to move the boat forward on the long miles upstream. Only if a favorable wind rose and they unfurled the sail would they have any relief.

Looking back, the upstream boatmen shouted their last farewells to the boat moving quickly downstream in the wind and current of the everwidening river. The boatmen and passengers, the President and the doctor, waved back. An hour earlier at the tavern, such waves and shouts had bid farewell to the Johnsons when they turned their horses north toward Frederick and home.

For all 14 men in the boating party, it had been a pleasurable river journey. The two travel days had each dawned rosy and golden, as today's would, too, upon the canopied boats. Daybreak's sky rivaled the reds and golds of the forest covering the river banks high and low. Except for a cold fog, soon warmed and wisped at Williamsport the hour they departed, and a little shower during the first night while lodging in a farmer's house near Swearingan's ferry, calm fair weather had held, with its clear, sharp, bright light.

From the farmer's house, word had spread of the President's whereabouts. When his boats stopped next morning at Swearingan's for breakfast, he had found the principal men from Sharpsburg, Maryland, and their neighbors from across the river in Mecklenberg, Virginia, a village everyone called "Shepherd's Town." The two towns had sent a petition, offers of money, and a jolly invitation to spend at least an hour in each place letting the people adore their hero while showing him the ideal location for the permanent capital.

Stopping places mostly the same as GW's 1785 trip (GW Diary Aug.1785)

Griffith's 1794 map of Potomac; also GW Diary Aug.1785

Gazette of US. (Philadelphia) Nov. 27, 1790 quotes letter from Shepherd's Town citing "late visit" of GW, and that "he..informed us.." (Bryan p114)

He had spent half the day climbing the hilly streets of little Sharpsburg, ferrying across the river and riding borrowed horses to the top of the 100-foot bluff for a "Shepherd's-eye view" of mountains and winding river.

Shortly after wafting away from Shepherdstown, the not-quite-flat bottoms of the boats had begun bumping the river mud, and the crews began poling the boats along. Washington asked for a measurement of water depth.

"Not even a foot, Sir!" called a boatman. "A long-legged dog could wade across easy!" Johnson added that settlers from Pennsylvania moving to the Shenandoah Valley and Carolina drove their packhorses across this shallow as if it were a bridge.

Hist. West. Maryland (Scharf)

At Harper's Ferry, only 12 river miles beyond, they had dined quickly, boated around the point to the Shenandoah River, and returned solemn and thoughtful at dusk to Morris Tavern.

Not much progress in two years, Washington had told his brother Charles, who had been fetched from Charles Town 10 miles west. With low water exposing a mass of boulders, and no money to continue canal work, his disappointment was keen.

GW Diary June 1, 1788

Come dawn, Charles had helped with launching their boats, then climbed the high bluff above the village to watch them work through frothing rapids a mile away in Shenandoah-Potomac waters.

Following the lead boat, the President heard scrapings of bottom rocks against the boards of his boat as it raced down a channel cleared of its largest boulders.

The rest of the day, the problem of too little water showed itself as the boatmen guided them around more shoals and stones, each casting a shadow on Potomac dreams. Johnson spoke again about worries that had grown for some time over the fact that, except for about four months a year, shallows, shoals, and rocky bottoms would hamper loaded boats as much as rapids and waterfalls.

Columbia Hist. Society, 1909 "Potomac Route to the West" (Bacon/ Foster)

Washington had responded after a while that a tidewater capital below rapids and falls would be accessible year-round. Then he had quietly added, "If I decide to locate it there instead of Monocacy where you own land, I would want to appoint you a commissioner to supervise the construction of the new city. I will not choose for Commissioner a landowner in the 10-mile square. Even if he were the Angel Gabriel, he would be charged with favoritism in making decisions. Governor, I greatly desire that you will favor me by consenting to serve should I announce for tidewater. You have all the qualifications that I or the Congress or the country could desire."

GW letter in late 1790's

Thomas Johnson had taken off his hat and run his fingers through his hair. His usually ruddy cheeks had flushed a deeper shade of pink. "You know I cannot refuse you, General. But you know just as well that I would much rather spend my time tending to my own business."

The President had answered sympathetically, "I, too, had rather be at Mount Vernon with a friend or two about me than to be attended at the seat of government by the officers and representatives of every power in Europe."

GW letter to Stuart June 1790

During the rest of that day, they had passed many large and small forested islands, and skirted river bottoms rich and luxuriant in appearance. At mid-morning, the two boats had tied up at Captain Smith's homestead where they had breakfasted during previous river inspection trips. In the afternoon, they had dined on cold meat and cider at Noland's Ferry before pushing off for the mouth of the Monocacy and "The Dutchman's" tavern, their lodging at the end of the day. It was also the end of the Johnsons' boat ride.

GW Diary Aug.10, 1785

Now, at the first crack of light on Sunday, October 24, with the Johnsons trotting off toward Frederick, Washington had only the company of Dr. Stuart and the five boatmen in the downstream craft.

River currents, a friendly breeze, and a boatman pushing a pole against the river bottom, ease the President's boat across Potomac to Seneca Canal on Virginia's side. Shortly he and his companions will dock near Great Falls, mount horses stabled there, and ride five to eight hours through woods and fields to Alexandria and Mount Vernon.

The navigation to Seneca was not as difficult as the previous day's journey, although one stretch above a large, forested island was quite shallow (to Washington's disappointment) "as bad as any we've seen, and fish pots (V-shape arrangements of stones) are clogging the passage elsewhere, as usual. No one can blame the Indians for these!"

GW Diary Aug.10, 1785

By 9 o'clock, the President and Dr. Stuart were breakfasting on Indian cornmeal hoecakes and coffee at the home of John Goldsborough on the banks of Seneca Creek. The talk carefully kept to canaling, moving stones, and deepening channels after the President politely but pointedly ignored his host's "feeler" question about the merits of the possible Federal city sites.

Since their horses some days before had been ridden back to Georgetown, ferried to the Virginia side, and walked the 15-mile wagon road upriver to the stables of the canal workmen at Great Falls, Washington and Stuart settled once more into the riverboat. Expertly, the boatmen crossed the river to the Virginia side where the new Seneca canal bypassed the rapids. ("Lower water here than we saw when we came through a week ago, David.") Through the canal and back into the Potomac, the boatmen then rowed close to the bank to reach the landing at the head of the empty, mile-long ditch around Great Falls.

By noon, Washington and his stepson-in-law were riding their mounts under a canopy of trees over a lane crossing hills and dales to Alexandria.

Shortly, the President excused himself to ride ahead, alone, deep in thought.

Artemus Harmon map, D.C. roads 1790

After an hour or so to cover five miles, he reined in his horse and turned to wait for Dr. Stuart. Their horses now side by side, baggage horse on a line behind Stuart, the doctor started a conversation with remarks concerning the exercise benefits of bouncing the body on horseback an hour or two daily.

The President nodded agreement. "A good time for ruminating also." He paused. "I have decided to tell you, very privately, that I am considering a proposal to include some Virginia land in the 10-mile square. If I should do so, and Congress approves, I shall need a Virginian to serve as one of three Commissioners to oversee the laying out and construction of the city. I need a man that through long and intimate association with me has proved trustworthy, a man who will keep me informed as to the true state of affairs—yourself."

Dr. Stuart, frowning, looked at him, looked away, caught his breath. "Suppose Congress does not approbate Virginia?" he responded. "The law it passed mentions only Maryland. Though I am much in favor of the proposal, is it not risky to open up the seat of government question again?"

Washington nodded. "I have gravely pondered the dangers. I am acutely aware that any amendment to the law could be rejected, and even the Potomac thrown out and Germantown or Delaware Falls put in its place.

"But," he went on, "as you have reported to me, Virginians and especially Assembly delegates expect some consideration for their authorizing more money than Maryland to begin buying land and start construction of a Congress House and a President's House. Virginia's pledge is substantial— $120,000 to Maryland's $72,000. Virginia as well as Maryland has agreed to give Congress total control of a 10-mile square."

The men fell silent for the time they took to ford a creeklet. "Mr. Madison and Secretary Jefferson, when they stopped at Mount Vernon on their way home from New York, discussed with me the Assembly's expectations," the President continued. "It had expressed a preference for locating the seat ABOVE Georgetown—above tidewater. The Assembly had understood that, should a site on the Maryland bank of the Potomac be chosen by Congress, Virginia would cede land opposite, be included,

No record shows GW sounded out Johnson and Stuart on this trip, but it would have been a practical time, the only opportunity to do so in person.

Action of Va. Assembly, Dec. 1789; Md. Assembly, 1790.

Amid October's colorful foliage, horsemen and packhorse pause on the Great Falls-Alexandria wagon trail. Soon they will cross Washington's Four-Mile Run Farm and his step-grandson's adjacent land opposite the Georgetown flats, prime candidate for the capital.

TJ Papers Vol.19, p32
(Boyd)
Hist.Natl.Cap. p7
(W.Bryan)

and share in the cost of erecting buildings—the same offer made in '83 just after the mutinous soldiers incident.

"But if Georgetown was the choice, and land opposite included, would the Assembly accept the tidewater location and still grant the money?

"Sounding out my neighbor George Mason might indicate what to expect from the Assembly. He has strong connections and influence with the members. When Jefferson and Madison left Mount Vernon in September, they stopped at Gunston Hall to see Mason, an old and close friend, particularly of Jefferson. By cautious questioning and by the manner in which he replied, we could perhaps assess how strongly the Assembly members felt about an upriver location for the seat.

TJ and the Natl. Cap.,
Sept.17 letter, TJ to GW

"Mason came into it with a shyness not usual with him, Jefferson wrote me. We think it proceeded from his delicacy about the land he owns—some 2,000 acres—on the Virginia side, across from Georgetown and Little Falls.

*Letter, Mason to his
son, April, 1791*

"However, he said enough to show his decided preference for tidewater Georgetown over sites upriver above the falls. His reasons were firm and specific. Georgetown's port he compared most favorably with Alexandria's. Eastern Branch he declared superior in all respects to Alexandria. His opinions will carry much weight in Richmond.

*TJ to GW, Sept.17,
1790*

"George Mason and I became somewhat distant," the President said slowly, "when he refused to sign the Constitution despite contributing much to its drafting. He opposed ratification, insisting that a bill of rights should be added by a second convention. Perhaps he didn't trust Congress to write them. Perhaps it was his poor health distressing him. At the end, he walked with Governor Randolph out of the convention. Still, his opinions are much respected, and could hurt us if adverse."

Life of G.Mason, Vol. II,
p335 (K.Rowland)

Washington paused. "But I would like to include Alexandria in the square. That might set off a dispute in Congress. Perhaps it should not be risked. The town would be so close to the federal district it would enjoy great benefits on that account."

The road now lay through Four-Mile-Run farm, its name taken from a large creek emptying into the Potomac by Dr. Stuart's residence north of Alexandria. Dr. Stuart inquired if a 10-mile square reaching into Virginia might take in the very ground their horses were now traversing.

*Harmon map, DC
roads of 1790*

"You mean my Four-Mile-Run farm," answered the President. "I believe so—yes, of course it would—and also it would include the Custis estate, the 1200 acres between my farm and the river that you administer for your wife on behalf of her son, Wash, my adopted grandson. I expect criticism on account of both farms if Virginia land opposite Georgetown is included."

*Columbia Hist.Soc.
Record 1935 "GW's
Woods on 4-Mile Run"*

Dr. Stuart shook his head vigorously while saying, "No, General! The country wants to give you anything you will permit it to, and woe to the Senator or Congressman who dares put on a frown."

Washington glanced at Stuart with a faint smile. "If I were to choose Monocacy and the Virginia bluffs across the river from it—Williamsport is in no way practical—I could avoid criticism of the Washington interest since I own no land there."

Dr. Stuart was shaking his head. "I cannot serve if I must travel to Monocacy! It's a full day's journey across hilly country, even after I move my family to my Fairfax farm!"

Quickly the President said, "David, you are one of the few men whose integrity and discretion I fully, wholeheartedly, trust. You live within a few hours of the two possible sites, and have a strong interest in seeing the Federal city rise on the banks of the Potomac. You are close friends with many of the landowners; all of them respect and trust you. You speak French, which may be necessary, for I have in mind a Frenchman to draw the plan for laying out the new city. I earnestly beseech you

*"Hope Park and Mill"
(Petersilia/Wright)
Fairfax Planning
Dept., p32*

to answer affirmatively should I call."

The horses clopped along for a mile before the doctor answered. He was a man of few words despite his European education; some even called the youthful doctor glum. But his reticence meant discretion to George Washington. Since leaving Mount Vernon for the inauguration, the President had relied on the younger man's acute observations, recent experience as a Virginia assemblyman, and solid common sense to keep him apprised of Virginia's political doings and public opinion. Their letters back and forth had been lengthy, frequent, and frank.

Eleanor Calvert and Her Circle, (A.Torbert) *p47*

Dr. Stuart said at last, "It would bear hard on me. I mentioned to you that I must move Eleanor and the six children in a few weeks from Abingdon.

"I expect the court to give Abingdon back to the previous owners because Custis paid them for it in worthless Continental money. One of them has already told me how much rent he will charge if we stay in the house. I can't afford it. At least 'Hope Park,' my little house and farm in the Fairfax countryside, will cut down on travel time to Monocacy—though not enough to count for much, in my opinion. It will be a long ride from Hope Park to Georgetown, too—20 miles—four hours!"

GW letter to Stuart Dec.12, 1790

More silence. Washington suddenly said, "As for the Monocacy, I know that my good friend Charles Carroll would like for his Carrollton Manor to become the federal district. I expect he will quickly offer land and probably money. However, our ride down the Potomac showed me that a site above the river's falls will not be practical any time soon. The canal work has not gone quickly enough."

Dr. Stuart waited for the President to continue. When he did not, Stuart tactfully nudged him by remarking, "With Congress offering no money for land or buildings, where is the money coming from? The sums Virginia and Maryland are giving will not be near enough."

They had arrived at a crossroad. Washington whoahed his horse, pulled a gold watch from his waistcoat pocket and read, "Two o'clock. By taking a left here and riding to the edge of the bluff on the Custis farm, we can have as fine an elevated view of Potomac as we had at Shepherds Town. Also, we can proceed homeward by the superior riverside road below."

Hawkins map of D.C. roads 1790

Harmon map, D.C. 1791 roads

With a nod, Dr. Stuart agreed. He knew the place they were going was the front yard of a cottage built 10 years before by Jack Custis, Mrs. Washington's son. He had planned to build a mansion with the grandest view of the Potomac from the high bluff on the Virginia side. Stuart, in looking after the property for his wife, Jack's widow, used the cottage for storage.

"Old Arlington" (Natl.Pk. Ser./Murray Nelligan)

A few minutes along the lane, Washington abruptly reopened the subject of Charles Carroll of Carrollton. "I am much indebted to him. It was he and Gouverneur Morris in the winter of Valley Forge, who vigorously defended me in Congress and in its Committee of Inquiry. Otherwise, the Adamses and, strangely enough, Virginia's Richard Henry Lee, now Senator Lee , would have bent to the efforts of Conway and Gates to replace me with Gates as Commander-in-Chief of the Army. Carroll had weight as the supporter of the Army who could give large sums of money. You know, of course, that Carroll signed the Declaration of Independence. He thus risked his great fortune to rid America of rulers who forbade Catholics like himself many rights, including that of holding public office. He was serving in the Continental Congress when he and Morris showed up the 'Conway' schemers and snuffed out their fire.

Life of C.Carroll (E.H.Smith)

"In addition, in this recent session of the new Congress, Carroll guided through the Senate the bill naming Potomac for the seat of government." Washington paused.

"The question now is, If Carroll of Maryland fails

Life of C.Carroll
(E.H.Smith)

to get the seat for Monocacy, will he be willing to introduce and see through an amendment to include Virginia land in a 10-mile square at Georgetown? If he remains silent and distant, he could signal disgruntled losers that they might upset Potomac by opening the fight in Congress again.

"His Carrollton land and money," the President went on, "would surely relieve our financial straits; a Monocacy, upriver Potomac location would place the capital city closer to the western settlements— fast filling with people who will want to form new states. Did you hear that Kentucky is applying for statehood? The just-completed estimate of the census takers gives United States population as 5,000,000! That will astonish Europeans and add consequence to the union of states."

GW letter to J.Monroe in France, Dec.17, 1790

The horses separated to go single file up a rough, wooded slope. Side by side again, Washington continued. "But Thomas Johnson is right: Our canals to bypass Potomac falls will not be ready for some years. Even worse, the river has low water most months, and often ice in winter. What criticism would rend the air if I chose Monocacy!"

The President shook his head. "Fingers would be pointing at me for placing Congress in a capital inaccessible by water OR land! Johnson said roads in the area are impassable in bad weather. Carroll himself does not travel to Carrollton when roads are deep in mud.

"Besides that," he went on, "were I to choose Monocacy, some would accuse me of making a deal with Carroll for his support of Potomac and Assumption."

Another pause. "Besides THAT, South Carolina and Georgia delegates would abandon Potomac, probably, were I to choose Carrollton. South Carolina considers Carroll a half-traitor for introducing in the Senate Ben Franklin's Quaker resolution last year to free the slaves. When Franklin died some months later, Carroll infuriated them more by

Maclay's Diary April 1790

making a motion for Senators to wear black armbands, as they do for every man of note. He met with such coldness, he withdrew his motion."

Washington seemed to be talking to himself in the presence of a most trusted friend. They were plodding across mostly flat, sometimes lightly rolling cleared land where slaves were gathering and husking corn, bush-axing the ditchbanks, plowing in wheat stubble and strewing stable manure. The pungent odor of dung floated to the travelers, drawing farmer Washington's attention to the scene about him. "We must be on Jack Custis' farm now. You have looked after it well. With this plowing, the ground seems in perfect tilth and in good order. My Four-Mile-Run land is almost all woodland with only a few acres of corn and pease. But you saw that when you helped me start a survey of the place back in '85."

GW Diary, late Oct. 1786

"It was a memorable occasion," Dr.Stuart responded. "Your Black Billy went with us to hold the chain, fell down a little ravine and broke his knee cap on the chain pile. We got him to Abingdon on a borrowed sled since he couldn't walk, stand, or ride."

Columbia Hist.Soc. Record 1935

GW Diary, Apr.22 1785

"A sort of portent for this acreage, perhaps," said Washington. "After waiting 10 years to clear the deed, the first day of survey ended in an accident. Now its possible location in the federal district will bring criticism on my head. With my adopted grandson's future inheritance AND my acreage included, I could not avoid stirring disappointment, resentment, even cynicism among those whose lands to the north lose out as a result of including Virginia land. My good friend Congressman Daniel Carroll of northern Rock Creek will be left out. He expects the base of the square to be Potomac's Maryland bank. The square would then embrace his plantation, which he thinks will bring him great future advantage."

After a moment's silence, Washington added, "To

GW letter to Stuart June 1790

No record mentions that Washington sought Carroll's pledge of support before proceeding with a change requiring Congressional action. But it is unlikely GW would have risked losing the hard-won prize without first assessing his support and chance for success. Carroll's sponsoring the Senate action was essential.

please everybody is impossible. I therefore have adopted that line of conduct which combines public advantage with private convenience, and which, in my judgment is unexceptional in itself."

On the last phrase, he reined his horse to halt. Looking straight into Stuart's eyes, he continued in a firm and forthright manner, "First and foremost, as we have seen on our river journey, Georgetown is the only feasible location for a capital. Next, in fairness to Virginia, I wish to include Virginia land in the federal district. I would want Alexandria within its boundaries.

"But before I launch a move in Congress to open up the seat of government law to possible vandalism, I need assurance from Charles Carroll that he will aggressively shepherd the amendment or supplemental bill through the Senate. With Madison working in the House, a Senate-approved action should move safely through."

Stuart nodded in agreement. In a less intense tone, the President said, "Carroll has just gone to Doughoregan from Monocacy, and soon he will move to Annapolis for the social season. I do not wish to write anything to him, and in such delicate and interesting matters it is advisable not to diminish their importance by sending another to speak my mind.

"Therefore, I would like to send you to learn from Carroll's own mouth when and how he and I can discreetly confer.

"For you to take my message to Doughoregan will require a long day's ride, and another to return. What I have told you today must be kept a tight secret, even in your speaking to Carroll. You need only to say to him that I urgently need to confer with him."

Dr. Stuart quickly agreed to make the trip and soon. "I can combine your business with some I have in Ellicott Mills near Doughoregan."

The President beamed, thanked him, and clucked

to his horse. He led the way until they saw the cottage in a grove of majestic trees at the top of a knoll that marked the edge of the high bluff.

They sat on their horses beside the cottage to gaze at the wide river and beyond it to the distant low hills. Pointing and naming the farms, creeks, and nearest heights, Stuart was moved to exclaim with the most enthusiasm he had shown all week, "It has everything! The point of flatland stands well above the water, exactly right for laying out a street grid! The wavy land rising behind it will raise the government buildings above the flats! Our Virginia bluffs are positioned exactly right for defending the capital city! It is all just right—just right!"

Suddenly embarrassed by his outburst of words and feelings, young Dr. Stuart cocked his head and cut his eye at the President. The President was looking at him affectionately, triumphantly.

"Old Arlington (Lee Mansion)" (M. Nelligan)

From Monticello at Charlottesville, Virginia, to Philadelphia, temporary capital, required eight days of discomforts from bad roads, bad weather, often bad food and beds at "ordinaries" along nearly 300 miles. Madison often made the trip with Jefferson in his coach. In their November 1790 journey, they would have discussed the exciting details of a capital city soon to begin rising on a Potomac site as yet unnamed.

CHAPTER 26

Sliding the Diamond Across Two Rivers

SCENE: A coach taking Jefferson and Madison from western Virginia
to Philadelphia, with a stop at Mount Vernon.
TIME: November 8, 9, 10, 1790.

Thomas Jefferson's coach rolled away from Monticello, the mansion he designed, built, and had never completed atop his little mountain in Virginia's Blue Ridge. He was setting out on the hundred or so miles between Charlottesville and Mount Vernon, an important overnight stop on the way to Philadelphia, temporary capital.

Above, a rumple of clouds sulked away the glow from the November morning's sunlight. The heavy gray mass hung motionless, sullen, threatening more rain. Below, hovering around the foot of the 500-foot height, a thick, white mist had already begun drizzling moisture on the earth.

Coach drivers, holding taut rein on horses stepping briskly down the long, steep hill cast anxious eyes on the signs of imminent bad weather.

Jefferson drew a deep, resigned breath. If he didn't have James Madison's company to look forward to, he would dread even more these days of travel—travail, he called them. The badness of the roads and discomforts of lodgings promised a certain torment of body. The job of Secretary of State took a high toll on a man's bones and bottom. He wondered which length of the road to Philadelphia would make him feel worse—the first 100 miles bringing him to George Washington's door, or the 165 miles from there to the temporary capital? What a relief it would be when the capital moved near

Mount Vernon!

With a sigh for the amusing, sunny, three-week journey homeward he and "Jemmy" Madison had made from New York in September, he looked back at his house on the hilltop. Monticello—Little Mountain. The sight of it set his heartstrings in motion. Even when November had stripped oak, maple, gum, and sycamore trees down to their naked network of branches; even when Indian Summer never appeared, but in its place arrived soggy, dull days, his Monticello high on its solitary hill stood out like a jewel box in the landscape.

"Monticello!" he said to himself. "Where has nature spread so rich a mantle under eye? Mountains, forests, rocks, rivers. With what majesty do we there ride above the storms! How sublime to look down into the workhouse of nature, to see her clouds, hail, snow, rain, thunder, all fabricated at our feet! And the glorious sun when rising, as if out of a distant water, just gilding the tops of the mountains, and giving life to all nature."

But today, he must leave it all behind for places far away. If only the road kept firm despite a week of rain! Jefferson thought with sympathy of Jupiter, his same-age slave since youth, today a bundled-up coachman managing the reins of a team of horses; of the postilions hanging on at the back; and his cook with the excited teen-age slave—his

*J.Madison (Brant)
p320*

*Restored Monticello is
open to the public,
Charlottesville, Va.*

*Life and Letters of TJ
(Hirst)*

TJ Papers (Boyd, ed.)

Mrs. Thornton's Diary (Mrs. Wm. Thornton)

first trip—taking turns driving a baggage-wagon. Most of the baggage was furniture for a rented house in Philadelphia since his Paris goods had not arrived, despite a year of letter-writing.

A few miles before the village of Orange, some five hours—25 miles—north, the drizzle faded. His coach turned into a lane winding uphill through a wild woods. Shortly, it reached the open lawn of Montpelier, the Madison family mansion with its dramatic view of the Blue Ridge.

As usual, Jefferson pondered the large, plain rectangular house. Too flat-faced, he complained. He had been teasing its pale, thin-faced occupant— "the GREAT little Madison" he called him, younger by a decade but an old friend—about adding some distinction to the facade of his birthplace, columns, portico, something. But Madison had little interest in changing facades.

"All you think about is politics, politics, ever more politics!" Jefferson twitted him.

TJ (F. Brodie) p301

A hearty repast, a loading of trunks and boxes, a last pat for Madison's saddle horse tethered to the wagon, and the two gentlemen—one a hatless, whitening redhead, a loose-walking six-footer in his late 40's; the other in his late 30's, rather colorless, thin, short, wearing a high crown hat to bring him up to size—settled into the coach.

"Away, Jupiter!" The whip cracked, and to the rhythmic strike of metal horseshoes on gravel, the Secretary and Congressman began discussing Congress, politics, and people.

Plans they had made by letter called for an overnight stop at the ordinary in Rhoadesville crossroads, 15 miles east—"downhill," they said—of Montpelier, and to proceed 35 miles to Fredericksburg the next day. They would lodge at convivial, even club-like Weedon's Tavern on Caroline Street. From Fredericksburg, it was 40 miles north to Mount Vernon. Pushing long and hard, they'd make it on the journey's third day.

"Unless rains catch us and deep-mire the roads," cautioned Madison. They were passing the courthouse in Orange where he had faced the voters on many a voting day, and celebrated victory in the nearby tavern. "Weather rules the traffic, and the traveler never knows what adventure will befall him," agreed Jefferson, taking a last look backwards at the Blue Ridge. "Last March when I began the trip to New York to take up my new duties as Secretary of State, a heavy snow fell. The roads were so bad the stage could never go more than three miles an hour, and sometimes not more than two, and in the night, one! Ten days on the road, Annapolis to New York—12 or more hours a day— being bounced back and forth, up and down."

Life, Letters of TJ (Hirst) *p253, letter to son-in-law Randolph, Mar. 1790*

During the hours while the coach rolled and bumped through soft rutted earth, pot holes, and creeklets, the two friends opened their minds to each other. Jefferson dreaded to return to work, work, work, which was hateful to him and no good to anybody else, he felt sure. Madison pleaded in a voice as soft and southern as his companion's, "But you are doing many things that are essential to help establish the new government! The President needs you! He greatly values your intellect and esteems you personally."

"Oh, yes—he exactly calculates every man's value, and gives him solid esteem proportioned to it— except probably in the case of Hamilton it is too much, I think," Jefferson said. "Washington gathers opinions and facts from all of us, takes them into his own counsel and from them renders his judgment. No judgment was ever sounder. But to me, it is slow in operation, little aided by invention or imagination, but sure in conclusion. No motives of interest or consanguinity, of friendship or hatred, are able to bias his decision. George Washington is, indeed, in every sense of the word, a wise, a good, and a great man."

TJ (Hirst) p480

"I applaud your delineation of his character,"

Thomas Jefferson

*All the quote from
TJ Autobiography*

*TJ memo to GW,
Aug.29 (TJ journal
entry date, with title
"agenda in the 10-mile
square") Papers of TJ
Vol.17, p454, 461
(Boyd)*

Madison said. "Would that I were able to work only with him instead of 66 Congressmen talking every subject into the ground, always contentious."

"Contentious!" exclaimed Jefferson. "It is the hallmark of Congress, old or new! In Annapolis, in the months after Washington resigned his commission, I sat in the old Congress enduring contentiousness. With great difficulty, we rounded up enough votes finally to ratify the treaty of peace with England! But I failed by ONE vote—the man who would have cast it was ill—to gain passage of my bill prohibiting slavery in any newly-created state, thus blocking future calamity in this land of ours. The fate of millions unborn hung on the tongue of one man! And heaven was silent in that awful moment! Instead, day after day was wasted on the most unimportant questions. I recall that a member, one of those afflicted with the morbid rage of debate, a copious flow of words, and impatience with any logic which was not his own, sitting near me on some occasion of a trifling but wordy debate, asked me how I could sit in silence hearing so much false reasoning, which a word should refute? I observed to him that to refute was indeed easy, but to silence impossible."

Madison exclaimed, "Hear! Hear!" and launched into his bent-necked, finger-pointing imitation of Elbridge Gerry bumbling out an opinion. When they had wiped away their tears of laughter, Jefferson declared that the only speakers he cared to listen to were Franklin and Washington—"they never spoke over 10 minutes, laid their shoulders to the great points, knowing that the little ones would follow of themselves.

"But," he quickly added, "AFTER the talking, as you know so well, Washington spends hours, days—many of them now MY days—collecting facts and opinions, querying about dozens of details. You remember how far into the night you and I worked the day before he left New York in August,

writing out answers to his questions concerning the law locating the seat of government on the Potomac?"

Madison laughed and recalled how amused they had been at playing the President's game, which they called "skirting around Blanktown."

"He kept saying, 'If I should decide on a position below Great Falls,' so we had to stop saying 'Georgetown' and solemnly say, 'If you decide on a position below Great Falls.'

"Oh my," Madison added, still smiling, "at the same time, he gave us a long list of questions to ask in Georgetown about Funkstown owners, land offers, prices. It took two days for Stoddert, Deakins, and Congressman Carroll to answer them and show us the site when we stopped there on our trip home in September."

"Well, well," said Jefferson, "he's better off playing a game of indecision—but certainly his face said a straightforward 'Georgetown!' even if his words did not when we stopped at Mount Vernon to make our report."

Jefferson credited Madison for phrasing the critical remark, "ESSENTIAL that the District should comprehend the water adjoining—ELIGIBLE that it should comprehend the opposite shore," that opened the question nearest their hearts: including Virginia land in the 10-mile square.

"I can still see the sudden flash of his glance when I mentioned Alexandria," Jefferson said. "Of course I prefaced it with 'if a position below the falls should be decided on.' Including Alexandria and its port is desirable but awkward since it lies just outside an extension of a line across the Potomac from Eastern Branch, the boundary set by Congress. He didn't like my idea of accepting only seven miles along the Potomac from Eastern Branch, but 10 miles upriver from Alexandria, Virginia. That would not make a square.

"What a devilish little problem! Ironical, too.

James Madison

*TJ to GW Sept.14
memo (Papers of TJ:
Boyd, p461)*

George Washington's hometown may have to stay just outside the magical lines of the nation's capital! Perhaps we should pray for a small, well-directed tremor of the earth that would shift the mouth of Eastern Branch a mere three miles downriver!"

Madison declared that he, like Washington had been hoping that Jefferson could see a legal interpretation of the law that would make a change in the law unnecessary. A rectangular shape had looked promising in August when Jefferson had included in his memo to Washington that "10 miles square" presumably meant 100 square miles IN ANY FORM. But in mid-September at Mount Vernon, Washington had turned aside the idea. Congress had always talked of a square; presenting a rectangle would give Potomac's enemies an excuse to attack it.

Jefferson reached for a carpet bag on the seat beside him, drew out a rolled-up paper, and spread it flat on the seat beside him.

"I made this tracing of the Georgetown-Alexandria area from a large-scale map, old but accurate, that my father made when he surveyed Virginia. (No, my bad wrist is no better, but I can trace and draw with my left hand now almost as well as I can write with it.)

"Look now—I have cut a paper square to scale for the 10-mile square. Let's lay it so it covers the area from the edge of Eastern Branch, the law's specific limit, to a point 10 miles along the Maryland shore of the Potomac."

Madison observed that the square included Georgetown, Little Falls, and several miles upriver while on the far northeast side it went a distance beyond Bladensburg, "and beyond Congressman Carroll's plantation on the northwest."

"Now let us slide the square straight down across the Potomac and five miles into Virginia," Jefferson said.

"It leaves Alexandria off to the side. At the top,

the Congressman and Bladensburg are out."

Jefferson's forefinger moved the paper square to the right, covering Eastern Branch and land beyond. "And now?" he asked.

Madison looked up, his face animated with pleasure. Jefferson's easy smile and shining eyes were waiting for him. "It's no longer a square sitting squarely," Madison said. "It seems to have turned magically into a diamond! With Alexandria anchoring the lower point!"

With an admiring look at Jefferson, Madison added, "The President will like this demonstration. In a glance, anyone can comprehend the problem. Your sliding paper square quickly tells the story."

"It would not surprise me if Washington, the surveyor, has already done this demonstration for himself!" Jefferson replied.

"It also makes clear," Jefferson went on, "that there is no legal way to include Alexandria under the present law. But, much as he—and we—might desire the law changed, I feel cautious about encouraging him to go back to Congress and re-open this subject. New York or Pennsylvania might well attempt to displace Potomac.

"If we should lose the measure we now have securing the federal seat for Potomac, it could never be regained," said Jefferson.

Madison murmured that Potomac's victory had been a lucky combination of circumstances that might never be repeated. "It would be devastating to see it grabbed away."

After a minute, Jefferson declared, "Perhaps the President should resign himself to being satisfied with five square miles of Virginia land without Alexandria—and avoid asking more from Congress. The present law does not prohibit including the river itself and land on both banks in the 10-mile square. On the contrary! By saying that government buildings must be located on the Maryland side, the law indicates an expectation that land in

TJ quote: Hist.Natl. Capital (Bryan) p107

284

Virginia will be included!

"However, if the President goes past the specific, named boundary of Eastern Branch, he will violate the law—which is unthinkable. Thus, he must ask for a supplementary law if he pursues his desire to include his hometown."

All of a sudden, a loud "Halloo!" from the road made them look up from their map study. A man on horseback, one of a file of a dozen or more, was waving and peering into the coach window. "Mr. Jefferson! I knowed I that werz you! 'Tis a fine coach, that it is, sir! Onliest one on the road, sir! Josh Jenkins at your service, sir!" Tipping his hat, Josh Jenkins, frontiersman, passed from sight, on his way home with bulging saddlepacks of salt, bartered for in Fredericksburg.

As the other horsemen in the little caravan passed, Jefferson continued to nod and smile at them. Madison pressed closer to the back of his seat, stiff-faced and motionless, ill at ease. "A few bushels of salt and saltpeter cost those men a pile of hides, pelts, ginseng and snake roots, whiskey, and bear grease," remarked Jefferson folding away his map.

At Roadesville, the candles had just been lit when Jefferson's coach pulled up in front of the door. The innkeeper directed the laying down of some boards for the gentlemen to step upon rather than in the bright red mud. "Tis a divine mercy the rains held back today!" he greeted them, then led them upstairs to a small room crowded with two narrow cots, "garn-teed bugless, as you know from previous stops here, yer honors."

"That little private room and the cook's bean soup raise this ordinary just over the line from indifferent to tolerable," Jefferson remarked next morning when the coach rolled away. Madison yawned. "Barely tolerable with the arguing and shouting of the crowd of men playing cards downstairs, clomping upstairs past midnight, and snoring like bass fiddles til rising time," Madison answered.

"However, the tune was just monotonous and dull enough, not being played next to my ears, that I slept soundly from time to time." Jefferson laughed appreciatively.

A chilly fog and mist hung over the rolling red hills of the countryside. Inside the coach, the Secretary and the Congressman stared out the window in silence, listening to the squeaks of the coach, the sound of wheels cutting through the wet, rutted earth, and the loud yawns of the coachmen who had spent the night in slave quarters above the tavern stables.

Shortly, after fording a small creek, Jefferson drew from his carpet bag a sheet of paper on which some sketches had been made. "To pass the time, you might be amused to see a more elaborate design than the simple grid I drew for our Georgetown report. The President seemed interested at that time to see how I fitted the government buildings into the area where much of the 400 acres, offered during our Georgetown visit, lie.

"Here in the upper left corner is Georgetown. In the shoulder of high land—Braddock's Landing—between Rock Creek and Tiber Creek, I have marked off the squares—18 of them—forming a long U around the President's House and the Capitol, each with spacious grounds. They face extensive public walks along the bank of Tiber creek where it joins the Potomac.

"Tiber water there is only 18 inches deep—not enough for commerce, as I have written alongside. But it will provide a fine prospect for those attached to the government.

"On the high corner—Braddock's Landing—the President's House. Two blocks up Tiber Creek, the Capitol. In the blocks behind and to the side will be buildings for the Secretaries of State, War, Treasury, and the Attorney General. Total acres, 300. Those acres we will have to buy. As much as 1200 adjacent would be surveyed for a town. As our

Travel in America
(S.Dunbar)

Dunbar p199

TJ sketch:
Wash.Architecture
(Fine Arts Office)

Jefferson's sketch became a matter of record in March 1791, although he probably drew it much earlier. How much earlier is unknown, but a likely time is autumn 1790 when he was home on vacation and the subject was on his mind. He had just examined the site and, being a surveyor, could easily have drawn its outline from memory.

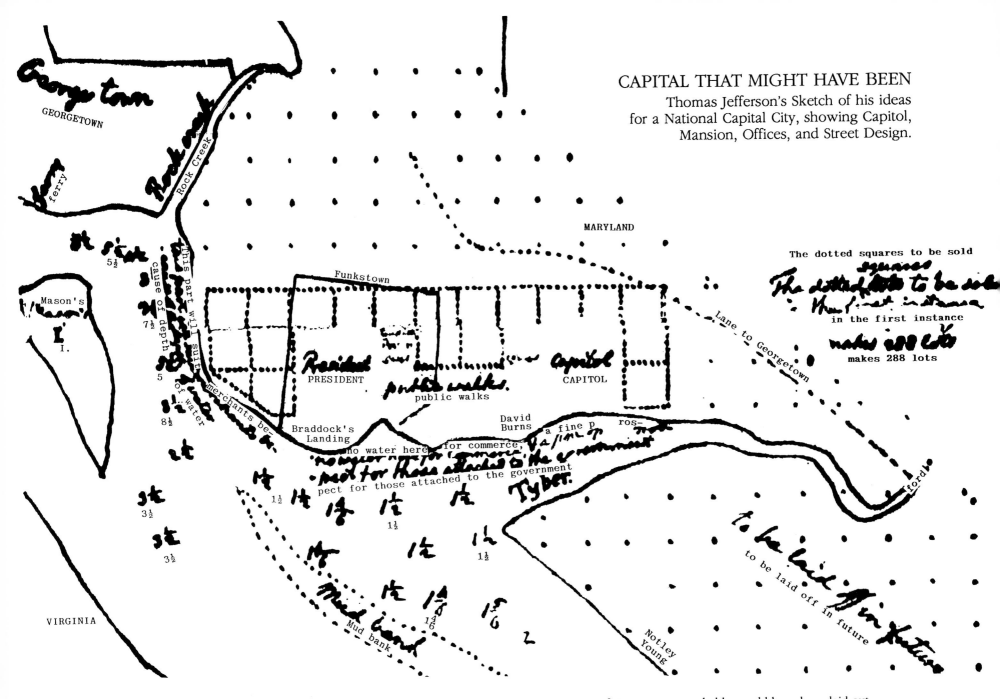

CAPITAL THAT MIGHT HAVE BEEN
Thomas Jefferson's Sketch of his ideas
for a National Capital City, showing Capitol,
Mansion, Offices, and Street Design.

GEORGETOWN

ferry

Rock Creek

Rock Creek

MARYLAND

5½

This part will suit merchants because of depth of water

Mason's I.

7½

5

8½

Funkstown

President

PRESIDENT

public walks

Capitol

CAPITOL

The dotted squares to be sold

in the first instance

makes 288 lots

Lane to Georgetown

ford

Braddock's Landing

no water here for commerce,

a fine p   ros-
pect for those attached to the government

David Burns

not for those attached to the government

Tyber.

3½

3½

1½

1½

1½

1½

1½

1½

1⁴⁄₁₆

1⁵⁄₆

2

Notley Young

to be laid off in future

VIRGINIA

Mud bank

Jefferson's plan for a compact capital village about a half-mile square, an extension of Georgetown, probably would have been laid out
had not Pierre L'Enfant asked Washington for, and gained, the job of city designer. In Jefferson's drawing (above), the President's
House sat on the high ground of the present State Department, the Capitol on the site of Constitution Hall, and government office
buildings in a two-block-wide line behind them. The rest of the town Jefferson drew as a few blocks in a simple grid pattern.

TJ memo to GW,
Aug. 29, 1790

memos have told the President, although the law does not say 'lay out a town,' it seems obvious that a town is implied. Recall that the Georgetown men who escorted us around the site in September—Stoddert, Deakins, and Congressman Carroll—calculated that 20 good houses for officials, 20 more lodging houses for Congress, and a half-dozen good taverns to feed everybody, were needed. On my sketch, the squares formed by these large dots could accommodate a conveniently laid-out town."

Madison looked up from studying the sketch to say, "The President has mentioned a letter that the architect 'Lanfang,' as he calls him, wrote to him asking for the job of designing a plan for the town."

"Oh?" A cloud passed briefly across Jefferson's pleasant face. "L'Enfant, the talkative Frenchman? A creature of Hamilton, I believe. Well, he has shown some style in renovating New York's Old City Hall into Federal Hall, though quite extravagant with money. But has he experience or aptitude for drawing up an appropriate city plan? My design is only a simple one—a grid of streets at right angles, like Philadelphia."

TJ Papers (Boyd)
TJ to GW
Aug. 29, 1790

Madison leaned to look at the sketch. "I see the President's grounds occupy most of Funkstown's acres. With 160 lot owners to find, acquiring the land could take much time. The Capitol will take that part of David Burnes' farm where his house sits. I can see it requiring much money to pry that land from him, even for a Capitol. The whole shoulder of land, as you call it, may turn out to be the most difficult to acquire of all the acres in the 100 square miles—the principal men's pledge of their acreage and lots notwithstanding—especially when there is no acquiring money."

Jefferson answered quickly that the Maryland legislature would then be asked for a law forcing consent of obstinate proprietors. "As for money to buy land for government buildings, there are the grants from Maryland and Virginia. For land enough

TJ Papers (Boyd) p462,

for a town, there is the idea of persuading the proprietors to deed their acres to the government, which would survey it and give back half the house lots to the proprietors as compensation. They can SELL their lots for much more money when, as the capitol rises, prices rise. The government could sell its half of the lots to get the money to construct the Capitol, President's House, and some offices."

"Mr. Secretary, your inventive genius extends far beyond your mechanical contrivances at Monticello!" Madison declared. Jefferson responded that the idea was not his, but the prospect of laying out and building a new city intrigued him. He had spent much of the past two months at home thinking about the Georgetown site, and perusing books about architectural styles.

TJ to GW Sept.14
memo (Boyd)p463

"Your plan for the government center in the new capital is also practical," Madison observed. "For some years at least, only the taverns and private houses in Georgetown will exist to board and bed officials and clerks. Of necessity—we know how well our Congressmen like their comforts and pleasures—the Congress should be close to those taverns and houses."

Jefferson quickly added, "At the same time, the Eastern Branch side of the area—four miles off my sketch—could be laid out for factories and commercial and shipping businesses, which should satisfy the landowners over there."

TJ Papers (Boyd) p463,
TJ to GW Sept. 14

Jefferson returned his drawing to his carpet bag, uncrossed and recrossed his long legs, and wondered aloud if the President would announce for Georgetown in his speech to Congress on the eighth of December—a month hence.

"I think not," Madison said. "It would be foolish to announce before all the southern senators and congressmen have arrived. They might not take their seats until after New Year's. Then the supplementary, if there's to be one, must start moving. In only eight weeks, the First Congress ends, and the Second Congress with many new delegates begins."

Jefferson agreed that was barely enough time even if everything went smoothly. "Charles Carroll should see it through the Senate this time, too. But will he? Or will he hold back when he learns that his upper river land lost out to Georgetown, to Virginia, and to Washington's hometown?"

Only time and George Washington hold the answers, Madison declared, and moved the conversation back to Jefferson's plans for the capital.

To this warmly receptive, trusted friend, Jefferson eagerly revealed more of his vision of what the seat of government should look like. With the Capitol and the President's Mansion only a few blocks apart in a compact area of public buildings, with their style embodying the best of the ancient Greeks and the Renaissance Italians, the whole would, he thought, provide the impressive view, elegance, harmony, even grandeur, desirable for a national capital.

TJ to L'Enfant Apr.10, 1791

"I should prefer for the Capitol," he said, "the adoption of some one of the models of antiquity which have had the approbation of thousands of years. For the President's house, I should prefer the celebrated fronts of modern buildings which have already received the approbation of all good judges—a place such as the Louvre in Paris. Simplicity, grandeur, and convenience, those are essentials. I believe the natural good taste of the President will select such a design whether it comes from the Commissioners (which I doubt likely) or obtained from ingenious architects." He glanced at Madison and smiled.

The U.S. Capitol (p.xv,xvi) (G.Brown) TJ Papers, (Boyd) TJ to GW Aug. 29, 1790

"Should I guess that you already have a sketch or two?" Madison smiled back.

Jefferson dug into his carpetbag and pulled out a sheet of paper. "Only a whimsical drawing for the Mansion, in a style now favored, which draws its inspiration from the architect Palladio and the Italian Renaissance. It has a small, elegant dome..."

Submitted anonymously under initials "A.Z" in 1792 competition

For the rest of the day, their animated conversation went on, Jefferson's low and slow, pleasant, bantering voice predominating. He was pleased to hear Madison urge him to offer to Washington his plan for the Mansion. He was inspired to describe the shapes and locations of buildings he envisaged for the federal rectangle with such vividness that Madison could see them standing full-size on the high corner bounded by creek and river, in sight of Georgetown.

While the horses pulled coach and baggage-wagon slowly through Wilderness Run, alongside pastures, dark-red earthy fields, forests leading to and past the crossroads villages of Spotsylvania and Chancellorsville, Jefferson told stories of Paris—delightful buildings, gardens, the King's palaces, the Bastille and the astonishing scene he witnessed when the mob demolished it. Then, General Lafayette and his city militia trying to keep order, himself and Lafayette drafting a Declaration of the Rights of Man.

Present Va.Route 15

TJ (F.Brodie)

Madison listened enthralled.

At dinnertime, four o'clock, when they alighted at Weedon's Tavern in Fredericksburg, it required as much effort to bring back their thoughts from Paris as it did to limber their stiff muscles into walking.

GW's Relations and Relationships in Fredericksburg (P.S.Felder)

In this superior hostelry, they were honored with a glass of wine and applause at dinner, a small but well-furnished room to themselves far-removed from the Richmond stage coming and going at the entrance, the loud voices in the bar talking horses and horse races, those in the parlors exclaiming at backgammon and billiards.

But during the night, their weather luck ran out. Heavy rains fell for hours, turned into a short but vicious cloudburst after breakfast, and calmed to a steady downpour for the rest of the day.

Equally steadily, Jefferson and Madison fretted about the black men on the outside of the coach, sheltered only by canvas roofs hastily set up on poles over the drivers' seats. Their baggage under already-soggy canvas worried them. They abandoned plans to walk a few blocks to the mansion of Washington's sister, Betty Fielding; the Secretary and Congressman had not personally spoken to her since the death of her mother, Mary Ball Washington, the previous year—before Jefferson had arrived home from Paris and while Congressman Madison was in New York fighting for a capital on the Potomac.

Instead, they nervously watched from the coach window as ferrymen slowly hauled on the chain drawing the great flatboat and its load of coach, wagon, men, and horses across a quarter-mile of Rappahannock river water.

GW's Relations and Relationships in Fredericksburg, Va. (P.S.Felder) p17

The road north climbed the riverbank to cross a corner of Ferry Farm, owned by Washington. As always, the two friends looked across the farmland to gaze with thoughtful interest at a sizeable, low frame house atop a knoll in sight of the river ferry— Washington's boyhood home.

There the future Commander-in-Chief and first United States President had lived with his widowed mother, three brothers, and a sister from age six until his teens, when he began living at Mount Vernon with a half-brother.

Wheels cutting deep into sticky mud, and horses and drivers half-blinded with rain, slowed the coach. Inside, anxiety silenced conversation. Finally Madison ventured, "What a pity nobody—not even you— loves poor John Fitch, and helps him perfect his steamboat. We might now be going eight miles an hour up the Potomac, without mud and rain holding us back."

Jefferson looked skeptical, shrugged, mumbled something about "that coarse, belligerent, wild man." He knew that Madison a few years back had tried unsuccessfully to persuade the Virginia legislature to vote Fitch some money—and that the first

History of Travel in America (S.Dunbar) p257

news they heard in Philadelphia two months ago concerned the steamboat's daily runs all summer between Trenton and Philadelphia. "A Dr. William Thornton and some other Philadelphians put up the ship-building money, so Fitch and his idea may amount to something after all," Madison added.

Jefferson thought a balloon with a steam engine would attract him more. "Instead of a week on the road from Philadelphia, I would be home within five HOURS!" They both laughed.

TJ (F.Brodie) p255, letter 1793

All morning and early afternoon, the little caravan made steady if bumpy and slow-to-slower progress across 23 miles of low hills to Dumfries. Fortunately, the large, high-bank creeks they had to cross—Potomac, Aquia, and Chopawamsic— had passable log bridges, the road having been the route of American and French armies on their way to Yorktown in 1781. "But one more day of this weather and we could have been stuck depressingly long in Fredericksburg," the gentlemen observed to each other.

Present Route 1, Alexandria to Fredericksburg, Va.

At Dumfries, the hungry and rain-oppressed men and horses stopped for food and rest at Leitch's Tavern. From there to the turn onto Mount Vernon's long lane, adventures undesired befell them at every waterway.

Creeklets could barely be forded successfully. The sizeable Occoquan Creek had spread a few yards out of its bounds; across its bridge coursed swift, inches-deep water. How secure was the bridge? A pair of local horsemen who had just come off that almost invisible passage splashed up. They shook their heads and advised the Secretary and Congressman to seek a nearby narrow ford— "turn left on this lane uphill, go a mile or so, take the left path at a fork, then a little ways on take a right to a rail fence, which you must follow alongside until you come to the woods of the upper creek—"

Travel in America (S.Dunbar)

"No," Jefferson interrupted, "we have only an hour before dark. To lose ourselves in the wilder-

Name places, taverns, details of the route from GW Diary, 1770-1790 travels on this road.

ness in a pouring rain, as sounds inevitable, will serve us poorly. We will take our chances here."

He directed the baggage wagon to try the bridge, testing its shakiness and the water depth. In a sudden downpour, coachdrivers and postilions stood at the water's edge, ready to plunge in should disaster seize the wagon driver and baggage.

The gentlemen in the coach peered nervously from its windows. The wagon body stayed inches above soaking, the bridge held steady, the driver waved and shouted jubilantly from unflooded mud beyond the creek.

On their way again—"but don't try hastening, Jupiter, we have uncertainty enough and wish not to invite further excitement"—along heavily wooded miles, up hill and down with a creeklet to ford at each bottom, they arrived by end of daylight at the turnoff for George Mason's Gunston Hall. Perhaps they should seek haven there.

No, the gentlemen in the coach decided, the old man is not well and besides, the miles east to his house are as many as the miles north to Mount Vernon's long lane—"provided we can get across Accotink Creek and its marshes." They did, with a mounted postilion holding a lantern to mark the bridge and lead the way through the darkness.

They knew from the roar of the waterfall when they were passing Washington's grist mill just by the lane to Belvoir on the Potomac. "Sad, sad Belvoir mansion—only burned-out ruins," said Jefferson. "I have several times heard Washington remark about the happy years he spent as a young man living at Mount Vernon with his half-brother and visiting George and Sally Fairfax at Belvoir almost every day." Madison began to tell him that, these days, George Fairfax's widow was living in straited circumstances in England—when a back wheel of the coach suddenly lurched into a deep hole and threw him against Jefferson. In an instant, the wheel pulled out of the hole and jolted Madison back into his seat.

In the dark, Jefferson was reaching to help him, exclaiming, "Good God, Jemmy, are you hurt!?"

"No..No," Madison half whispered. Then he began laughing softly. "Ridiculous how this reminds me of a verse I composed and recited at one of our more boisterous outings at the college in Princeton. It's memorably bad, and goes like this: 'Urania threw a chamber pot, Which from beneath her bed she brought, And struck my eyes and ears and nose, Repeating it with lusty blows——'"

Jefferson, with a whoop of laughter, cried, "Stop, Jemmy, stop! Remember that your college President, the Rev. Dr. Witherspoon said, and I quote, 'During the whole time Madison was under my tuition, I never knew him to DO, or (Madison chanted with him the rest of Jefferson's favorite tease) to SAY an IMPROPER thing!'"

In the coach slowly rolling through the night, they struck up singing old college songs, merrily remembering the days of their youth.

An hour later, the coach had pulled close to the middle door at the back of George Washington's home, and a postilion was rapping on it urgently.

The President received his guests cordially, enthusiastically, and led them to the dining room. On the bare table lay a large map—and a small square of paper. "I have again studied the Alexandria problem," he said after calling a black man to bring brandy. "Unless you two have thought of an acceptable way to avoid it, I will be obliged to risk a supplementary law in Congress. Anticipating that, I have spoken to Carroll of Carrollton. He consents to see it through the Senate. I think we can confidently predict success." After they had toasted that success in brandy, Washington turned to the map.

"Perhaps even the square on the map predicts success. When it embraces both rivers to include Alexandria, it becomes that most valuable of jewels, a diamond."

GW (D.Freeman)

J.Madison (R.Ketcham)

Jefferson and Madison often stopped overnight at Mount Vernon on their way to and from sessions of Congress and their homes in western Virginia. In November 1790, much of their talk with Washington would concern sliding the 10-mile square across Potomac and Eastern Branch Rivers to include Alexandria.

TURNING A SQUARE INTO A DIAMOND

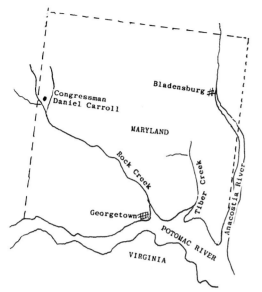

At left, the dotted-line 10-mile square on its eastern (right) side borders the Eastern Branch, or Anacostia River, Maryland, as prescribed by the Seat of Government, or Residence Act, passed by Congress. On the south, the Maryland bank of the Potomac is the boundary line, perhaps implied but not specifically stated in the law.

At right, the dotted-line 10-mile square, still with its eastern border the Anacostia, has slid straight down into Virginia, taking in a section of the Potomac River. Since the law did not prescribe the Maryland river bank as a boundary, nor specifically confine the Federal District to Maryland land, the slide into Virginia does not violate the law.

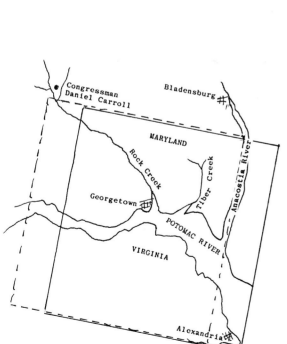

At left, the dotted-line 10-mile square, also shown above at right, will be declared the Federal District by the President in the event that Congress refuses to allow a second slide to the east as shown in the solid-line 10-mile square. By moving the eastern boundary three miles beyond the Anacostia, then extending it southward, the town of Alexandria, Virginia, can be included in the Federal District.

At right, the solid-line 10-mile square standing alone in the location that Washington asked Congress to grant him before the end of the last session of the First Congress, impresses the eye less as a square, more as a diamond.

Part Five
Risking an Amendment
Third Session, First Congress
December 1790-March 1791

In Philadelphia, Washington once more settled into quarters too small for 23 people—14 of them servants—even though it was "the best single house in town" (left). He rented it for $3,000 annually from Robert Morris, and lived next door to Morris in his just-renovated mansion at Sixth and Market Streets. Washington ordered an extension built to a "back building" for servants, and renovation of four rooms (darkened windows) over the kitchen for himself, Martha, and the two grandchildren.

CHAPTER 27

Not Leaving Chance in Charge

SCENE 1
PHILADELPHIA STRAINS AND STRATEGIES

PLACE: Washington's third presidential mansion (Robert Morris house), Philadelphia.
TIME: Thursday, December 9, 1790

GW Diary
Dec. 9, 1790

At breakfast a month later, on Thursday, December 9, the three Virginians were meeting to go over again the delicate and interesting details of locating the federal city in the exact place they wanted it to be.

Jefferson and Madison had knocked at seven o'clock on the front door of the President's new home, a flat-faced, four-story brick mansion sitting flush with the sidewalk at 190 High Street near Sixth Street in Philadelphia.

Am. Phil. Soc.
Vol.43, 1953, "190 High Street" (H.D.Eberlein)

In the small family dining room—"the Blue Room" with blue draperies, rug, and chair seats—on the right by the front door, Washington sat alone, waiting for them. His four aides, not yet settled in the house, would arrive in an hour; Mrs. Washington and her two grandchildren breakfasted in their family quarters.

While the three Virginians ate hoe cakes, honey, tea, and sliced tongue, they talked about Washington's new home. City officials had selected it as the best available house in town. Its owner, Washington's close friend, Robert Morris, had offered it rent-free; he would move into his other mansion, which was on a lot next door.

*High (Market) St.,
south side between 5th
and 6th Sts.) (House
demolished 1833)*

Washington was well acquainted with the house chosen to be the third executive mansion. He had visited the Morrises there, even living with them all the 1787 summer of the Constitutional Convention.

Before accepting the Morris residence as the President's house, he insisted on paying a fair market rent of $3,000 a year, but let it be known that the house was too small and would require a number of expansions and alterations.

*Private Affairs of
Washington (Lear/
Decatur p159*

Soon after Congress adjourned in New York in August, Senator Morris returned to Philadelphia. About a month later, he moved his family to his newly renovated house only a half-block from his old one. A 7-foot-high brick wall reached from the front corner of his new home to the front corner of the President's house, shielding from public view a fine formal garden between them.

In early October, workmen directed by Tobias Lear, Washington's trusted, efficient, endlessly patient young secretary, began slowly carrying out the President's detailed instructions.

*Amer. Phil.Soc. Vol.43
(1) 1953 p.161–78
(Eberlein) "190 High
Street"*

They were to replace two-thirds of the back wall of the house with a bow window to lengthen the main room on each of two floors; construct a one-story servants' quarters by extending the "back building"; renovate the back building to make a 52-foot long kitchen on the first floor and living quarters for the Washington family on the second.

"The small bathing room at the far end of our quarters has been converted into a study and dressing room for me," the President confided to his visitors. "But there is an outbuilding with marble

*Washington Mansion
in Philadelphia
(N.Burt)*

Eberlein p166n

and wooden bathtubs, a copper boiler for hot water and heat, and pipes to conduct them. It's the first of its kind in the city. A most useful apparatus!"

GW Writings, Letter to Lear, Nov.7

The building and rearranging had progressed so slowly, however, that only a few rooms were habitable when the family arrived, he added.

During the last week of November, the President, Mrs. Washington, and the two children journeyed in a hired coach from Mount Vernon 165 miles to Philadelphia.

GW Writings p159

For six days they suffered "the most infamous roads that ever were seen." When they, their maids, slaves, servants, baggage, and extra horses at last arrived, jostled and sore, at their new home, the carpenters, painters and masons were much in evidence. The President's household would have to crowd in and live a month or more among the busy workmen, and the mounds of furniture from 58 wagon-loads brought by sloop from New York.

Private Affairs of GW (Decatur/Lear) p161

Washington's explosion of words expressing his disgust made the chandeliers shiver. Adding disappointment to his fatigue from traveling bad roads worsened by "incessant and heavy rains" and a drunken coachman who twice overturned the baggage wagon, had worn holes in his patience. Now, 10 days and numerous complaints later, his temper had not cooled much.

GW letters, Nov. 19 (Knox), Nov. 23 (Lear)

As they left the Blue Room and walked through the long, adjacent state dining room to see the new bow window, Washington exclaimed, "You'll see litter and rubbish in the yard! That's what the dinner guests have to look at. The yard should be as clean as the parlour! But unhappily the People of Mortar and the Carpenters will make it unsightly for weeks more!"

GW letter to Lear

Jefferson, examining the pattern of the moulding around the new windows, and the red silk damask draperies, answered that, with every big house in Philadelphia undergoing repairs for government officials, there were not enough workmen to go

Decatur/Lear p161

around. His house wasn't ready either. Vice President Adams had moved into Bush Hill but not comfortably.

"I went to see them yesterday and had tea with Mrs. Adams—Abigail has been a favorite correspondent of mine since '84 when I arrived in Paris just as they were getting ready to leave. She's a woman I much admire—witty, vivacious, just a little noisy. A strong character, as you know. She told me the house had been vacant for years, and had fewer bushes and trees than expected, and no firewood. It was so cold she was forced to spend the first night in City Tavern, then nearly gave up the next day in the midst of building fires, getting the beds up in cold damp rooms that smelled strongly of paint—linseed oil and turpentine.

TJ (F.Brodie) p188

Private Affairs of Washington (Decatur/Lear) p161

"But at least they have moved in. I am still waiting." Jefferson shrugged, smiling. "I have only a weak, fretful promise of ONE room on the third floor by the end of the week—to serve as parlour, bedroom, study, and dining room. Still, it won't look crowded for a while. Few furnishings I'll have until I find the money to pay a staggering freight bill—$544.53! Furnishings I bought in France have just arrived."

TJ, Biog. Vol.1, p416 (N.Schachner)

"So much!" exclaimed Madison. "How many packing cases do you have?"

TJ Papers (Boyd) Vol.18

"Oh—86, the bill of lading says. Elegant French chairs and sofas—59 of the one, six of the other—tables, beds, mirrors—everything desirable for a comfortable house. One piece you, Mr. President, will find quite astonishing and amusing as well as highly practical: a suspended bed! It sits on the floor when in use, but within a system of hanging ropes and pulleys. The rest of the time, it's hoisted to the ceiling, out of the way!"

TJ (F.Brodie) p255

The President laughed appreciatively, diverted for a moment from the disarray in his own house. Madison's laugh was admiring, his upward gaze moving from his tall, playful friend Jefferson to his

Washington lived in cramped style in the Presidential Mansion in Philadelphia. In addition to his family of nine, including five aides, 14 servants needed housing. Essential for an executive obliged to entertain hundreds of people every week, the maids, butlers, steward and housekeeper, valets, body servants, cooks, pastry cook "Hercules," scullery help, washerwomen, coachmen, and stableboys crowded into the house and outbuildings. They lived in the attic, behind the stairs, in the new extension of the "back building," the bathhouse upper floor, above the stables, in the converted smokehouse, and in trundle beds of grandchildren. Stables and 4-carriage garage sheltered horses and coaches. Two of Morris's first-in-Philadelphia innovations added to the President's comfort—a bathhouse with hot water piped to marble or wood tubs, and a storage facility for ice blocks cut from nearby streams. Washington had lived in the house with the Morrises during the five months of the Constitutional Convention in 1787. Morris had just rebuilt the burned-out shell—wartime headquarters for British General Howe, then American General Benedict Arnold. In 1796, when newly-elected President Adams moved in, he and his wife Abigail declared that for them, the house was too big.

Details from "190, High Street" by H.D. Eberlein, American Philosophical Society, Vol. 43 (1), 1953. Also, Washington Mansion in Philadelphia, by N. Burt.

America's first two presidents lived in this house on Market Street near Sixth in Philadelphia during 10 years of construction of the Potomac capital.

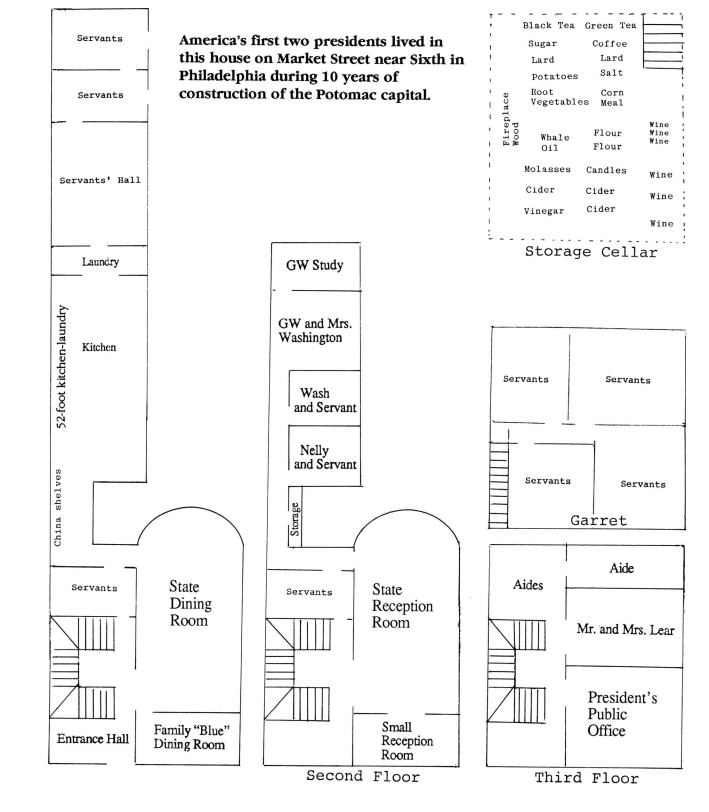

equally tall, stately friend Washington, both silhouetted in the bright light of the window.

Private Affairs of GW (Decatur/ Lear) p160 GW letter

"We could use a number of such beds," the President said, "for we barely have enough for everybody even with the new addition to this house, or even with the smokehouse, old bathhouse, and space over the stables all made into servants' quarters. We are nine in family and 20 servants. All must be comfortable if I am to have the smooth-running household necessary for frequent and sizeable public entertaining.

"One of the most serious inconveniences is the location of my office for the public. It's on the third floor—no space elsewhere. You'll have to walk up three flights of stairs."

Maclay Journ. Dec.7, levee

The Washington Mansion (N.Burt) (1875) house plan illustration

He led them out of the dining room ("no rug yet—a red one is being made—but reasonable order was attained in here day-before-yesterday") into the grand entrance hall with its grander staircase winding up three floors.

On the second floor, they glimpsed the great mirrors and chandelier of the Green Reception Room where they had attended the levee two days before, and the small adjacent drawing room where punch was served. "On this floor in the back building—that is, above the kitchen in the ell—are the family accommodations, and a small private study for me," the President remarked, raising his voice above the sound of hammering upstairs. They mounted the steps to the third floor. Crates, chairs, baskets, and baggage sat in heaps in the hallway.

Private Affairs of Washington (Decatur/ Lear) p160 GW letter

"The workmen have at least finished the public office," the President intoned. "They're now partitioning space beside it to house Mr. and Mrs. Lear, and two rooms for the other three Gentlemen of the family—my aides. The garret has four rooms for Mr. and Mrs. Hyde (the steward and housekeeper), and other servants. In the yard, there are good stables for only 12 horses, but the coach house will hold all my carriages. Two other out buildings

Eberlein

are an ice house and a hot house—the first in America, Mr Morris tells me—and two large reservoirs for a steady supply of pure water.

"But come now into the office and pull up a chair. We need to consider how best to present to Congress the request to include Alexandria in the seat of government's 10-mile square.

"Until my annual address to Congress was written—" the President glanced appreciatively at the men who had arranged on paper his stated thoughts. They smiled, and assured him that his speech yesterday had elicited favorable comments among Senators and Congressmen.

N.Burt

Wash.After the Rev. (W.S. Baker) p201

"Good. But the time left is short for drafting the seat of government proclamation and a request to Congress for the supplementary law. The First Congress should alter its own law before going out of office in less than 90 days. A new Congress will bring a number of new members, who not having endured the tedious argumentation of the past few years, might unwittingly move to re-open the subject of location of the capital."

"Heaven forbid!" exclaimed Madison.

"We might lose Potomac and find our capital rising on the Ohio!" laughed Jefferson.

"More likely, we might lose to Philadelphia," said Washington, not smiling at all. "I hear at every hand that Congress will be coddled in this city, and made so comfortable that the members will vote to stay, abandoning the Potomac's half-built city—which many keep referring to as 'Conna-ca-chig,' or 'that Indian place.'"

Washington did not join in the laughter. Quickly Jefferson spoke up. "All I have heard about Philadelphia from other officials are complaints—less comfortable houses, higher prices, reserved and gloomy Quakers, and a law that says a slave is free if settled here with his master for six months."

Washington's sharp glance caught Jefferson's own. "Are you sure about that?" Jefferson nodded.

Private Affairs of GW p223

After a moment of silence while the President, frowning, seemed to study a paper on his desk, he looked up and said briskly, "I would like for the two of you to draft a proclamation naming Thomas Johnson, David Stuart, and Daniel Carroll of Rock Creek as commissioners, and the Georgetown site as my choice for the seat of government. This proclamation will go to Congress, the newspapers, and the public—but only after Charles Carroll is ready to make his move in the Senate to amend. What have you heard about his arrival? I have not had news lately."

When Madison informed him that a Maryland delegate arriving the day before had told him Carroll was still sick and would not arrive until after New Year's Day, Washington's frown showed disappointment and concern. Madison hurriedly added that the two months left of the session would be enough, he thought, for Congress to approve a request of the President.

Washington looked unconvinced. Jefferson added that short time might short-shrift the bickering and tinkering.

"I think," the President proceeded without further comment, "that the public proclamation must cite both Virginia's and Maryland's gifts of money and grants of jurisdiction for a 10-mile square of land. That should go a long way toward taking the surprise out of my including Virginia land and the town of Alexandria.

"The public as well as Congress will want to see the exact bounds of this federal square. For the Maryland side, I have recently received from Mr. Deakins in Georgetown a plat showing the land parcels and their owners between Georgetown and the Eastern Branch. Deakins, I remind you, also secured for me similar plats for Monocacy and Conococheague lands.

"But if I should ask anybody in Alexandria to send me such a plat of the Virginia land involved,

it would be the same as advertising my decision in the newspaper. As a surveyor, and particularly as the one who in my youth surveyed the street grid for building the town of Alexandria, I could easily choose a starting point like the Courthouse, and describe the directions of four lines, the 'lines of experiment' defining the square."

"Mr. President!" exclaimed Jefferson. "You have just pointed to the surest means of drawing Virginia lands into the square without stirring a resistant word. YOUR descriptive details of the encompassing lines will hold like granite markers. For any one who tries to fault you, we need only to cite the law, which says 'ON the river Potomac'—NOT 'all in the state of Maryland.'"

Jefferson's soft voice rose. "There remains, however, the Eastern Branch limit as stated in the law. Mr. President, I regret to say that neither of us see a legal way to move the boundary that Congress placed on the west bank of that river. It will take another Act of Congress to relocate the boundary three miles east, and thereby include Alexandria directly opposite in Virginia."

Washington, stroking his chin, turned a keen gaze on Jefferson, then Madison. "Disappointing. But not surprising. How can the new act be presented so that the Potomac site is not endangered?"

Each expressed his ideas. A strategy emerged that softened the expression of the President, and brought smiles to his adviser's faces.

First, no uncertainty about the present law permitting Virginia land would even be hinted at. Second, the lines of experiment (with starting point Alexandria) would tell Congress exactly what the President desired. Third, the President would declare "fixed" all the land from Eastern Branch westward on both sides of the Potomac, and order an immediate survey. The three-mile extension east of Eastern Branch would not be "fixed" until Congress approved it. Should Congress not see fit to

GW letter to TJ, Jan.4, 1791

299

approve, then Eastern Branch would remain the boundary on the east, and the square's western boundary would move three miles farther west, thereby eliminating Alexandria.

"Some embarrassment is possible, but I believe Potomac is safeguarded," Washington said, "provided that no one makes a serious attempt to repeal the Potomac law."

Jefferson shook his head, "That would amount to a personal attack upon you, Mr. President. Since that would be foolhardy for any member, Potomac will be safe. Only Alexandria may not."

Washington was about to answer when his attention and gaze suddenly went to the door, which had silently opened. "Excuse me, Gentlemen," he said and rose from his chair. He walked to the door where his stepgranddaughter, Nelly Custis, waited. She beckoned to the President to lean down for her to whisper in his ear. He did, and whispered his answer in hers, bringing a giggle and a kiss before she ran away.

Smiling, Washington closed the door, turned to the Secretary and Congressman and said, "I shall leave to you gentlemen the exact language of the Proclamation and request to Congress. Could you bring me a draft by Christmas? Good. I will work out the lines of experiment.

"Who in the Senate might seize upon an amendment as a heaven-sent opportunity to attack the Potomac law? Who will vote against the eastern extension, rebuffing my request? Who will raise an objection to including Virginia land? The same ones who for years lobbied and made deals, tricked and tripped, orated and offered land, even money, for Philadelphia, Germantown, Susquehanna, Falls of the Delaware, and Baltimore. Proposals, deals, and close Senate votes now would stir a like fuss in the House. With quiet acceptance in the Senate, the House most likely would peacefully approbate the requested change."

"I think," Madison declared, "the successful votes for Assumption and Potomac have quieted Senator Butler's rambunctiousness. For the rest of the Senate, the surest way to a quiet change of the law is to say privately to the Senators, 'Do not embarrass President Washington: Defer to his request.' It's the one thing most of them can agree upon—to give you your expressed choice."

Washington pursed his lips and gazed briefly out the window. "That is a flattering sentiment, but one we must not fully rely upon. We dare not leave chance in charge. My good friend Robert Morris waged a vigorous campaign for seven years to bring the federal city to the Falls of Delaware.

"In September of '89, I was much dissatisfied with what he was doing in this business, and in fact troubled enough to speak to him—cautiously, of course—about his agency in it. It did not stop him. He came within a hair's breadth, the measure of Mr. Madison's amendment, of winning the seat for Germantown.

"I have also been informed that he wrote Gouverneur Morris that it has been constantly in his view to bring the capital to the banks of the Delaware, but that the obstinacy of only one or two, and the schemes of some OTHERS, had prevented him from getting it as high up as the Falls.

"He has recently said again and again that Philadelphia will hold on to the seat after its 10 years as temporary are up, implying an attempt to change the law. He may not be able to resist making the try NOW. He has the instincts of an aggressive, successful businessman and those instincts served us well during the Revolution. Without the hard money and the Army supplies he miraculously found for us, we could not have survived. You may not know this, but even Yorktown might have been lost, except for him.

"On the march south across Jersey, I wrote him in great anxiety that I needed hard money to come

TJ Papers, Vol.XI, p7, letter of R.Morris to his wife Sept.15, 1789

RM letter to G.Morris quoted in <u>Robert Morris, Audacious Patriot</u>, p122 (F.Wagner)

<u>Robert Morris, Patriot and Financier</u> (Oberholtzer) p.81

on wings of speed. The kegs of coin Morris sent arrived at the head of Chesapeake Bay just in time to pay the Northeastern soldiers—half the army— who had sat down, threatening to go home. The money—$20,000— was poured out in a heap on the ground so the men could see that it was truly silver coins they would get, not silver words. Pockets jingling, they went on to Yorktown."

Great Triumverate of Patriots (H.Barnard)

Washington paused, remembering. "If any individual were to be singled out for his role in the fight for independence, Robert Morris is perhaps most responsible for our success."

Fixing his gaze first on Jefferson, then on Madison, he said, "Nevertheless, neither of us has ever let our long friendship stand in the way of working assiduously for whatever each considers the best interest of the country, which at the same time may combine with private interests—interests that may compete, his against mine and vice versa."

Jefferson and Madison glanced at each other. Then Jefferson began with, "Another Pennsylvania Senator who will cause trouble with needling questions and an accusing finger is William Maclay, 'big as a bear and stiff with rheumatism,' as John Adams says. Those two can't abide each other. Maclay might choose to subject your request to his last big flare of heat and feathers before leaving the Senate. The word flying around says the Pennsylvania legislature will NOT reappoint him.

"Next most dangerous," added Madison, "are Senator Rufus King of New York and his loyal supporters from New England and New Jersey. They might find it entertaining to plot one more time with Senator Morris to topple Potomac, no matter the offense to you."

The President nodded agreement. "Mr. Madison, you are most effective at influencing the members of the House. I will ask Mr. Hamilton to speak to Senators King, Schuyler, and those from New England. Mr. Jefferson, it will take a diplomat and

magician to turn Senator Maclay in our direction, but please try at some appropriate moment."

"If ever there comes one," answered Jefferson. "But I may laugh when I oughtn't, forgetting I'm seeing and hearing the real man instead of our Jemmy here doing his imitation of Maclay!"

SCENE 2
FOUR LINES OF EXPERIMENT

PLACE: Jefferson's house and office (State Department), Philadelphia.
TIME: A month later, Tuesday, January 4, 1791

In the rented quarters of Secretary of State Thomas Jefferson, a three-story brick duplex on High (Market) Street near Fifth, Jefferson and Congressman Madison were sipping coffee in a just-completed, elegantly furnished study. They had arrived from a snowy walk from the President's house, only a block or so away. On the desk before them lay two well-marked papers, the results of their morning meeting with Washington. He had given them his lines of experiment, a tentative survey by description, defining the federal district, and his changes to their drafts of his proclamation.

A great log of oak flamed high in the fireplace, antidote to unusually bitter cold swirling within a curtain of snow that ticked against the window glass.

"So—you copy the proclamation with all the changes, and I'll rewrite the message to Congress," Jefferson said.

"You're taking the harder half," answered Madison, smoothing his paper and preparing to dip his quill. "Yours is a redrafting job; mine is simple copying. Small changes in the paragraphs describing the actions by Assemblies of Maryland and

Jefferson's door, right. State Dept. door, left

Jefferson and his Times (II) (D.Malone) p321

GW note to TJ, Tues., Jan.4, 1791

GW Proclamation, Jan.24, 1791

Thomas Jefferson

TJ (F.Brodie)

TJ and the New Nation
(Merrill Peterson)
p.420–1

Virginia to cede to Congress a 10-mile square for a capital.. Ditto for the paragraph summarizing the seat of government act of Congress.. Then the 'I hereby make known' paragraph, onto which I must add his 'four lines of experiment' directions delineating the 10-mile square that he would like.."

He paused, reading silently a page of surveyor's directions in Washington's handwriting.

"Then comes 'fixing' the Maryland area from the Eastern Branch to Georgetown and Little Falls— AND the Virginia area exactly opposite it across the Potomac. Then, his 'reserving the direction of contiguous parts' parenthetical phrase.' He insisted on that wording."

Jefferson grunted. He folded his arms over his chest, stretched his long legs under the table to cross his ankles, and tilted his head against the chair to gaze at the ceiling.

Madison looked up quickly. "Something wrong, Tom? Headache again?"

"Eh?" Jefferson straightened up, rubbing his brow.

"How is your headache, Tom?"

"Thumping. But not the worst it could be. Last year, as in many other years, it put me in bed off and on for six weeks. Waves of brutish pounding. This one is an insistent little thumper, always there, rising and falling, but never savage—thus far. Well, now, let's see what unprovocative, invulnerable language we can wrap the President's ideas in. I'll start midway the first sentence, where it says 'I have directed Commissioners to survey.'"

For a few minutes, only the scratchings of Madison's pen on paper, tickings of a golden mantel-clock, and snappings of the fire were heard. Jefferson, chin in hand, stared past his blue damask draperies to High Street's rows of snow and ice trimmed poplars twisting and jingling in the wind. His gaze came back to the man he called "the great little Madison." He was concentrating hard, dipping quill in ink, and scratching words on paper. "Many a

year he's written the words Washington wanted to say," Jefferson mused to himself.

A few minutes later, his long, loose legs took him into the wide center hallway, now lined with shelves filled with books. He looked for his favorite on botany, brought it back to the study, hoping to distract his painful brain. Madison still sat bent over his paper, his quill scratching rapidly. Suddenly with a last jab at the paper, he looked up and announced, "Done!"

Jefferson laid his open book on the desk, leaned back, and looked through half-closed eyelids at Madison. "My dear Jemmy," he said, "You have a style more sympathetic to the President's than I do. With the notes you took this morning while he was talking, you could more quickly and easily than I write the one-page message to Congress. If you will consent, I will retire to my couch and lay my head down."

Madison, his face drawn with concern, rose quickly to ring for a servant. "We'll have your French couch lowered in one minute," he said, and hurried to the library. In a recess, once a pantry between library and breakfast room (dining room until renovators completed the dining hall) hung the Moroccan leather couch at the ceiling. Madison was already working the pulley when black Jupiter appeared and took over.

"With a stiff wrist and a pounding brain, I'm not much good as a writer," Jefferson said, stretching out on the couch.

Madison smiled wryly. "I'll just scribble out what the President said. Also, there's a small, separate proclamation he decided on, to announce the names of the commissioners. I'll do that too. Send Jupiter for me in the study when you feel better."

An hour later, Jefferson quietly returned to the study, drew out his chair, and said, "Even with three quilts, my feet stayed cold. I must write home and ask the women to knit some heavier wool socks

TJ (N.Sachachner)
p416

TJ Papers, Vol.18
(Boyd), letter, TJ to
daughter Jan.1791.

GW message to
Congress, Jan.24, 1791

for me. I hate cold weather! Ahh—I see you're ready. Let's hear it."

Madison cleared his throat and began. "'I have, et cetera, directed Commissioners to survey and limit a PART of the territory of 10 miles square, on BOTH sides the river Potomack, so as to comprehend George Town in Maryland, and to extend to the Eastern Branch. I have not, by this first act, given to the said territory the whole extent of which it is susceptible IN THE DIRECTION OF THE RIVER' (that's Eastern Branch)—"

"Splendid word 'susceptible,'" interrupted Jefferson, "impeccable choice," he said approvingly.

"—because I thought it important," Madison continued with a little smile, "that Congress should have an opportunity of considering whether, by an amendatory law, they would authorize the location of the residue at the lower end so as to comprehend Eastern Branch itself and some of the country on its lower side in Maryland, and the town of Alexandria in Virginia. If, however, they are of opinion that the Federal Territory should be bounded by the WATER EDGE of the EASTERN BRANCH, the location of the residue will be made at the upper end'—that's the Georgetown end— 'with some Virginia land opposite.'

GW Message Jan.24,
1791 except word
emphasis and
parenthetical words.

"Paragraph. 'I have thought best to await a survey of the territory, before it is decided on what particular spot on the northeastern side (meaning Maryland, of course) of the river the public buildings shall be erected. George Washington.'"

Madison looked up to find Jefferson smiling broadly.

"Sounds just like him!" Jefferson declared. "Forthright—giving Congress a chance to say 'no' to the national hero—repeating his convictions with succinct phrases—'on BOTH sides of the river,' without admitting any question about including land in Virginia—then bowing courteously to Congress while saying firmly what he wants—in terms that

require looking at a map to be comprehensible. I predict the President will NOT change a single one of your phrases!"

"I am flattered, Mr. Secretary. The short proclamation announcing the names of Thomas Johnson, David Stuart, and Daniel Carroll of Rock Creek is routine, but——"

"No need to read it to me." Jefferson waved it aside. "The main interest is that the President decided to name the commissioners in a separate proclamation—possibly for use at a separate time. Further, perhaps in his haste this morning, the President did not speak of having sounded out Congressman Carroll of Rock Creek about his appointment. 'Old Dan'l' as some of the Maryland men say, arrived here weeks ago, didn't he?"

Madison nodded. "He was at the President's New Year's reception. I think...well, we know from our two visits with him in Georgetown on our way to and from home, that he was sure the federal square would envelop his plantation, 'Forest Glen', north of Georgetown. He was very pleased at the prospect—remember?"

Letter TJ to D.Carroll,
Sept. 1791

Jefferson agreed with a slight nod.

"My guess is that the President's caution keeps him from asking the Congressman—who will leave Congress March 4—to serve as a commissioner. If he had sounded out Old Dan'l, it would have revealed that his land will not be in the District. It's been repeated around, and Carroll would have heard, that the President says it would never do to appoint a resident landowner as Commissioner of the federal district. The President has told us (Madison could not suppress a short laugh), 'Even if the landowner were the Angel Gabriel, he would be charged with partiality to himself, whatever his decisions.'"

Life of D.Carroll
(E.H.Smith)

GW letter to Deakins
1796

"Hmmm," murmured Jefferson, "A delicate situation. The President has to wait for Carrollton Carroll to arrive to start the Senate action. With that

James Madison

History of Congress
(Gales/Seaton)
Jan.22–24, 1791

Carroll on hand, the President will quickly make public the appointment of the other Carroll. Daniel smiles acceptance. A day later comes the proclamation—Alexandria in, Daniel's land out. Commissioner Daniel frowns dismay. But what can he do? To refuse and huff off will make him the poor loser, insulting to the President, selfish, not serving. So the President plans to appoint, then dis-appoint."

Madison, a master political strategist himself, beamed, fully appreciating the President's insight into the likely reactions of his almost life-long friend.

"But," he added, waving a forefinger at Jefferson, "His cousin Charles Carroll's introducing of the supplementary bill in the Senate provides only half the support the President must have to succeed there."

"You mean Robert Morris must provide the other half, of course. Yes—Washington implied to us that he will speak to the 'financier of the Revolution' who is now America's biggest public-debt and western land speculator. Now there's a conversation I would give my best gold-leafed sofa to hear.

"But let's ease my headache now—" Jefferson reached for the botany book on his desk—"let's plan a vacation in the country beginning the day Congress adjourns. Botanizing we must go! There are in this land flowers we can discover and name, wild shrubs we can examine, berries we can pick. Politics I can live without—but not natural science, my lifelong passion. We must fish in crystal cold lakes from birchbark canoes, sit by campfires discussing the habits of the Hessian fly—"

TJ and the New Nation
(M.Peterson) p115

"Oh, yes!" exclaimed Madison. "I know just the place—the Hudson River, Lake George, Lake Champlain—where I went in '83 with Lafayette on an Indian treaty mission. Its beauties and interesting botanical objects have great restorative powers for mind and body!"

"To the mountains and lakes we must go!" said Jefferson rubbing his temples. "I'm certain they will

banish my headache—and improve you,too, my dear unhealthy-looking friend. When we return, my remarkable French chef, Petit, will just be arriving from Paris, bringing a strange and delightful dried noodle called 'macaroni'—and other exotic edibles—and wines! What a difference it makes to have each day Petit's fine cookery to look forward to! That prospect, and our botanizing trip in the spring, will buoy me just now when, to hold our 10-mile square in place, I must gird with 'there now, there now' words to soothe Maclay and lead him to the path of righteousness."

TJ and New Nation
(M.Peterson) p421

Although just completed for a county courthouse, the building to the right of Pennsylvania's State House on Chestnut Street, Philadelphia, underwent an extensive renovation to please Congress. For the House of Representatives on the first floor of Congress Hall, a visitors' gallery, a Speaker's dais, and a room-size platform tiered for two rows of desks, were built. In the Senate chamber at the far end of the second floor, handsome new furnishings and a canopied seat for the Vice President were installed. Philadelphians planned to make Congress delegates so comfortable they would never consent to move to a Potomac "wilderness capital."

President Washington enjoys one of his favorite diversions, a witty comedy at the theater. Between acts of <u>The School for Scandal</u> seen on January 5, 1791, he had a chance to talk capital business with a guest sharing his box. Philadelphia theaters, closed during the war, had just reopened with the same company and plays Washington saw in New York.

CHAPTER 28

Capital Courting

SCENE 1
A MORRIS PLAY

PLACE: Southwark Theatre, Philadelphia, South and Apollo (Charles) Streets.
Playbill: "The School for Scandal" by Richard Sheridan of London.
TIME: January 5, 1791 at 6 o'clock.

George and Martha Washington, Tobias and Polly Lear, and the three aides arrived at the bright-red, half-brick, half-wood theater exactly a quarter before the hour. Theatrical company manager Mr. Wignell (also the town's favorite stage comedian), dressed all in black, his wig freshly curled and powdered, greeted them with flowery words. He and a little parade of actors bearing lighted candles in silver candelabra escorted the President and Martha to his private box, and his staff to one nearby.

On the main floor and in the gallery, the audience broke into applause. "Washington! Washington!" shouted several voices. Even after the President had sat down, many in the audience continued to stand, staring and smiling at the President's box until military guards quietly bade them sit.

Before Mr. Wignell departed, bowing and bowing, the President said to him, "Whenever Senator and Mrs. Morris arrive, I beg you escort them here, Mrs. Morris to sit on Mrs. Washington's left, the Senator to sit beside me."

At 10 minutes after the hour, the Morrises, she tall and full-bodied, he tall and fatter than ever, both whispering apologies, took their places. The players immediately appeared, and the scandalmongers on stage, Lady Sneerwell and her flunky, Snake, began their mischief.

"Ah, General! It's such a relief to laugh at fools

and foibles other than those in Congress," Morris remarked at the end of the first act. His round, pink face shone even in the dim light of the theater. "My one complaint," he added, tossing his long, loose hair back and crossing his arms over his buttoned overcoat, "is the cold. If they had another Franklin stove or two in here, the play's witty lines would draw far more laughter."

Washington smiled and observed that he had seen the play three or four times in various seasons and its wit and humor each time had provided him complete and pleasurable diversion. "Some of the lines I can repeat by heart, and sometimes do when they well fit an offstage occasion."

Quick to sense a message of importance aimed in his direction, Morris replied, "You have an offstage occasion well fitted to a line on-stage tonight, Mr. President?"

"In the next scene," came the reply, "Lady Teazle excuses herself for the disturbances her words and actions create. She says, 'I vow I have no malice against the People I abuse when I say an ill-natured thing—'tis out of pure Good Humour.'"

A commotion at the back of the box interrupted Morris's move to pose another question. The Vice President and Mrs. Adams were entering to thank the President for his invitation to attend the theater as his guests. Behind them pressed Senator and

The Theatre in America, Vol.1, p120, 183 (A. Hornblow)

Washington After the Revolution (W.Baker) citing newspaper notes that GW attended *The School for Scandal* on this date.

The School for Scandal (R.Sheridan)

(That the President spoke to Morris about the amendment is almost certain. Had such an event taken place at the theater, it would have given Washington special circumstances and control).

The School for Scandal (R.Sheridan) Act 2, scene 1

Mrs. Rufus King of New York, and Senator and Mrs. Oliver Ellsworth of Massachusetts. They hurried back to their adjacent box as the second act was opening. Senator Morris, still thinking about the President's remark and what message there could be in it for him, suddenly heard Lady Teazle on the stage saying the line the President had quoted. He glanced around at Washington, who was glancing around at him. Both men smiled.

At intermission, Morris had no chance to say a word to the President. The President stood with the ladies, and the audience turned from applauding the play to applauding the President. Senators and Department Secretaries crowded in, departing only after the actors on stage began to speak.

The witty talk on stage greatly amused the President who laughed frequently. He laughed loudest when the good Sir Oliver was taught how to act the part of a crafty moneylender. During the applause at the end of the act, the President remarked that despite its being a comedy, the play had some serious points to make.

"My dear friend," Morris replied, "I gather you have some serious point to make with me, and I would prefer a straightforward quote from you."

Quickly the President responded. "I hear that you continue to assure all men in and out of Congress that the seat will never leave Philadelphia. That you say this out of good humor, for amusement, seems less probable than out of the belief that you will be able to upset during the next 10 years the majority vote of this Congress. You may decide you see your best opportunity during the next 30 days when I present to Congress a request to adjust a detail in the present law. Charles Carroll will introduce it in the Senate. It will be just that—an adjustment, not an opening of the act for further amendments concerning location. I trust that you will respect it as such."

"Ah, Mr. President—a small adjustment!" sighed

Morris glancing around at the door of the box and noting gratefully that the doorman, his eye upon the President, had made no move to admit visitors.

"For two acts of this play," Morris said, "I have agitated a list in my mind, looking for some ill-natured item that could be disturbing you. I am much relieved! The seat item has not enough fire left in it to warrant blowing the coals—in Congress. More dangerous for the Potomac winners are Philadelphia's fine food, comfortable hotels and rooming houses, elegant social events, music, theater, Peale's museum—all the culture, entertainments, and conveniences in this handsome city! Their allure will do the job that none of the machinations in Congress could do—that I promise you. We are so certain, we are about to appropriate money to build you a proper mansion, big and elegant, not far from the new building we have given Congress for its meetings. We love you, Mr. President! We aim to keep you!"

Washington rose, and with a small bow to Morris, turned to attend the visitors now beginning to enter the box.

The next act on-stage opened with the famous scene of the auctioning of the wastrel's family portraits—"raising money on your own flesh and blood." Washington, jarred at hearing with his own ears his friend's well circulated threat, missed some of his favorite lines though hearing all of Morris's free and easy laughing.

Soon came the even more famous and hilarious scene when the hero joyously hauled out a surprising number of his embarrassed friends caught hiding in the villain's closets. The scene triggered an upsurge of relief in the President, and he began laughing as freely as Morris and the audience. He had hauled out his fears and heard the Senate lion promise he would not attack! Potomac was safe—for now! Morris's 10-year siege upon the weaknesses of men for comfort and amusement was a worry for the future—this season, the lion would not do battle!

The President's obvious enjoyment drew all eyes to his box and a delighted hand of applause.

SCENE 2
A PLAY FOR MACLAY

PLACE: Senator Maclay's rooming house, Ogden's Tavern on South Second St.
TIME: January 20 about 6 p.m.

Senator Maclay, having just come home from the President's house where he had been invited for dinner, felt like telling someone about the remarkable incidents of that occasion. He walked next door and knocked loudly until Congressman Wynkoop called, "Come in!"

"Oh, there is no question about it, Mr. Wynkoop," he said as they sipped Madeira. "The President paid marked attention to me today! I was invited to dine and I did my duty and went. Sundry gentlemen met me at the door, and though I rather declined, they pushed me forward. The President rose from a sofa to receive me. I made my bows and inclined toward a vacant seat, but the President edged about on the sofa as he sat down, and said, 'Here is room.'"

(That IS remarkable, murmured Wynkoop.)

"But I went on and sat on the opposite sofa with some New England men."

(Oh. You shouldn't've, Will.)

"I am not a courtier! At dinner, more attention. First, the President spoke to me—I was just across the table—offering to help me to part of a dish which stood before him. I had just declined more food from Mr. Lear at the end of the table, even indicating I had my fill. So, for the sake of consistency, I had to thank the President negatively. Was

All the scene and quotes taken from Maclay's Journal Jan.20, 1791

ever anything so unlucky!"

(Consistency! Will, you'll break your back on that word one day.)

"Then the dessert came. He was distributing a pudding. He gave me a look of interrogation. I returned thanks positive.

(Thank God.)

"The best came last. He soon after asked me to drink a glass of wine with him! I readily agreed. Most remarkable! I did not see him drink with any other person during dinner!"

(Perhaps you weren't watching?)

"Marked attention he gave me. So unexpected."

(Can you think of any particular reason?)

"He knows the weight of political odium under which I suffer. He knows I will be no Senator after the third of March. To the score of his good nature must I place these attentions."

(Just good nature? Hm.)

SCENE 3
THE CARROLL CLINCHER

PLACE: Indian Queen Hotel where Senator Charles Carroll of Carrollton had arrived from Baltimore the night before.
TIME: Friday, January 21, at 5:45 a.m.

The President delayed breakfast to take a brisk walk with two of his aides. First light of day barely made the street visible. Frost lay white on browned grass and shrubs.

The three men, cloaks drawn about them, hands gloved, hats firmly settled above long, braided queues, turned off High (Market) Street into Fourth Street. Just ahead was the Indian Queen Tavern, where Charles Carroll of Carrollton had spent the night following his arrival in Philadelphia. Wash-

Probable, but unrecorded meeting.

ington knew Carroll was a predawn riser like himself, and would most likely be sitting in his elegant hotel room reading the newspapers or one of his French or Latin books, any of which, as a result of his daily reading sessions for 40 years, he could recite by heart.

The news of Carroll's arrival had come the evening before, shortly after the President's last dinner guest had departed. At breakfast every day for a week, the President had inquired of his aides, "Is Carroll here?" Three WEEKS of January gone! Little more than a month before the First Congress would adjourn, and not a move made for slightly adjusting the seat-of-government law. True, Hamilton's bank bill had consumed the Senate's attention, but that ended yesterday with the vote approving it.

Equally delaying was the absence of both principal Potomac supporters—Richard Henry Lee of Virginia and Charles Carroll of Maryland.

Nothing could be done except wait. The only news was a brief letter to the President from Carroll that he hoped to start from Annapolis on the fifteenth, doctor and weather permitting. Last evening, news came—he had finally arrived.

"I would have hurried over last evening when Mr. Madison first brought the news that you were at the Indian Queen," the President declared to the sickly little man sitting by the fire in his hotel suite. A large dog with auburn-colored hair lay at his feet. "But to call, even for urgent business, before the weary traveler has slept at the end of a week of journeying produces little except more fatigue," the President added. "I trust you have fully recovered from your bout of chills and fevers? (How extremely thin and frail he looks. But his father looked the same, lived 80 years, and died from a fall off the front porch.)"

Carroll's bright blue eyes lighted up and a sweet smile softened his usually quite compressed lips. "I am flattered Mr. President, that you would be the

President Washington discusses the 10-mile square with his life-long friend, Maryland Senator Charles Carroll of Carrollton, considered the richest plantation owner in America.

first to pay me a visit in this temporary seat of government. The infirmities of old age are coming fast upon me but I am hopeful that I may see the day 10 years from now when the Congress moves to and meets upon the banks of the Potomac."

"Being five years younger than I," said Washington, "you have a much better prospect than I for seeing Congress sitting in a Potomac capital in December 1800—provided our efforts during the next five weeks succeed. We must move quickly; for that reason I have come to tell you how I expect to proceed.

"Tomorrow, Saturday, the newspapers will be given a public proclamation, but it will only name the three commissioners—Thomas Johnson, Daniel Carroll, and Dr. Stuart—as I told you when we met some weeks past.

"On Monday the twenty-fourth, I will submit to Congress copies of the public proclamation naming Georgetown, and describing my lines of experiment defining the 10-mile square. In my message to Congress at the same time, I will advise them that, in regard to those lines, I have not FIXED the one that takes in unauthorized land east of the Branch, and includes Alexandria, but await Congress's approval for that.

"I am greatly relieved, Carroll, that you are here and in good health. Your unequivocal show of approbation by introducing the request to the Senate, and seeing it through, greatly reduces the risk of attack upon the original law."

Carroll leaned to stroke the dog, which had stood up, stretched, and laid its chin on Carroll's knee. "From which Senators do you expect opposition?" Carroll inquired.

Washington named the New England men and King of New York. "Hamilton gives us hope for Schuyler."

"Morris is no threat?" queried Carroll.

"I have spoken to him," the President said, "and

History of Congress, Senate Journ.(Gales/ Seaton) Jan.22, Jan.24

he declared he had no interest in blocking the 'adjustment'. He has more confidence, he says, in the effect that 10 years of Philadelphia's 'charm' will have on Congress."

"Then there is hardly any risk left!" Carroll exclaimed. "With no Robert Morris and a tame Senator Butler, the Northern men have no one to lure into a deal. The worst that can happen is rejection of our bill to include Alexandria. You'll still have the site west of the Anacostia!"

"If the request is rejected," Washington replied calmly, his steady gaze meeting Carroll's, "we could consider re-introducing it in the newly elected Congress next month."

Carroll burst out laughing. "Mr. President, I will introduce it as many times as you wish—until Virginia gets its share of the glory, the half-million a year in trade, the advantage of knowing today's news today instead of some days or weeks hence, and a short ride to the capitol!"

Washington's smile and expression thanked his old friend. "I had hoped you would be able to make this first introduction on Tuesday. However, we still lack one of Virginia's senators, Richard Henry Lee. He, too, has been ill. Each day he has been expected, but we are still waiting."

"Let us say, then," Carroll responded, "that the day after he arrives I will bring forth the amendment in the Senate. I will prepare it, and bring it for your approval. With little or no opposition, it begins to look possible that in 10 days the Senate could be sending it to the House for final action."

The President rose to leave. "Speed is of the essence in order to beat the March third adjournment. If we miss that deadline, the next Congress might cause us more trouble than this one."

Carroll walked with the President to the door while saying the new Senate might cause LESS trouble—"My old friend William Maclay's sharp and sour wit will be gone, for one thing. The new

Senators should be as willing as most of the old ones to approve moving a survey line three miles east if that's all it will take to spread capital glory and good fortune to the hometown of our hero and President. They would have asked the same favor for their hometown—certainly I would have. As it is, Excellency, I will support Alexandria as if it were my own hometown."

SCENE 4
PROCLAMATION

PLACE: Senate Chamber, second floor of Congress Hall at Sixth and Chestnut, northwest corner of Independence Square, Philadelphia.
TIME: Following Monday morning, January 24.

History of Congress, Senate Journal, Jan.24, 1791 (Gales/Seaton)

The voice of the clerk droned on and on, reading voluminous communications sent by President Washington. For a half hour, he read a long letter from somebody in Kentucky describing a coming fight with squatters in Yazoo country. For another half hour, it was the Secretary of War's alarm over the horrible Indian raids against settlers in the Ohio country. Send troops to help us, was the message from both. The President was going to rely, he wrote, on the wisdom of Congress to make arrangements to keep good order, and to protect the frontiers from thieves and Indians.

The Senators on the floor busied themselves throughout the readings with tête-a-têtes, note writing and passing, disappearances and re-entries. Mr. Adams in his chair behind the rostrum brushed the lace at his wrists, smoothed his velvet kneepants, swept his waistcoat, patted his wig, and smiled toward space.

Maclay's Journal, p29

The scene began to change as two clerks moved to hand each Senator a paper headed in large type "Proclamation." At the same moment, a clerk read, "Message from the President to the Gentlemen of the Senate and House of Representatives: In execution of the powers with which Congress were pleased to invest me, by their act 'An act for establishing the temporary and permanent seat of Government...'"

The murmur of senatorial voices faded. All Senators faced the clerk and Speaker, eyes watching the clerk's mouth, the better to catch every word. Several glanced at each other questioningly when they heard "on BOTH sides of the river Potomac." Others murmured at the name of Georgetown. The murmur was considerably louder a minute later at the words "amendatory law" and the name of Alexandria "in Virginia."

President's Letter to Congress Jan.24, 1791 Hist. Cong., Senate Journ.(Gales/Seaton)

Hardly anyone heard the last sentence—that the President would decide later exactly where the public buildings would be located on the Maryland side. Adams rapped his silver pencil case on his desk, ordered the President's message to lie on the table and asked for the next order of business.

When it was apparent that no business would pull the attention of the Senators from their reading closely—even noisily—the Proclamation in their hands, Adams called for a move to adjourn.

The rest of the day, on the Floor and off buzzed with talk and map study concerning the details of the President's lines defining the 10-mile square. Maclay, sitting alone, studied the Proclamation silently, pondering the picture it was drawing, and grumbling to himself that the President had "taken on to himself to fix the spot by his own authority when Congress intended that the Commissioners should fix it."

Maclay's Journ. Mon., Jan. 24

His mouth twisted by dissatisfaction, he painfully raised his sore and aching body from his chair. His face tightened with words crowding behind it, pressing to be expelled. He looked about for Senator Morris, who often came late and took an empty seat near the door. But not today.

The small figure of Senator Carroll sitting nearby attracted him. Standing over him, he spluttered, "I really am surprised at the conduct of the President! Saturday, when the Senate had no session, he sent to the newspapers a Proclamation only naming the Commissioners for the Federal District. Today, a message was read to us while a clerk was putting into our hands another Proclamation with a profusion of lines of experiment to announce for Georgetown—AND Alexandria through an amendatory act! He is opening up the whole matter of locating the seat! An amendatory act! That is the most imprudent of all acts! Another chance for New England and Yorkers to kill Philadelphia!"

Adapted from
Maclay's Journal,
Jan.24, 1791

Carroll looked up at Maclay, whom he quite liked, and smiled. "I will present the bill myself. Since it is only reasonable that Virginia be included in the Federal District—especially since, for the safety of the city, both sides of the river are needed, and especially since Virginia is giving a lot of money—I trust that you, being a reasonable man, will support the President's decision."

Maclay glared at Carroll, turned aside and walked away. He hurried downstairs, entered the House Chamber and looked about for a Pennsylvania delegate, preferably one from Philadelphia.

The House had also just listened to a reading of the President's message, and received Proclamation copies, but had gone on to debate a new tax on whiskey. Maclay spotted Daniel Heister of Philadelphia standing alone, blowing his nose near the end of the room where two doors opened into a handsome garden.

Maclay hurried to him; the two whispered for a moment, then proceeded outside.

Sunny skies had taken the edge from the cold. The formal garden still had the charm of design Samuel Vaughan had given it, but Maclay neither felt nor saw the scene. His feelings and thoughts were exploding in the direction of the President, Virginia, Philadelphia, Morris, Congress, Commissioners, amendatory acts, Carroll. "The President is unsettling the whole affair! What an unexpected manner of treating this subject! He took it on himself to fix the spot by his own authority! He ought to have placed the three commissioners in that post of responsibility! Thoughtless act!"

Maclay Journal
Jan.24, 1791

"But I seem to recall that the law says the Commissioners act only under the President's direction," Heister tried to say. In the same instant, Maclay declared, "I may raise a query whether the words of the law warrant his different construction!"

"He must have consulted lawyers about that. Probably Hamilton, Jefferson, maybe others," Heister ventured. "You could look foolish challenging Washington on the point."

"I really think it not improbable that OPPOSITION—you know who I mean—"Maclay arched his brows and spoke through clenched teeth—"may find a nest to lay her eggs in! Most likely he—Morris—will move fast, call a meeting of our delegation, and alliances and trade-abouts will begin working to scuttle Carroll's bill—"

"Carroll?"

"He told me just now he will bring it to the Senate floor. We can move to postpone, just as he always did to our seat of government bills," Maclay growled.

"Ahchoo! Ahchoo!" Heister sneezed. "Let's get back inside," he said. "My cold is worsening out here. Tell me, why couldn't we AMEND Carroll's bill? Merely killing it only keeps the President's hometown out of the Federal District! Why not turn it into a new permanent seat of government bill naming Germantown?"

Inside the House Chamber, they shook hands and parted. "Yes," Maclay repeated, "the President has unsettled the whole affair. Most imprudent! Most imprudent!"

From the second-floor bay windows of the Senate Chamber (above, as restored), Senators could look down on the park behind Congress Hall, Philadelphia. Vice President Adams presided under a canopy hung with green silk and a red damask swag like those at the windows. Above him hovered a ceiling mural of a ferocious eagle. On the floor, a dark green rug's bold medallion displayed signs of the Zodiac. Here in late February 1791, Senator Morris delayed Washington's "Alexandria" addition to the federal district law, then helped it to a two-vote victory a few days before adjournment.

CHAPTER 29

Tottering Capital Columns

SCENE 1
BAD NEWS

PLACE: Peale's Museum of Natural History, Third and Lombard streets, Philadelphia.
TIME: Saturday, January 29, 1791, about noon.

TJ and the New Nation
(M.Peterson) p420

Mr.Peale's Museum
(C.C.Sellers) p21

Stepping carefully on the brick pavement of the poplar-lined street, Thomas Jefferson in fine Parisian blue silks, ruffled shirt, and crimson-lined cloak, his powdered, perfumed queue of hair tied with a ribbon, approached the front entrance of a house at the corner of Third and Lombard Streets.

There, James Madison in his tall, round hat, heavy coat and boots, waited in the doorway. Portrait painter Charles Willson Peale and his numerous household were living in part of the two-and-a-half storey brick; the other part had become the now famous "Peale's Museum of Natural History."

Madison, seeing his friend Mr. Jefferson approaching, waved a hand.

On this fine, crisp, cloudless day, they were going to a 2 o'clock reception at the mansion of "dazzling Anne Bingham" and her rich merchant husband William, but until the hour came closer, they would do what everybody in Philadelphia did sooner or later—see the new curiosities Peale had added to his collection of "Wonderful Works of Nature."

"Your face is not reflecting your usual good-humored self this noontime," Madison greeted Jefferson. "That, I fear, portends some rather unpleasant news?"

Jefferson grimaced, with a little shrug. "This seat of government business will harry us all to death.

It might have been a blessing if Robert Morris had run off with the capital to the Falls of the Delaware or Germantown and left us to feel simple disappointment or anger. I took a route by the President's house at his urgent request, and found him agitated with bad news from three directions."

Madison moaned, "Oh, no."

Two couples with children arrived, recognized Jefferson, started a round of "Good day, sirs," and held the door open for the Secretary and Congressman to enter the entrance hall. After another round of bows and "Good day, sirs," the families proceeded past a staircase along a narrow corridor toward the exhibit rooms in the back of the house. Jefferson in a lowered voice proceeded to recite to Madison the list of crumbling columns in the Federal District structure.

The worst news concerned Daniel Carroll. He had written Washington a stiff and formal note to say he could not accept the appointment as commissioner for the Federal District. His reason was, he said, that he understood that he could not act as an official for the Federal district while he was a Congressman.

"But he will not be a Congressman a month and two days from now—probably the same day the Alexandria bill passes!" said Madison.

"I know," said Jefferson, "BUT—he returned the

*TJ to Stuart and
Johnson Jan.29, 1791*

Congressman
Daniel Carroll
of Rock Creek

*Jefferson's portrait was
hung in Peale's
Museum in 1792*

appointment certificates that we expected him to take to Georgetown to Stuart and Johnson when he went home. That means he has no intention to serve AFTER Congress adjourns and he is a private citizen again. All of which means he is peeved. 'Appoint then disappoint' didn't work with him. Now I must write to Johnson and Stuart that the two of them will have to carry on any business that needs doing until a third commissioner can be found and appointed. I expect that will be more than a little time from now."

Madison shifted a bit to turn his back on the entrance where several new visitors had stopped to stare and whisper. "I think you are recognized, Mr. Secretary. Perhaps we should proceed to the exhibit rooms where, among stuffed birds and animals, we will not appear to be conspirators."

Jefferson looked toward the visitors, smiled, bowed, and replied casually to Madison that he understood Mr. Peale was as good a taxidermist as he was a portrait painter—"which is so good that I shall have him paint my portrait, even display it, if he likes, among the others in his museum, but never ever would I say the same for a stuffing."

Slowly they followed the other visitors past the stairs, speaking of the "January thaw" milder weather, letting distance and low voices curtain their words. Jefferson picked up where he had left off.

"But Daniel is not the only Carroll causing nervousness. His cousin, the Senator, has studied the proclamation, the message to Congress, and the bill we helped him draft. He would like a survey map, he says, to show Senators whose geographical knowledge is limited to their own backyard what the Carroll bill will ask for. The President thinks he should order a quick, preliminary ground survey to confirm the lines of experiment he worked out. If we can have one quickly, it will not only satisfy the Senator, but also add substance to the Proclamation and the bill.

"I'm required to write a letter today to our surveyor and Geographer, Andrew Ellicott, who has just fixed the northwestern border between Pennsylvania and New York. The President wants him to hasten to Georgetown, quickly run the lines, and send him a rough map in, say, two weeks. I doubt a man can walk the 40 miles around the square, clearing away brush and trees, shooting a straight line, and measuring it in less than three weeks."

GW to TJ Feb.1, 1791

TJ to Ellicott Feb.2, 1791

Madison clasped his hand to his forehead. "And Congress adjourns in four weeks! But worse than having no survey in two weeks is having no Virginia Senator Lee for another two weeks! We have to hold off the vote until he arrives—MID-February he has just sent word.

"Now, now! What if Carroll's bill is doomed this session? We have the original law—we still have Georgetown," Jefferson whispered.

"The President is going ahead, trying to buy land there. He is disturbed that the landowners have started a little tug of war to pull the Capitol and Mansion sites to their own property. He has asked Deakins and Stoddert in Georgetown to SECRETLY buy for him 350 acres on one side of the creek, 250 on the other, at a low price, all next to Georgetown as if they were speculating for themselves, and without setting off a speculating frenzy! (Jefferson rolled his eyes toward heaven and groaned.)

GW to Deakins and Stoddert, Feb.3 and Feb.17, 1791

"But naturally, the instant the owners knew his decision was for Georgetown, land prices ballooned—in the owners' heads. As soon as it's known which portion of the land the public buildings will sit upon, the adjacent land for a town will double or triple in price! He wants the landowners to think he hasn't decided yet—Funkstown or Eastern Branch or Carrollsburg? He has told Deakins and Stoddert that their success in buying Funkstown and Burnes's farm will help him decide! My, my! I wonder if this will work any better than 'appoint then disappoint.'"

"Ah—Funkstown and the Burnes farm! The exact section you chose for your sketch of a city plan," Madison said. "But Burnes told us himself he wouldn't sell at any price. He's an obstinate man, and he's no fool. I expect he long ago decided that the Capitol and President's House will be built close to, if not on, his land. He'll probably hold out for 25 pounds an acre!"

"At least!" laughed Jefferson.

Despite their slow progress, they had reached the end of the corridor and were stepping into the art gallery. Almost instantly their hands were being wrung by "soft, tender, affectionate" (as John Adams said) Mr. Peale himself. "My dear friends! Mr. Jefferson! Mr. Madison!" he said in his quick, energetic, yet musical voice. "I have been looking for your visit since sending notice of my latest acquisitions! A feathered cape and cap from 'O'whyee' to add to John Galt's donation of Indian clothing from the Pacific Coast of our continent! Please—you don't need to show your annual tickets—certainly not Thomas Jefferson, the successor of Dr. Franklin in science as well as politics—certainly not James Madison whose interest and book knowledge have long supported me! Come now through the portrait gallery, and the room of glass show cases—I have some new birds and background scenes in them—no, the moving pictures are not here any more, they've been put away. But look! In the next room we are creating a seaside grotto with an opening at the top—my skylight! We're displaying marine life, reptiles, and amphibians—all preserved, of course—in their natural environs! Beautiful, eh? And scientific!"

With a stride as rapid as his flow of words, Peale had led them to the main gallery, and quickly to a corner where the "new acquisitions" had been hung. He had begun the exciting story of how the "O'whyee" cape and hat were acquired, when his young son Raphaelle ran in, eyes flashing with

25 pounds equalled $67. Hist.Natl. Capital, p124 (W.Bryan) $67 was later set for all land bought for public use. (p134)

"Peale's Museum" (C.C.Sellers) Historic Philadelphia, Am.Phil.Soc.

Mr.Peale's Museum (C.C.Sellers)

"Philadelphia 1787" (H.Holzer) Am.History Illustrated, May 1987

Peale's Museum offers a natural meeting place for Madison (right) and Jefferson, both much interested in science. Bumping into Hamilton (far right) spoils their visit. They will not tarry to talk politics with him, resented as the President's most influential adviser.

excitement. "Father! Come quick! Somebody stuck the five-legged cow with a knife to see if she'd bleed, and she's bleeding, and bellowing, and—"

"WHO DID THAT?!" Peale stormed, rushed toward the door, turned back to apologize for leaving, and rushed away again.

Jefferson threw back his head and laughed. "The five-legged cow! Why does that remind me of the Federal District business and its appalling disjointedness?! Let me go on with my recitation of its present lamentations."

Madison, who was facing the door, bumped his elbow against Jefferson's arm. "We have company," he murmured.

Alexander Hamilton with his young daughter had entered, paused to look around, and now bowed toward Jefferson and Madison. He spoke to the child, pointed the way to the new gallery where trees and bushes on a mound were filled with birds, wild animals, and reptiles. At the foot of the mound, a beach by a glass-covered "pond" held an array of shells, turtles, frogs, and waterfowl; in the pond were many kinds of fish. All the creatures had been artfully preserved and displayed by Mr. Peale.

Hamilton, having stationed the girl to look at these wonders, approached his fellow Secretary and the Congressman, and greeted the two men cordially.

"Oh yes," he said. "I have completely recovered from my ailments of last month. I'm feeling especially well just now—with my Bank plan accepted by the Senate a week or so ago, the House just now accepting my excise tax plan to raise money to back our war debts and pay their interest. It looks as if I'll have bank and taxes in hand before adjournment! Merciful heaven, I hope so! How long would you say the House will take to pass the bank bill, Mr. Madison?"

"It might take longer than you like, Mr. Hamilton," answered Madison. Their eyes met. Madison's held no smile. Jefferson, tall and lanky, bent towards the two shorter gentlemen a little and changed the subject.

"You were so helpful last summer in breaking the impasse on the seat of government, Mr. Hamilton. I hope your persuasive talents can help us now in the matter of the President's request."

Hamilton, vivacity somewhat subdued, answered, "The President has mentioned that matter. My father-in-law, Senator Schuyler, you can count on. Possibly something can be done with New Hampshire. But with the rest of New England and New York—" Hamilton raised his hands in a gesture of helplessness. "And with you Virginians short one Senator—where IS Richard Henry Lee? Is he ill? You'd best send word for him to hasten here or you may run into a tie—or worse—with the President's amendatory act."

Seeing Jefferson flush and Madison look uncomfortable, Hamilton added jovially, "Well—a late date for that bill will be good for my bank and tax plans! Without the distraction of gnashing teeth over small issues, the Senate and House will be able to act without delay on large ones!"

Abruptly he excused himself as daughter Angelina called to him. A few feet away, he stopped, turned, and said, "I suppose you know that my good friend L'Enfant, the French architect, who renovated my New York house and Federal Hall in New York, will definitely make the street design for the capital on the Potomac. The President has just told me. I assured him that the Frenchman was also the best architect available to design Congress Hall and the President's House."

Jefferson's face flushed again; he smile faintly, bowed politely to acknowledge Hamilton's remarks, and bowed again at Hamilton's, "Good day, Gentlemen." Madison barely nodded, his face like stone.

"Let's go," muttered Madison, walking toward the door. Jefferson leisurely followed, pausing to look at a display of Indian pottery, weapons, clothing,

History of Congress, Senate Journ. (Gales&Seaton) Feb.15, 1791

318

History of Congress, House Journ. (Gales and Seaton) Feb.2, 1791

TJ (F.Brodie) p264

dried scalps, and skeletons. "I am preparing to strike his bank bill dead!" Madison half-whispered when Jefferson caught up with him just outside the front door. "My speech is ready and waiting. A government bank is unconstitutional! I shall let the Congress know why!"

"Oh, Mr. Hamilton will not care about that," Jefferson laughed. "He says the Constitution is a shilly shally thing of mere milk and water. It cannot last, he says, and is only good as a step to something better—specifically, the ENGLISH way!"

"Of course, it was expected that the Senators would approve Hamilton's bank!" blurted Madison in a low, tense voice. "If the House approves it, money merchants in northern cities will rush to buy bank stock, starting up new waves of speculation. How can the President support such a thing? I shall warn him that the Constitution gives the Congress no power to create a national bank. But will he listen to me? More and more the Treasury Secretary acts as if he is the President's prime minister! Washington still asks for your and my advice but his decisions reflect advice Hamilton gives him."

Jefferson nodded. After a moment's silence, he said, "At least the Secretary's creature L'Enfant has displayed some architectural sense. And I will be in a position to critique his work. I hope the President remembers that the Federal Hall L'Enfant renovated in New York cost double—or was it triple—the money in hand. I am surprised that Washington told Hamilton before he told me that L'Enfant is definitely his choice to draw up the city plan—which means, of course, L'Enfant will decide, or at least recommend strongly, where the public buildings will be located. Did you notice Hamilton's expression when he flung the L'Enfant news at us? He does enjoy flaunting—especially to you and me—his position as Washington's current confidant.

"But he enjoys flaunting ALL his intimacies, it seems. In New York" (Jefferson said softly as they strolled toward the Bingham mansion a few blocks away) "our Treasury Secretary has made—still makes—a fool of himself, flaunting his affection for his wife's married sister, Angelina!

"Yes, Jemmy—Angelina Schuyler Church, Senator Schuyler's daughter, exquisite woman, full of wit and humor," whispered Jefferson to his wide-eyed companion. "In Paris," he went on, "she and I had an amusing flirtation. But when she and her husband returned to New York from London, our ardent correspondence abruptly ended. At balls, levees, the theatre, she flirts scandalously in public with Hamilton, her 'petit Fripon' she calls him. He shows his affection for her so warmly, it's an embarrassment to everybody—except his wife, it seems. Others in the Schuyler family, all of whom appear to think Hamilton can do no wrong, also pass it off as 'amusing.'"

TJ (F.Brodie) p265

With gracious bows and greetings, the gentlemen began to acknowledge others turning into Third Street, on their way to the Binghams' mansion at the corner of Third and Spruce.

Philadelphia the Federal City (R.G.Miller)

For some moments, Jefferson and Madison ceased talking while their thoughts worked busily on Hamilton, the Federal District, Senate votes, the President, and back to Hamilton. When they arrived at the corner of Spruce and Third, they saw the President stepping from his great canary-colored coach, turning to extend his hand to Mrs. Washington as she alighted, and with courtly grace, escorting her to the house.

The Secretary and the Congressman stopped, looked at each other, and spoke at the same instant:

"BUT—!" Both laughed, and Jefferson finished the sentence: "But we must mind our manners for the moment—the President's request needs all the help we can find for it—including Hamilton's."

Smiling, Jefferson shook his finger playfully at Madison, and added, "I only wish Hamilton had

TWO fathers-in-law in the Senate to vote for that amendatory act! Now, on to the Binghams' extravagant party. We can practice our most winning smiles and polite bows for hours—and listen for clues as to how to pry Mr. Treasury Secretary from the President's side."

SCENE 2
LAUNCHED AMENDMENT

PLACE: President's house on High Street.
TIME: Thursday, February 17 about 1 p.m.

Washington, in his third-floor office, studied a large map spread out on the table. His secretary, quiet, mannerly young Tobias Lear, sat beside him writing down the names of towns and distances as the President called them out. They were planning Washington's journey through the Southern states, an event he hoped to begin in early April after a stop in Georgetown to start the work of creating a capital city.

"Petersburg, Virginia, to Halifax, North Carolina, 67 miles," Washington said. "Hm. Halifax. Hometown of Wi'lie Jones, who led the anti-Constitution campaign and kept North Carolina in the status of a foreign country for 16 months. Wi'lie Jones of Halifax let Patrick Henry lead him astray. I am told that Jones withdrew from politics when the call in the legislature for a second convention to ratify was successful. He didn't run for a delegate's seat, had no part in ratifying last fall. As the principal man of Halifax, in what way will he participate in the ceremonies during my stay in that place? I hear he wants nothing to do with a federal government and its officials."

"I'm sure your presence there will win him over, Mr. President," Lear answered, "as it will all the way to Charleston and Savannah."

Washington replied that he had heard stories that dissatisfaction with the new Government permeated the South. "I want to see for myself if that is true," he said, "and learn what the dissatisfactions are, and why. I think the southern people may feel they have received little attention, while the northerners have had the Congress in their midst, and I have visited all their states. My wish is that my journey through the South will cause them to feel more a part of this union of states. I want to carry them word that work has begun on surveying the boundaries of the Federal District, and acquiring the public land that will bring Congress and the President much closer to them geographically."

He looked up at the mantel clock with a frown. "Almost 12 o'clock. I was expecting Charles Carroll to arrive from the Senate before now. Since the Senate had little on its docket today except Carroll's introduction of his bill and its first reading, I am surprised that it's taking so long. There must be some difficulty. Could it be that not having a survey map from Mr. Ellicott gave the opposition an excuse for delay?"

Washington glanced out the window to see if rain had begun falling from the somber February sky. "The weather is holding at least. Well, let's us go on, Mr. Lear. The noise of the coach turning the corner onto the cobblestones will announce Carroll's arrival well in advance."

They worked another hour with the map, plotting the course of Washington's newly furbished coach to North Carolina's current capital in New Bern, thence to Wilmington, onward to Georgetown and Charleston in South Carolina, finally to Savannah, Georgia, and Augusta west of it pointing a backcountry route home.

Washington was looking at his watch and clock again when they heard the clop, clop of hooves, and the rumble of heavy wheels. By the time Char-

GW Writings, 1791

Private Affairs of Washington (Decatur/ Lear) p201

Philadelphia, temporary capital of the United States, 1790-1800

Congress met in a newly-built hall beside the State House of Pennsylvania on today's Independence Square. Two blocks away, the President lived and had his office in a rented mansion. In the same block, Madison, other Virginians in Congress, and the Maryland delegation lived in a large rooming-boarding house. A half-block beyond, Jefferson occupied one side of a double house, the State Department the other. Most of the blocks shown in this map were solidly built up, mostly with rows of attached buildings used for businesses and residences. The city's population in the 1790 census numbered 28,500.

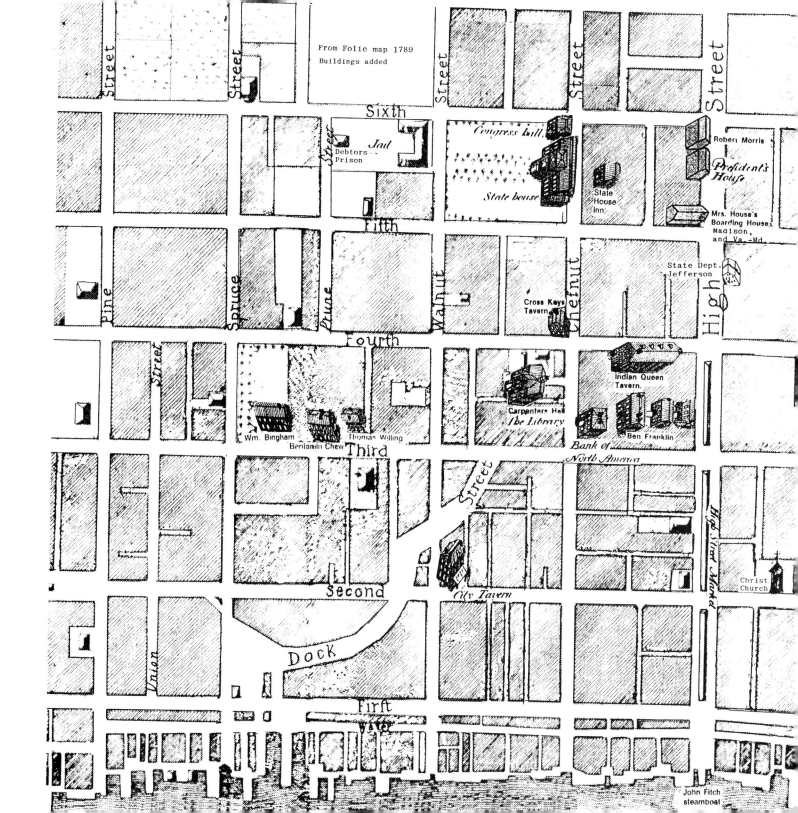

les Carroll entered the house, all was ready for tea in the Blue Room. With Carroll came Richard Henry Lee, the Virginia Senator against whose arrival the launching of the amendment had been timed.

"Gentlemen! I am anxious to hear your news! Is it launched?" the President greeted them as they entered the front door.

"Yes, Mr. President, it passed on a vote of 17 to 7," answered Carroll.

"Seven voted NOT to allow the amendment to be presented for discussion?!" Washington asked. "Who were they? Morris was among them?"

"Not Morris—though Mr. Maclay turned upon him a sour look when he called out 'aye.' The seven were no surprise—all from the North and East: Dalton of Massachusetts, Ellsworth and Johnson of Connecticut, King of New York, Foster of Rhode Island, Maclay, of course, and Wingate of New Hampshire."

"Schuyler?" asked Washington.

"Absent," spoke up Lee, "as was Basset of Delaware—but I, who have been absent so long, was present voting 'aye.'"

"Excuse me, Mr. Lee," the President said, "for my lack of courtesy. I was extremely glad to hear of your arrival yesterday, and appreciate your coming now to pay me your respects. I trust you have completely recovered your health. Come into the Blue Room, Senators, for a cup of tea, and relate all the details concerning the bill. Was there any discussion, for example, Mr. Carroll, of the provision assuring Congress that all public buildings will be placed on the Maryland side?"

"Only Senator Maclay asked for an amplification of the reasons for including any Virginia land at all," Carroll responded. "I reminded him that the Virginia legislature had voted to give $120,000 for land and buildings and was not satisfied to be a part financially without being a part physically. Maclay saw no need for it. He suspected Virginia

gave the money on the very principle of having Alexandria included. Then the 17-7 vote came for leave to read the bill, and it was read. Mr. Adams declared that the second reading could be called for tomorrow, and went on to other business."

"So there was no move to commit it?"

"Mr. President," replied Lee, "any motion maker could see that we had the votes to shame him if he tried to suffocate the President's request."

"So the bill is finally launched," the President said with a wry smile. "Let us drink to that first step with a cup of Hyssop green tea. Robert Morris brought it to me from the cargo of his recently returned ship, the 'Enterprise,' second from our country to make the voyage for trading in China. May our bill now finally launched in the Senate come home as safely as that worthy ship!"

Maclay Journal Feb.16, 1791

The Empress of China (P.C.F.Smith)

SCENE 3
FUTILE LOBBYING, POSTPONED VOTE

PLACE: Senate Chamber, Congress Hall.
TIME: Two days later, February 18.

Senators, finely dressed and hair well-powdered, visited their neighbors, and read newspapers, all with dignity and decorum. Vice President Adams, seated in a plain chair on a low platform, sorted papers on a small mahogany table before him. Curtains of green silk hung behind him, swags of crimson over him, fringing a canopy. A few Senators conversed discreetly while gazing out the windows at Rickett's Circus across the street.

Just in front of the Vice President's platform sat the clerks at their desks. Facing them and Adams, the 26 desks of the Senators made a semi-circle of two rows. Each Senator's mahogany armchair with red leather seat sat within easy shot of a spitting

Diary of Independence Hall, p318-9 (Eberlein and Hubbard)

Diary of Independence Hall, p317 (Eberlein and Hubbard)

box, essential for coughers and snuff users.

Red window swags and a mammoth medallion in the green rug enlivened the rather small chamber. On the ceiling, two paintings hovered: Over the Vice President, an eagle clutched thunderbolts in its talons; in a center circle, grape vines with tendrils enclosed 13 stars.

Fires burned in stoves inserted into two fireplaces, one at each side of the room. Secretary Jefferson had taken a place by one of them while he watched the entrance to the chamber. He talked to Senator Langston of New Hampshire for some minutes, but he was obviously waiting for someone, and rather impatiently.

Maclay Journ. p386
Feb.18

When Senator Maclay entered, Jefferson excused himself and walked quickly to him. "Good morning, Senator! I am pleased to have the opportunity to see you before departing from doing business here. I have been much disturbed that you found so unsatisfactory my explanations for finding invalid the French arguments concerning our ship tonnage tax. Friend though I am of France, I was bound to the terms of our treaty—"

Tall, plainly dressed Maclay, his long, thin face stern and lined by physical pain and political disappointment, looked searchingly at Jefferson before interrupting. "Some person wishes, it seems, to destroy the confidence between us and France and bring us back to the fishpots of British dependence. That you, of all persons, seem to countenance this with your interpretation of the treaty is a thing that will forever astonish me!"

Maclay Journal p369,
370-1

Jefferson in his most gracious Parisian manner managed a slight smile and bow, citing something about creating precedents, then changed the subject. "I also wanted to explain more fully my proposal to build up the whaling and fishing fleets of New England—"

Maclay Journal p373

Maclay with a wave of the hand interrupted in an embarrassingly loud voice. "The great object of your proposal seems to be making these fleets a nursery for seamen, that we, like all the nations of the earth, may have a navy—so setting aside a portion of our citizens for the purpose of inflicting misery on our fellow mortals!"

"Truly that was not the intention, Mr. Maclay—no more than it was the intention of Virginians to demand (as you phrased it) inclusion in the Federal District. The President's decision to include the Potomac's south shore resulted from logic and caution while studying a map. He was considering the safety of a seat of government lying next to a river navigated by large ships. Then, for the boundary line to come so close to Alexandria—within a mile or so—and not include it would have seemed a rebuff to the President. Were you not pleased when Harrisburg was once seriously considered for inclusion in a 10-mile square for the seat of government? Should we not consider the feelings of General Washington, who brought us to independence, and was the unanimous choice for President?"

Maclay glared. Just then, three raps on the table of Mr. Adams's silver pencil-case signalled the opening of the session.

"Good day, Mr. Secretary," Senator Maclay said, and walked away.

"Good day," said Jefferson, adding under his breath, "Mr. Ex-Senator-to-be," and left the chamber, annoyed that his lobbying effort for the amendment had been so futile.

*Diary of Independence
Hall,* p318 (Eberlein
and Hubbard)

Senate business concerning the western lands droned away an hour. Robert Morris, arriving quite late, was still in good time for the debate on Carroll's amendatory bill. He listened for an hour as tempers rose. Senators from New England resisted allowing a change to the seat of government law, while Senators from the South passionately resisted the New Englanders.

Maclay's Journal
Feb.18, 1791

"Are you going to speak?" Morris leaned toward Maclay and whispered.

Maclay shook his head.

The argument went on. After Langdon of New Hampshire made a strong stand for the bill , Maclay suddenly rose. "Mr. President!" Morris rose and stared at him. "Changed my mind!" Maclay flung toward him, and launched into a criticism of the President for laying out the 10-mile square himself when his appointed commissioners (Maclay felt certain) were supposed to do it. The same argument applied, he implied, against the President's asking for a change in the law.

On the Speaker's platform, Vice President Adams, who could never disguise his feelings, stared at Maclay with his coldest, most disapproving face.

"The expectations of the people have been disappointed!" Maclay declaimed. "But I do not arraign the President's authority! I do not call it into question! BUT, the fact is, he has done himself what should have been done by others. But I will neither pull him down nor build him up. But let the measure rest on the law we passed. If all was right, the law should support itself. If wrong, our mending of it is IMPROPER!"

Morris had remained standing, shaking his head at almost every word Maclay said. Immediately that Maclay sat down, Morris gained the floor. He complained about the ifs, ands, and multitudinous buts, the gentleman's using up of limited time with petty arguments.

"As for me," he concluded, looking about the chamber, "should anyone move for a week's postponement, I would gladly vote for it!"

Senator Gunn of Georgia jumped to his feet. "What are Pennsylvania's Senators up to, Sir?! We all know postponing is an indirect way of getting rid of the measure! This Congress adjourns in only two weeks!"

"No, sir, I'm not trying to get rid of it," Morris said soothingly. "A week's delay will not jeopardize the bill, and when it comes up, I will most surely vote FOR it! I repeat—I will vote FOR the bill next week when tempers are cool and logic is steady. This week, time is being wasted that needs to be spent on other important matters."

He was looking at a bill supporter, Langdon of New Hampshire, who gained the floor as soon as Morris's last words were out. "Mr. President, I move for postponing this bill for one week!"

"I second the motion!" called out Schuyler of New York in turn.

The vote was taken. Postponement won 15 to 10, with Morris, Langdon, and Schuyler voting for it with the Northeast men.

"They want to make sure nothing interferes with passing Hamilton's infernal whisky tax bill," grumbled Gunn to Carroll and Virginia's newly appointed senator, James Monroe, as they left the Chamber. "That money will make their speculations in debt certificates very, very profitable!"

"A week's postponement brings us to the twenty-fifth," said Carroll. He paused. "That is also the date by which the President must sign the bank bill—or not."

"Oh? Do you see a connection between the two?" asked Monroe.

Gunn, wide-eyed, added, "You think Morris and the Northeast men intended the postponement as a pressure for the President to sign the bill? No Alexandria if he vetoes the bank?"

Carroll hesitated. "Perhaps they don't know themselves. But Morris must realize that Washington, if confronted with a choice of Alexandria OR the Constitution will support the Constitution. Jefferson and Madison knew that when they raised the Constitutional question about the bank bill. But Hamilton has answered, knocking down their arguments. I feel certain that the President, who has made no secret of his support of Hamilton's bank, will favor Hamilton's logic now, and turn his deaf ear toward his distinguished fellow Virginians.

John Adams
(biography)

Maclay's Journal
(Feb.18, 1791)

Hist.Cong., Senate Journ., Feb. 18, 1791
(Gales/Seaton)

Hist.Cong., Senate Journ., House Journ.,
(Gales/Seaton)
Feb.8-Mar.2, 1791

"No, Gentlemen," Carroll concluded with a slight head shake, "Morris sees that he has less than two weeks to push the revenue bill through—important for his debt speculation—and to roadblock western land-sale rules that Mr. Madison likes but Morris does not—and even to sway votes for keeping the Senate's door closed to the public and press.

"I had hoped," Carroll's soft voice added sadly, "that the Senate would act on my Alexandria bill by next Tuesday, to give Washington the birthday present he most desires. Instead, all we can offer is Morris's promise that he'll jump to our side next Friday.

"Unpredictable character," he mused, "ruthless in getting what he wants, yet boundless in generosity when he likes; gracious and amusing one minute, vulgar, profane, talking bestial badney, to quote Maclay, the next minute. Well, we'll see which way he talks next Friday."

SCENE 4
PROMISE KEPT, POTOMAC SECURE

PLACE: The Senate, then Maclay's rooming house, and afterwards the President's House.
TIME: Friday, February 25

Hist.Cong., Senate Journ.,Feb. 25; House Journ., Feb.25 (Gales/ Seaton)

Less than a week before the end of the first Congress—the day the President signed the bank bill, and the two Houses agreed on the last details of the tax bill—Carroll's Alexandria bill came to the Senate floor for action.

Quickly, the Northeast Senators moved for indefinite postponement.

Morris, Langdon, and Schuyler, joined by Elmer of New Jersey and Read of Delaware, voted with the Southerners against postponing action, and won 14 to 12.

In a few minutes, all five voted with the Southerners again on Carroll's bill. Another 14 to 12 victory, foretelling final victory on the third-reading vote next day.

While Morris, tall, bulky, rosy-cheeked and smiling, was shaking the hands of all the Southern Senators, Maclay stalked stiffly out of the chamber. In his room at Ogden's Tavern, he wrote in his journal with ink of venom and dark suspicion.

Maclay's Journal, p389-90

"This victory is astonishing, indeed. It is plain the President has bought them. I know not their price–" but he felt angry enough to guess: a conspicuous station abroad for one; a job for a relative for another. "Schuyler is only a supple-jack for his son-in-law, and Read is shaken by something else besides the wind."

As for himself, Maclay wrote his epitaph. "I have drowned in the Potomac Jefferson's good regard of me. I already had Hamilton's gladiators and speculators down on me in the Senate. The city of Philadelphia hates me, and I have offended Morris, so my place in the Senate must go, and it has gone. When I leave that Hall, I will be fully satisfied that many a culprit has served two years at the wheelbarrow without feeling half the pain and mortification I experienced in my honorable station."

p401

He then figured his accounts, and began laying his belongings in his trunk to depart.

A few blocks away, Robert Morris was lifting a wine glass in the President's Blue Dining Room, and looking at Washington with his most jovial, almost impish smile. "To the victors belong the— bank!" he declared.

Washington raised his glass and said, "To the Potomac belongs the seat of government!"

The site chosen for the capital of the United States embraces Georgetown, Maryland (left),
downstream flat to lightly terraced land, and land across the Potomac in Virginia, including Alexandria (steeple, extreme
right). During the 10 years between 1791 and the end of 1800, a Capitol wing, an Executive Mansion, several groups of
row houses, and a few dozen scattered houses would begin the city of Washington, District of Columbia.

CHAPTER 30

End and Beginning

SCENE 1
TAVERN-TABLE DEBATE

PLACE: City Tavern, on Second Street by Logan's Alley between Walnut and Chestnut, Philadelphia, in the second floor "Long Room" and adjacent small, private dining room.
TIME: Monday, February 28 about 4 p.m.

Mid-way the Long Room, a quartet of Southern Congressmen had risen from their table by a window, and begun moving across the noisy, crowded room toward the stairs.

When they reached the door opening onto the stairs' landing, a quartet of Northeastern Congressmen in the two-table dining room adjacent caught sight of them. "Look! It's Madison and Jackson, Stone and Giles," Fisher Ames said to his friends Elbridge Gerry and Theodore Sedgwick, also from Massachusetts, and to John Laurence of New York. "Let's hail them," said Ames. "Let's needle them a bit about the vote coming up tomorrow in the House on Charles Carroll's Alexandria bill."

"Ames, you do enjoy being p-provocative, don't you," laughed Gerry. "Oh, I just like to hear them drawl Southern," said Ames.

"Mr. Madison!" called Ames, standing up to wave at the Virginian. "Gentlemen! Come join us in a glass of Madeira! There's an empty table here!"

Madison, in his tall round hat and surcoat, hesitated. His companions, William Giles of Virginia, Michael Stone of Maryland, and James Jackson of Georgia, smiled, lifted their tricorns, and nodded. All then proceeded into the little room where their convivials were drawing the two tables together and rearranging the chairs.

"Plenty of room, plenty of room," Ames said

jovially. "These tables are reserved regularly for us, you know, but half the usuals didn't show today. They're probably at the fine new Oeller Hotel across from Congress Hall," he added as the visitors settled in. "I might forsake this old place, too, if the street noise keeps rising in volume, and the old chef quits as he's threatened. Ah! Mr. Madison, your Madeira! And a toast to your predictable success tomorrow when the Carroll bill comes to a vote!"

Having drunk, Madison looked bemused, which inspired Ames to prick him with a reminder that not ALL the House felt as pleased as the Virginians about the bill. "It's UNCONSTITUTIONAL!" pronounced Ames, raising his eyebrows high and, with a smirk, looking down his nose.

Madison smiled faintly in return and said, "Even though the Constitution contains a provision for a seat of government in a 10-mile square controlled by Congress? And even though that provision excludes no town or state?"

Ames leaned forward and raised a forefinger. "Ah, but elsewhere in the Constitution, giving commercial advantage to one port over another is forbidden! And you, Mr. Giles of Virginia, forsaw that the principal effect of a National BANK would be to give decided preference to the port of Philadelphia, and THEREFORE was, as Mr. Madison had already proclaimed, UN-con-sti-TU-tional!"

City Tavern,
Philadelphia.
Restored.
Public restaurant.

Hist.Congress, House Journ., Feb.1 through 8, 1791, Bank debate

House Journ., 1791, Column 1940, Giles remarks

Cols.1894-1902,
Madison remarks

Col.1909, Ames
remarks

"Now, the distinguished citizens of another port, Alexandria, Virginia, want their town included in the seat of government district. This, even more than a bank will give that port commercial advantage—even over Georgetown, Maryland! Such favoring is SPECIFICALLY FORBIDDEN by the Constitution! People in Georgetown and other less favored ports must cry out in protest!"

Laurence of New York broke in eagerly, "Think, gentlemen, how strongly we, in places without a seat of government drawing money to our area, will feel the UNCONSTITUTIONALITY of Alexandria's position 10 years from now—1800—when Congress moves into the Federal District! (His voice trembled.) And Georgetown will be wailing and wailing at having its commercial advantage cut in half! (He wiped a tear.) A great Constitutional crisis will shake the country in 1800!"

Even Mr. Madison smiled as the others laughed in varying degrees.

Sedgwick jumped in to add, "And think of the turmoil and agony that would have been going on RIGHT THIS MINUTE in Philadelphia—IF you Southerners had decided last month that a Federal bank was constitutional—PROVIDED it was built inside the Federal District on the Potomac!"

The Virginians' good humor vanished. Giles, stony-faced, slid his chair back as if to rise. Gerry leaned toward Madison to say jocularly, "We are only making use of your anti-bank artillery to shoot at the Alexandria bill! No, no, no—you shouldn't stretch the Constitution to cover something you want! Stretching it is UNconstitutional, remember? Or so you argued last month against something you DIDN'T want! It all depends, doesn't it? Alexandria in the permanent seat is more constitutional than a Federal Bank in the temporary seat!"

Ames burst out with, "As I said in the bank bill debate, in two years Congress has made no law except where we exercised power not expressly

Fisher Ames

Col.1946-50, Gerry
remarks

granted! We can hardly proceed without using implied power!"

"Will that cause you to support the Carroll amendment tomorrow?" asked Madison.

"I well remember the time," spoke up Sedgwick, "when the energy of Mr. Madison's reasoning impressed on the minds of the House a conviction that the power of removal from appointive office is vested in the President—although the Constitution doesn't say so. You were very persuasive, Mr. Madison, when you argued in 'The Federalist Papers' that the business of legislating is a practical interpretation of the powers given to Congress—that no Constitution could be drawn with such precision and accuracy as to leave nothing to necessary implications. But you abandoned that view when it came to authorizing a Federal Bank."

Madison raised a hand in protest, but Sedgwick surged on.

"Now that you espouse letting the federal district straddle the Potomac and the Eastern Branch so as to encompass Alexandria, you have moved back to 'the practical' view, extending it even to include stretching laws Congress has passed—"

"Gentlemen!" Stone of Maryland fairly shouted, noisily backing his chair and rising. "You have rudely and mercilessly lashed Mr. Madison with your tongues! You make it sound as if his REAL reason for opposing the bank bill was not his concern with the bank's constitutionality, but with preventing Philadelphia from gaining a pot of federal gold—which would make it more able to lure the government away from its square on the Potomac. PHILADELPHIA is the port that will have special commercial BANKING advantages—not Alexandria!"

Madison abruptly stood up. "Mr. Ames, Mr. Gerry, Mr. Sedgwick, Mr. Laurence—the Federal District matter was entirely irrelevant to the banking bill, and the banking arguments involved different principles from the Carroll bill. That bill simply expresses

Col.1904, 5, 8, Ames
remarks

Col.1910, Sedgewick
remarks

Col.1946

Col.1930, Stone
remarks

Col.1958, Madison;
Col.1915, Madison

President Washington's judgment and desires, none of which infringes on the Constitution. With your good graces, it could be—it should be—a unanimous vote tomorrow. Alexandria is the gateway to the Federal District from the South; Georgetown is the gateway to the Federal Government from the West and North. It is a farsighted leader who tries to make the center of government more conveniently available to more people, now and in the future. Good evening, Gentlemen."

No one at the table spoke as the other Southerners pulled back their chairs, rose, and followed Madison and Giles. The Northeast men had stood at the same time, watching them go.

"Well," said Ames after they disappeared down the stairwell, "we got the bank we wanted by arguing against strict limits; they'll stretch their Federal District into Virginia by doing the same."

Laurence gave a short laugh. "We won't need to use floor time tomorrow debating the Southerners before the House votes. We've won the tavern table debate today, but tomorrow you can be sure they will win the House. Not many men will be able to say 'no' when they're told, 'George Washington wants you to say 'aye.'"

SCENE 2
THE FATEFUL HOUR

PLACE: House of Representatives, Congress Hall.
TIME: Next morning, Tuesday, March 1, 1791.

With the First Congress expiring in only three days, scores of gentlemen and a few of their ladies were crowding through the doorway of Congress Hall and up the stairs to the gallery of the House of Representatives. So much unfinished business would be hurried to the floor, every minute would have its excitement. Speeches would not drag on boringly, and votes might be taken hourly.

True, only the House had a gallery and permitted the public to sit in it and watch its elected officials. Occasionally, only watching was possible; what was said on the Floor did not rise above the cacophony of voices—about 100 on the floor, as many in the gallery, and a crowd in the front entrance lobby—all talking with little regard for ongoing House business.

Certainly in the minutes before the Speaker called for order, any voice except those within six inches, was as likely to be heard "as a popgun in a thunderstorm," Maclay had once observed.

Standing at the doorway of today's buzz-roar-chatter, Madison and the Virginia, Maryland, Carolina, and Georgia delegates strained their voices to greet four Pennsylvania delegates who had just arrived. They tipped their hats, the Pennsylvanians tipped theirs, smiled, nodded, shook hands, and shouted back their greetings.

"I see the Massachusetts men over there in the corner are hovering around Fisher Ames," George Clymer said close to Madison's ear.

Madison turned to look along the open space between the wall and the wooden back of the two-tiered semi-circle of desks facing the Speaker's platform. When he turned back, he said, "A knot of negative votes."

Clymer leaned close again. "I've heard that they won't say a word today. News of your encounter with them last evening spread fast and they have fended off our comments with the news that it was debate enough—they are ready to vote."

Madison replied that he was glad to hear they had worked the venom out of their systems. "They seemed determined to repeat more bluntly and rudely the barbs they threw underhandedly at me during the debate about creating Mr. Hamilton's federal bank," he added. "They won that one—but

Independence Hall Group (E.M.Riley) p27–28

329

I hope they will, indeed, help US win this one for the President. I hope you help, too."

Clymer squeezed Madison's arm, smiled, and moved on.

For a few minutes more, while Madison greeted a steady stream of arrivals, he watched the Massachusetts men from the corner of his eye. Just beyond them, he saw the New Yorkers gathered in a huddle and engaged in agitated conversation. Abruptly they broke up, all heading for their seats on the second row. He knew they would fill six chairs there, just in front of the 10 desks and chairs of the Virginians.

"Good morning, Gentlemen!" boomed the familiar sonorous voice of Speaker Frederick Augustus Muhlenberg, just entering the chamber. A path quickly opened for the tall, portly man with the pleasantly fat, oval face. Hats tipped, and greetings momentarily reduced the noise level.

Madison signaled his Virginians to move to their place on the House floor. As they settled themselves in their red leather seats behind the row of desks, the New Yorkers gave them not a glance.

On the Speaker's platform, Muhlenberg filled his chair with his generous dimensions. His handsome satin vest seemed to spread a full yard across his chest. In his hand he held a small silver gavel, and now he let it fall against a block of wood on the desktop. "The House will come to order!" his deep, strong voice commanded.

"The fateful hour has come", Madison mused. "The President is waiting anxiously for the vote; I hope to God the amendment does better than squeak by. We have 26 votes for sure. If the Pennsylvanians give us four, and New Jersey and Delaware give us three, we will have a respectable 33 to their 27... IF.."

To relieve the tension, Madison stared at the Speaker's face, at the newspaper stenographers at tables beside the Speaker's low platform, at the clerk's table in front of it. He turned to look up at the people in the long gallery behind him, then to look across the room to the bay windows where trees swayed outside in the wind. The round-top windows, trimmed with swags of green damask, were glares of light in the somber room.

All the time he was aware of the backs of the heads of the New Yorkers only a few inches away.

What was going on in those heads, he wondered.

The clerk began to read. It was only a bill to pay officers in the courts. At last the House was chorusing "Aye!" followed by a few shouting, "Nay!"

The clerk was reading again and it was the bill from the Senate "to amend an act to establish the temporary and permanent seats of government of the United States."

There was a call for its second reading. It was read again. There was a call for its third and final reading. It was read again.

Madison rose and moved that the vote be by rollcall. Giles seconded his motion.

No one raised a question. No one made a comment, or brought forth a change.

The rollcall began. "Ames." "No!" "Ashe!" "Aye!"

Among the C's and F's, Clymer and Fitzsimons of Pennsylvania and Cadwalader of New Jersey made Madison smile. But in the G's, he gasped——Gerry of Massachusetts who had jabbed him so hard the day before had called out, "Aye!" And soon, there was Hawthorne, Laurence, and Sylvester of New York doing the same! They turned to face a smiling Madison, bowed, and tipped their hats.

In a moment, three from New Jersey and three from Connecticut and one from Delaware brought tears to the Virginian's eyes. The count was 39 for Washington's request, 18 against.

The gallery visitors stood and applauded, the Carolinians whooped and beat each other on the back. The Virginians crowded around Madison, and delegates on all sides joined in the applause.

Hist.Phil. Vol.III,
p1821 (Scharff/
Westcott)

Hist.Congress, House
Journ. (Gales/Seaton)
March 1, 1791

Hist.Phil. Vol.III
(J.T.Scharf)

p1821

Hist.Congress, House
Journ. (Gales/Seaton)
March 1, 1791

Last action in an eight-year contest: James Madison (seated center), leader of the Virginia delegation, receives the applause of friends, long-time antagonists, and the public gallery on March 1, 1791. The House has just voted 39 to 18 to grant Virginian George Washington his request to include his hometown, Alexandria, in the 10-mile-square Federal District on the Potomac River.

SCENE 3
TEN YEARS OF TOIL AHEAD

PLACE: President Washington's office in the executive mansion on Market Street.
TIME: 6 o'clock, Friday, March 4. The chandeliers and whale oil lamps have just been lit.

Although there is no record of it, a meeting more than likely took place between Washington and L'Enfant when he stopped overnight (as the NY–Phil. stagecoach would have done) on his way to Georgetown. The President would have needed to instruct him and would have wanted to hear L'Enfant's ideas.

"Major L'Enfant! I am pleased that you have started on your way to Georgetown so quickly!" President Washington greeted the French engineer and architect Pierre Charles L'Enfant. "You made good time from New York. Good evening, Mr. Jefferson!" he added as servants helped the visitors out of overcoats and hats. "Thank you for escorting Major L'Enfant so expeditiously from the stagecoach and City Tavern. I am glad to be able to confer with him before he goes on to Georgetown."

Jefferson bowed and smiled; L'Enfant bowed and bowed and expostulated, his English words distorted by his French accent and the rhythm of his sentences. "Mr. President! I am greatly moved, greatly honored, to speak to you concerning this noble, this momentous work which you have entrusted to me and for which honor I present ardent gratitude. Since I received a month ago the letter of my appointment, I have been preparing myself to depart New York as soon as the Congress acted and your instructions arrived in my hand. I boarded the stagecoach only an hour after Mr. Jefferson's letter, posted on the day of the final vote, was handed to me!

"I have left behind a multitude of proposals already placed under my immediate agency for the erecting of houses to the amount of one millions of dollars in the least. But for acquiring reputation, that is nothing when compared to this great occasion for planning and establishing a Federal City which is to become the Capital of this vast Empire which will—"

L'Enfant and Washington (E.Kite) p33, TJ to L'Enfant Jan.29, 1791

Washington, seating himself at his desk and waving his visitors to chairs, interrupted. "May I use this occasion to express my admiration of your architectural style and artistic elegance in the renovation of Federal Hall and decoration of St. Paul's Chapel in New York. Having voluntarily come to America as a young man to fight in our army for the independence we now enjoy, you now give us evidence in your artistic work that you love America, and share the spirit of this new nation. I believe, Major, that you are peculiarly qualified to examine the features of the ground now chosen for the seat of government, and to fix on the most advantageous area for the public buildings."

"I only wish I had seen this sacred spot!" exclaimed L'Enfant, clasping and unclasping his hands in excitement. "I have heard, I have read, about riverside flats, terraces of hills, but it is their size, their location, their relation to each other that inspires the imagination!"

The President turned to Jefferson. "You have journeyed about the site, and you are well-known for your skill with words. Your description would serve the Major better than mine."

Jefferson nodded, and agreeably brought forth from an inside pocket of his coat a folded paper. "I am pleased to have occasion to show the Major my sketch—crude as it is—of the site, with my suggestion of locations for the government buildings." He unfolded the paper and smoothed it out on the table in front of L'Enfant.

He pointed out that his small drawing showed only one end of the site—the rest stretched about four miles to the right, then went across the Eastern Branch to include three miles of Maryland land. As for his small sketch, he pointed out Tiber or Goose Creek emptying into the Potomac near Georgetown, and flat farmland extending south of the creek a mile or two.

"On the north bank of the creek, the land begins

L'Enfant Memorial Aug.30, 1800 (Kite, p84)

L'Enfant and Washington (E.Kite), Sept. 11, 1789, p34

(Kite) p33, TJ to D.C. Commissioners Jan.29, 1791

to rise, particularly where creek and river join. There, almost sheer rock 50 feet high faces the heights of Georgetown across a bend in the river."

"Which is higher?" asked L'Enfant, "this cliff or the heights of Georgetown?"

"Oh, Georgetown is higher," Washington volunteered. L'Enfant's eyebrows went up as he pursed his lips. After a few seconds' pause, Jefferson continued calmly.

"The cliff, as you call it, gently declines as it curves inland north, then east, a modest ridge edging two miles of a strip of level land lying alongside the north bank of the creek. But abruptly, here on the east, the ridge rises above the flats to a substantial height—oh, about 100 feet (Washington nodded) "called 'Jenkins Hill' for a long-gone owner. The top of that hill extends like a wide plateau toward the Eastern Branch—I prefer the Indian name, Anacostia, for this river—but it is a slightly declining plateau abruptly ending as high river banks."

L'Enfant, fingers pulling at his chin, pointed to the small grid of streets that Jefferson had drawn along Goose Creek, beginning with the rocky height at the creek mouth. "This corner is your government center?"

"Yes, this is about 350 acres, and my agents are quietly attempting to buy them, as if for themselves," the President replied.

"It is very small and— (L'Enfant visibly struggled to decide between passionate opinion and tact) — and ORDINAIRE, and Georgetown's heights will overshadow it."

Jefferson's face crimsoned. "It is a simple design like Philadelphia's."

"What would you do with the rest of the land?" L'Enfant said.

Jefferson pointed to a scribbled note he had written on his sketch, and read it aloud: "To be laid off in future."

"Mr. President," L'Enfant began, a touch of impa-

tience in his voice, "the first national capital in history to be established by law on a space requiring an overall plan for a great city must not be small or ordinaire, especially for this extraordinaire country destined to enlarge state by state across the continent.

"It must be a revolutionary expression of a new form of government, new science, new technology—the whole proclaiming that the people of America control their destiny. This capital's hills should enshrine views, its boulevards point magnificent distances, its grid of streets made exciting with circles, great rectangles, squares, even angles. It should have fountains, cascades of water, canopies of trees, heights crowned with monumental architecture——a magnificent city renowned throughout the world for its beauty of form, its visual delights! Think of Rome, my dear Mr. President— think of Paris!"

Washington had listened absorbed, his eyes bright and focused intently upon the architect-engineer. It was apparent to Jefferson that L'Enfant's concept of a grand and elegant capital city had fired the President's heart and mind.

"But can we pay for such a grand, even grandiose, capital?" Jefferson said softly.

L'Enfant, waving both hands, rushed to reply. "Although the means now within the power of the country are not such as to pursue the design to any great extent, it is obvious that the plan should be drawn on such a scale as to leave room for that aggrandizement and embellishment which the increase of the wealth of the nation will permit it to pursue at any period, however remote!"

Jefferson, looking straight into the President's eyes observed that the scale of such a grand design would require buying many hundreds of acres, not just 300 or so. "Unless," he added, "the land owners agree to cede ALL the land that the Major's design will encompass, and take back as fair payment every

Derived from L'Enfant and Washington (E.Kite) p18–19, p36–37, p14

"L'Enfant's Washington, an Architect's View" (D.Jackson) Col.Hist.Soc. Records 1978

(Kite) p37, L'Enfant to TJ Mar.11, 1791

L'Enfant letter to GW, Sept.11, 1789

Pierre Charles L'Enfant, French artist-engineer-architect who fought in the American Revolution, designed the City of Washington in the District of Columbia during a few weeks of the Summer of 1791. A 1785 silhouette, cut out of paper by artist DeHart is the only known authentic likeness of L'Enfant. Artist Sofia Zarambouka has added the facial features and hair style suggested by the silhouette lines (right column).

other building lot, which they can sell at the inflated prices of the future."

The President looked at L'Enfant and asked, "How many acres do you estimate will be needed for your grand design?"

"No less than 3,000." The President and Jefferson stiffened in surprise.

"Perhaps no more than 5,000," L'Enfant added. "Mr. Jefferson's ingenious method of acquisition will, furthermore, defeat the land speculators. May I inquire, Excellency, about the money available for surveying and beginning construction of public buildings?"

Jefferson gave a short, hard laugh. Washington leaned back heavily in his arm chair. "Nothing will come from Congress—neither now nor in the future," he said. "The states of Virginia and Maryland together have voted $192,000 for the work. However, to date neither has issued any of the money. When I visit Richmond on my journey through the southern states next month, I will express to Governor Randolph our dire need. Almost certainly he will send to the Commissioners a draft for a goodly amount before I depart that city. But that will barely get the work started. We must sell building lots to supply more money as soon as you have completed your city design, and it is marked on the ground as streets and city lots. You can see that haste is essential or we will have no construction funds.

"I expect to arrive in Georgetown by the end of March, only three weeks after your arrival there, Major. May I expect that you will have drawings of the particular grounds most appropriate for the Capitol and Mansion? Be pleased to begin on the Eastern Branch, and proceed from there towards Georgetown, sketching the hills, valleys, morasses, and waters," the President said.

"Your Excellency, the confidence with which you honor me is too highly flattering to my ambition for me to fail to exert the best of my ability."

TJ letter for GW to L'Enfant, Mar.1, 1791

Kite p41, L'Enfant to TJ, Apr.4

"Good," the President said, rising from his chair. "I view you as a scientific man, one who has added considerable taste to your professional knowledge. For prosecuting public works and carrying them into effect, you are better qualified than anyone who has come to my knowledge in this country, or indeed any other, whose services could be counted upon."

Washington began to rise. "Now, I am obliged to bid you good evening. Today being Friday, Mrs. Washington is expecting guests, including myself, at her weekly levee, which begins in a half-hour. Today being the first day of the Second Congress, and the weather fair though chilly, the public rooms will be crowded. If you feel inclined to stay, you will have but a short time to wait for other guests on the floor below."

Jefferson and L'Enfant declined the invitation, donned their hats and coats, and were saying their goodbyes at the President's office door when he added, "Mr. Jefferson has already told you perhaps that our geographer-surveyor, Mr. Andrew Ellicott, is surveying the 40 miles of boundaries of the 10-mile square. Ellicott will work with you later to survey and mark the streets and the lots—no less than 20,000 of the latter, I calculate.

"The first Commissioner you see will probably be Daniel Carroll of Rock Creek—"

"Oh?" said Jefferson.

Washington, smiling and nodding, said,

"Yes, just before starting for Georgetown this morning, he called upon me and asked to withdraw his resignation. I was pleased— relieved—to re-instate him, having proposed this step when he came to dinner here on Wednesday."

Looking steadily at L'Enfant, the President said, "Major, I must emphasize that the Commissioners I have appointed—former Congressman Carroll, Dr. Stuart, and Gov. Johnson—live nearby the Federal District, and will, by law, be responsible for direct-

Writings of GW , GW letter to D.Stuart, Nov.20, 1791

Pierre L'Enfant

Hist.Natl. Capital, p161 (W.Bryan)

No record of D.Carroll's reinstatement, but he did accept his commission and take up the work.

ing the overall job on the spot. They are responsible to me, though communicating through Mr. Jefferson. So you will be also, particularly in regard to the city plan and the designs of the main public buildings."

The three men, almost equally tall, two with military bearing, one walking with relaxed informality, had reached the head of the stairs.

His face aglow, Washington said, "The work starts! Our dreams for a capital on the Potomac must, by law, be transformed into bricks and mortar by December 1800! We have 10 years of toil ahead of us. Let us hasten the start! Good night, Gentlemen!"

"Good night, Mr. President," said his visitors, who lifted their hats, bowed, and started down the stairs.

L'Enfant stopped on the first landing and looked up to see Washington still looking after them. The Frenchman again lifted his tall, round hat. Fervently he said, "My General and my President, I shall create for you a city design of such beauty and distinction that hundreds of years from now, the nations of the world will still be looking toward America's capital with envy and admiration!"

"I believe you will," replied George Washington.

Acknowledgements

To the reviewers of chapters whose places, people, and events came within their areas of expertise, I offer many more thanks to add to those I have already conveyed. The book is far more accurate as a result of their comments, advice, and corrections. Any errors remaining are all mine.

I wish to acknowledge a special debt I owe to three scholars whose knowledge and research material significantly altered some of my concepts, causing me to rewrite whole scenes. Dr. E. James Ferguson, widely recognized as the authority on Hamilton's finance plan, meticulously reviewed the six chapters describing the Second Session of the First Congress when the plan was taken up. Dr. Kenneth Bowling, historian whose specialty is the Federal District and the First Federal Congress, generously pointed out a recorded episode that enabled me to replace surmise with substance. Almost as important was his enthusiastic interest in my non-textbook style of telling history. Dr. Elizabeth Nuxoll, editor of the Robert Morris Papers, gave me valuable direction and information, including xeroxes of material otherwise unavailable to me.

Many historians will owe thanks to Betty Huber of Morrisville, Pennsylvania, whose research into land records and maps has clarified many details of Morris's acquisition of land at the Falls of the Delaware. The Cox 1789 land survey map of Trenton-Morrisville to which she led me was judged to be the original by Dr. Andrew J. Cosentino, Library of Congress, who visited the Trenton Public Library to examine it.

To Florian Thayn, Art and Reference Specialist, Office of the Architect of the Capitol, I owe a gold medal not only for the great quantity of material she helped me find during many years, but for her wonderful compliments for each chapter as it came out of the machine. Without her help and encouragement, this book would have required not five years but 10—or perhaps I would never have finished.

Reviewers

Chapters
1,11,8,27 Philadelphia
David Dutcher, Historian, Independence Historical Park,
Philadelphia, Pennsylvania.

2 Morris
Dr. Elizabeth Nuxoll, Editor; Dr. Mary Gallagher, Assistant Editor, The Papers of Robert Morris, Queens College, Flushing, N.Y.

Betty Huber, Researcher, Morrisville, Pennsylvania.

3 Annapolis
Maryland State Archives, Annapolis, Maryland

4 GW in the Alleghenies
Marion County Historical Society Museum, Fairmont, West Virginia
Betty Harr Koontz,
Herschel Ice,
Jay S. Moler (National Park Service),

5 Richmond
Minor Weisinger, Virginia State Archives, Richmond, Virginia

6 Mount Vernon Conference
John Riley, Archivist, Mount Vernon Ladies Association,
Mount Vernon, Virginia

8 Fitch
Charles Harris, Historian, Papers of William Thornton, Washington, D.C.

9 Hillsborough
Clarence Jones, President, Hillsborough Historical Society,
Hillsborough, North Carolina

Dr. Jerry Cashion and Steve Massingill, Historians, North Carolina Archives and History, Raleigh, North Carolina

10 Madison election
Dory Twitchell, Assistant Director, Montpelier, Virginia (Madison home)
Carol Deakin, Fairfax County Park Authority, Fairfax, Virginia

12,13,14,15 First Congress, 1st Session
Dr. Kenneth Bowling, Associate Editor, First Federal Congress Project,
Washington, D.C.

16,17,18,19,20,21 First Congress, 2nd Session
Dr. E. James Ferguson, author of *Power of the Purse,* Laguna Hills, California

16 (scene 3), 17(3), 18(5), 19(2), 26, 27, 29(1), 30(3)
Dr. Eugene R. Sheridan, Associate Editor, The Papers of Thomas Jefferson,
Princeton University Library, Princeton, New Jersey

24 Monocacy, Frederick
Clem and Harriet Gardner, Catoctin Furnace Historical Society,
Thurmont, Maryland

24 Monocacy, Frederick
W.G. Wilman, President, Frederick Historical Society, Frederick, Maryland

24,25 GW Potomac trip
Richard L. Stanton, Superintendent, C and O National Historical Park,
Sharpsburg, Maryland

24 Conococheague
Melvin Kaplan, President, Williamsport Historical Society,
Williamsport, Maryland

23,24,25,26 GW Potomac trip
**Kathryn Smith, President, The Historical Society of the District of
Columbia,** (formerly The Columbia Historical Society) Washington, D.C.

23,24,25,26 GW/Potomac
Donald Hawkins, Architect, D.C. maps collector,
Washington, D.C.

23,24,25,26 GW/Potomac
**John Frye, Historian, National Park Service, Sharpsburg; and Hagerstown
Library,** Hagerstown, Md.

30,11 L'Enfant
James Ogilvie, Director, District of Columbia Archives,
Washington, D.C.

General

**Florian Thayn, Art and Reference Specialist, Office of the Architect of the
Capitol,**
Washington, D.C.

Jean van der Tak, Editor, Population Reference Bureau,
Washington, D.C.

Judith Frank, Editor, Writer,
Washington, D.C.

Hobart McDowell, Jr., Senior Editor, Writer, *National Geographic
Magazine,* Washington, D.C.

Merrill Windsor, Editor, *Arizona Highways,* Phoenix, Arizona; formerly
Editor, Special Publications, National Geographic Society, Washington, D.C.

Janice Windsor, Family Counselor,
Phoenix, Arizona

Peg Morrison, Administrator, Woman's Clinic,
Wichita, Kansas

Marion Boyars, Publisher, Editor, Marion Boyars Publishers,
London, England, and New York, N.Y.

Suzanne Snell Tesh and Bradley Tesh, Bethesda, Maryland

**James L. Snell, Asst. Professor Computer Science, State University of New
York,** Brockport, New York

Kirby C. Loftin
Kinston, North Carolina

ILLUSTRATIONS AND CREDITS

Cover: From the poster "City of Washington - 1800" by T.L. Loftin. Full-color, 25 X 31-inch poster available from the publisher. See page iv.

Old State House, Philadelphia, 1783. Based on engraving by Charles Willson Peale in the collection of the Historical Society of Pennsylvania.

Robert and Mary Morris Portraits. Based on paintings by Charles Willson Peale in the collection of the Philadelphia Academy of Fine Arts.

Trenton, N.J. Based on painting by J. Califano, 1789.

Morris note. Collection of National Archives, Washington, D.C.

Annapolis, Md. 1783. Based on 19th century engraving.

Cabin in the Alleghenies. Engraving from 19th century magazine.

Cheat River Valley, Alleghenies. Engraving from 19th century magazine.

Map of Richmond drawn by British officer. From collection of Virginia State Library.

Mount Vernon, aerial view. Based on newspaper drawing of 19th century.

Mount Vernon, Washington's study. Based on old engraving, with figures added.

Mount Vernon with frigate on river. Old engraving. Courtesy of Old Print Gallery, Georgetown, D.C.

Broad Street to City Hall, New York, 1786. Based on 1797 painting.

New York City Hall floor plan before 1789 renovation. Tracing of a diagram in Independence Historical Park, Philadelphia, collection.

Fitch's steamboat "Perserverance." From Fitch's drawing.

St. Matthew's church, Hillsborough, N.C. From local historical drawings.

Campground during Ratification Convention of 1788, Hillsborough, N.C. Based on watercolor by W.C. Weisel, in collection of Boston Museum of Fine Arts.

Map of North Carolina 1788. From *Ratification of the Federal Constitution* by Louise Trenholme.

Courthouse polling scene, first federal election 1789. Based on 19th century magazine illustration.

Inaugural scene, viewed from rooftop. Based on 19th century magazine illustration.

Inaugural night fireworks seen from Bowling Green, 1789. Based on old engravings.

Federal Hall 1789 after renovation. Based on various drawings of the time, with added details from 1789 newspaper, magazine descriptions.

Senate Chamber, Federal Hall. Drawn from 1789 newspaper, magazine descriptions, no accurate picture having ever been made.

Dinner at the President's. Based on Henry Sargent oil, 1820, in the collection of Boston Museum of Fine Arts.

House of Representatives, Federal Hall. Drawn from newspaper, magazine descriptions, no accurate picture having ever been made.

Map of Trenton-Morrisville at Falls of the Delaware. Based on 1789 "Cox Land Survey" map in collection of Trenton Public Library, and on the research of Betty Huber, Morrisville, Pennsylvania.

Ferry on the Susquehanna near Havre de Grace. Based on Pavel Svinin painting in the collection of the Metropolitan Museum of Art, New York.

Map of New York in 1789. From *City of New York in the Year of Washington's Inauguration* by Thomas E.V. Smith. Buildings added.

Morris and gentlemen at President's reception 1789. Section of a cartoon of 1789 by R. Pollard, London. Courtesy of Old Print Gallery, Georgetown, D.C.

Hot air balloon begins to burn. Based on old engraving.

Wall and Water intersection, New York, 1789. Based on Francis Guy oil, 1797, in collection of New York Historical Society, New York.

Countryside at Germantown, Pennsylvania. Based on Charles Willson Peale oil in private collection.

Cherry Street home of President, New York, 1789, with coach and six. Based on old engravings.

Broadway home of the President, New York, 1790. From an old illustration.

Richmond Hill with John and Abigail Adams. Based on old engravings.

Broadway, Battery Park, across the river to Jersey, view from rooftop. Based on 19th century magazine illustration.

Cartoon of Morris dragging Congress from New York to Philadelphia 1790, and cartoon of Morris-guided ship heading for disaster. Adapted from copies in collection of Historical Society of Pennsylvania.

Washington departs from New York. Based on old engraving.

Georgetown waterfront 1790. Old engraving.

Washington on horseback at Jenkins Hill. Based on drawing by Betty Wells.

Looking downriver from a bluff near Little Falls, 1790. Courtesy of Old Print Gallery, Georgetown, D.C.

Great Falls of the Potomac viewed by Washington and companions. Based on old engravings.

Potomac map of 1794 by Dennis Griffith, in collection of Library of Congress.

Banquet in Hagerstown, Md. Based on drawing by Betty Wells.

Harper's Ferry, W.Va. 1790. Based on old engraving.

River Boat of 1790 moving downstream near Seneca. Boat from *History of Travel in America* by Dunbar. Scene adapted from old engraving.

Coach waiting outside an "ordinary". Based on old diorama.

President's house, Philadelphia. Old engraving.

Philadelphia city center 1791. Based on Folie map section greatly enlarged, buildings added. Library of Congress collection.

Theater scene. Based on John Searle watercolor, 1822, in N.Y. Historical Society collection.

Peale's Museum scene. Background based on painting by Charles Willson Peale.

Senate Chamber, Congress Hall, Philadelphia. Based on photograph of restored room.

Site for the capital on the Potomac, 1791. Based on newspaper illustration of 1860's.

L'Enfant silhouette in U.S. State Department Collection.

All other illustrations were composed by T.L. Loftin.
Tracing and artwork by Sofia Zarambouka.

INDEX